the complete story

CORVETTE®

CRESTLINE

This edition published in 2005 by Crestline, an imprint of MBI Publishing Company, Galtier Plaza, Suite 200, 380 Jackson Street, St. Paul, MN 55101-3885 USA

First published in 2002 by Motorbooks.

For a free catalog, call 1-800-826-6600, or visit our website at www.motorbooks.com.

ISBN-13: 978-0-7603-2372-4
ISBN-10: 0-7603-2372-0

Printed in Hong Kong

CONTENTS

FOREWORD

Celebrations are important to everyone associated with Chevrolet. Whether it's to acknowledge a record sales month for one of our product lines, the recognition by a magazine for a vehicle's outstanding qualities, or taking of the checkered flag at one of the many hundreds of motorsports events held throughout the season, it's a reason to be proud.

It was just a year ago that our division turned 90. When the first vehicle rolled through the doors of Louis Chevrolet's small shop in 1911, little did he know that the cars and trucks that carried his name would become the cornerstone of corporate parent General Motors' success.

A multitude of product lines have worn the Chevrolet name. While a few are no longer around, many still command great respect for their perseverance and success in the ever-changing marketplace. One of the most famous Chevrolets of all—Corvette— will celebrate its 50th anniversary on June 30, 2003.

For all of those fifty years, Corvette has remained true to its two-seat sports car heritage. Carefully crafted from a precise blend of power, performance, style, and comfort, Chevrolet's flagship continues to reign as one of GM's design and technology bellwethers. A fiberglass body, 'T-top' removable roof panels, and a fiberglass-reinforced monoleaf rear spring are among many mass-production firsts introduced on Corvette.

No single vehicle in automotive history has a heritage as rich or as celebrated. Corvette has been the only American-produced performance car to consistently challenge the world's top sports cars, both in its on-track achievements and its popularity with consumers. With total sales of nearly $1.2 million, it has become not only America's favorite sports car but also a true American icon.

When the first Corvette rolled off a makeshift assembly line in Flint, Michigan, the Corvette "enthusiast" had not yet been born. Over the following decades, however, there has been a Corvette revolution as evidenced by the numerous owners' clubs in the United States and around the globe. As if further testament is required, the independently-operated National Corvette Museum in Bowling Green, Kentucky, is the only museum in the world dedicated to showcasing the history of a single vehicle line.

There is simply nothing to compare with the dedication of every man and woman who has had a part in designing, developing, manufacturing, marketing, and selling this great automotive nameplate. Nor is there any doubt that Corvette owners are the most devoted enthusiasts imaginable.

As we celebrate Corvette's golden anniversary, we must honor the glorious past yet stay focused as we cast a bright eye toward what we envision for the future. Those fortunate enough to shape that future promise that it will continue to make Chevrolet proud.

Kurt Ritter

Kurt Ritter
Chevrolet General Manager

ACKNOWLEDGMENTS

Dedication: For my son, Paul, with admiration for his taste in cars and for his decisions in life.

My sincere thanks to Peter Brock, Redmond, Washington, for providing his extraordinary photos of the C5R racing efforts. Peter has chronicled this effort from the rollout, and as designer of the legendary Cobra Daytona Coupe, brings an unmatched perspective to his racing coverage. I am further grateful to Gayle and Peter for their generous hospitality and ongoing encouragement.

I also wish to thank fellow author Mike Mueller, Atlanta, Georgia, for his help and the introductions he made to collectors in the southeast.

I am extremely grateful to John L. Stein, editor of *Corvette Quarterly*, for opening his files to me and for generously allowing me to quote from the magazine. As the journal-of-record of this fine automobile, this publication was an immeasurable help in filling many of the holes I uncovered in other histories.

While many car owners proved heroic in their help and encouragement while shooting the photos for this book, I want to single out Kenn Funk, Glendale, California, whose 1969 L88 we rolled out for multiple photo shoots. His patience never flagged. Thank you so much, Kenn.

I visited the four corners of the United States to find and photograph significant cars for this book, logging 23,000 miles by the time it was done.

Tom and Susan Armstrong, Issaquah, Washington; Sheldon Aubut, Esko, Minnesota; Laverne Berha, my best friend in Texas, Houston, Texas; Ellen Bierly and Jan Leyden, Indianapolis Motor Speedway Museum, Speedway, Indiana; John Carefoot, Cincinnati, Ohio; Otis and Bettina Chandler, Ojai, California; Steve and Debbie Earle, Buellton, California; Dave and Jan Ferguson, Quartz Hill, California; Marty Fowler, Kennett, Missouri; Henry and Rita Fuchs, Oxnard, California; Kris Gardner, Camarillo, California; Jim and Dee Gessner, Mentone, California; Steve and Keith Goldin, Homestead, Florida; Bill and Sandie Herron, Sarasota, Florida; David and Merideth Hmura, Homer Glen, Illinois; Mark Hyman, St. Louis, Missouri; Jim and Nancy Jaeger, Indian Hill, Ohio; Doug and Carol Johnson, Maryland Heights, Missouri; Roger Judski and David Judski Jr., Roger's Corvette's, Maitland, Florida; Ralph Kramer, Indianapolis, Indiana; Leslie Krause, Santa Paula, California; Bob and Cheryl Lawton, San Jose, California; Kevin Mackay, Corvette Repair, Inc., Valley Stream, New York; Larry Martin, Houston, Texas; Rich and Shar Mason, Carson City, Nevada; Chip Miller, Carlisle, Pennsylvania; Leonard and Marjorie and son Jonathan "Hoss" Nagel, Buena Park, California; John and Sally Neas, Tulsa, Oklahoma; Kent Rockwell, Orcutt, California; Glen Spielberg, Merrick, New York; Robert Taylor, Santa Barbara, California; David and Cynthia Thurber, Santa Barbara, California; Bob Tomczak, Wauconda, Illinois; Bill and Betty Tower, Plant City, Florida; Ed and Linda Van Scoy, Gilbert, Arizona; Dave Wiehle, Cortland, Illinois; Mike and Laurie Yager and Nathan Sheets, Mid-America Direct, Effingham, Illinois; Harry Yeaggy, Cincinnati, Ohio.

My deepest thanks go to Jim Gessner, Mentone, California, for his tireless efforts in unearthing fantastic cars and wonderful stories, and for his careful and detailed scrutiny of my text.

Equal gratitude goes to Ed Wittwer, Corvette Service, Inc., Carpenteria, California, for his countless introductions, his gentle manner and his limitless enthusiasm and encouragement.

At MBI Publishing Company, I want to thank my editor, Darwin Holmstrom, for his patience, direction, and wisdom, and Senior Editor Lee Klancher for years of making me a better writer and a more focused photographer.

Almost last but far from least is my friend and fellow author/photographer David Newhardt, Pasadena, California. David, a *Motor Trend* staffer, came to my rescue as the deadline approached, tirelessly filling in countless shoots for me and adding his wonderful images to this book. He and Susan were with me as the saga of this book became one of the most significant journeys of my life, and I'm forever grateful for their friendship.

Standing beside me on that same demanding journey were my dearest friends, Otis and Bettina Chandler, whose love and encouragement are indescribable sources of strength and peace to me.

Finally, to my best friend and partner, Carolyn, thank you for everything. You have helped me become the man I want to be. I love you.

—Randy Leffingwell, Santa Barbara, California

CHAPTER ONE

A NEAR INEVITABILITY

he Corvette could only have come from General Motors. This is not just because Chevrolet general manager Tom Keating, chief engineer Ed Cole, and vice president of styling Harley Earl agreed this new car would be badged as a Chevrolet. It was more involved than that. The Corvette resulted from 30 years of work by GM's greatest thinker, Alfred Pritchard Sloan. Sloan and Donaldson Brown together devised a far-sighted management strategy in the early 1920s. Brown became Sloan's co-conspirator in the years after GM's board elected Sloan president in May 1923. By then, these two men had undone the conglomerate mess that their former boss, the entrepreneurial automobile enthusiast William Crapo Durant, had left behind.

Durant was the father of General Motors. He envisioned a system in which GM owned and controlled every part and product needed to manufacture his automobiles. The term for this, *vertical integration,* was not coined yet. What Durant created was a less laudable free will among the companies he owned. By the time he walked out in December 1920, his system had devolved into a corporate free-for-all. Durant had too many automakers producing too many similar models at too near the same price with no central control.

The healthy post–World War I U.S. economy collapsed in 1920 as Europe's recovery hit full speed. The recession hit hard in the United States. The fundamental difference between Billy Durant's car company and Henry Ford's operations took giant General Motors down to second place. In the best of times, Durant's products competed with one another. As money tightened, he had no small, basic, cheap car to sell, as Ford did. Durant soon had no corporate income.

Sloan joined GM in 1916. Brown arrived at GM when Pierre S. du Pont stepped in to become GM president as part of du Pont's *(previous pages) For half a century, the Corvette has defined the American sports car.*

Called Anniversary Red, this one-year-only color is part of the optional package Chevrolet created to celebrate half a century of its sports car. The 50th Anniversary package was available on coupes and convertibles only, and not for the Z06.
2002 General Motors Corporation. Used with permission of GM Media Archives

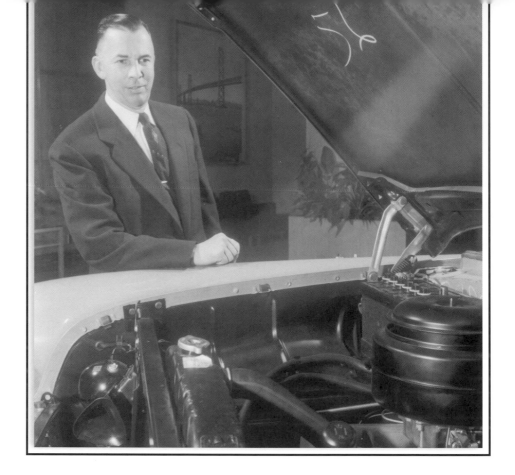

Ed Cole was chief engineer at Chevy in 1952. Cole and Earl worked together to create a running prototype to present to Keating and GM president Harlow Curtice for production approval. 2002 General Motors Corporation. Used with permission of GM Media Archives.

A clay mock-up of the 1953 Corvette in the design studio. 2002 General Motors Corporation. Used with permission of GM Media Archives.

efforts to bail GM out of its enormous troubles in 1921. With du Pont in place as the hard decision maker, Brown became GM's financial brain and Sloan became its backbone. Together, they made something rational out of the chaos.

Brown, Sloan, and du Pont monitored each company's performance individually, examining and revising GM's entire product lineup. By late 1921, they offered cars ranging from $700 Chevrolets to $6,000 Cadillacs.

Brown established the goal of achieving the highest possible return on rate of investment, a theory that guides most successful companies today. Sloan and Brown believed the purpose of any company was to protect and enrich the investment of its owners, stockholders—in GM's case—a philosophy that would affect product decisions to this day. He and Brown accepted delayed corporate gratification, as Sloan wrote years later in his autobiography, *My Years with General Motors.* "The question is not simply one of maximizing the rate of return for a specific short period of time. Mr. Brown's thought on this was that the fundamental consideration was [to achieve] an average return over a long period of time." If ever any single product in automotive history demanded patience to achieve its return on investment, it was Chevrolet's sports car. That was only one of several elements needed for the Corvette to succeed, however.

As Arthur Kuhn wrote in his book, *GM Passes Ford 1918–1938,* Brown and Sloan recognized that offering an automobile "exclusive in design, possessing superior engineering qualities and carrying with it a peculiar appeal to fashion afforded the opportunity for a favorable rate of return." This, as Brown wrote in his own book, *Some Reminiscences of an Industrialist,* required "ingenuity in anticipating the changing tastes of the buying public." They levered that philosophy into place and pressed forward in other ways that enabled the corporation to serve its stockholders best.

A CAR FOR EVERY PURSE

It was Sloan who, as early as 1921, had verbalized the evolving General Motors philosophy as a slogan: "A car for every purse and purpose." By 1925, Sloan and du Pont recognized a growing market in Europe for their cars, but they concluded it was wiser to buy an existing company and its products and factories than to start from scratch. GM acquired major interests in Vauxhall Automobiles in the United Kingdom and Adam Opel A. G. in Germany. At home, new customers were created when GM began financing purchases of its cars. It not only brought in first-time buyers, it benefited shareholders who realized there were new profits in interest payments. By late 1925, General Motors produced one of every five automobiles sold in the United States and kept one dollar in every three dollars of profit the auto industry reaped.

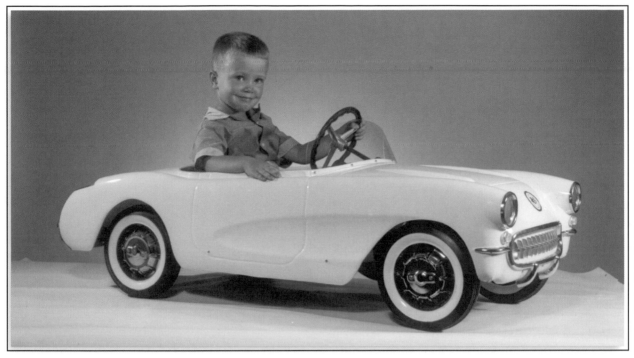

Sloan demanded his divisions communicate with each other on everything from engineering to advertising. He and other vice presidents began touring the United States and Europe to see firsthand new mechanical and engineering developments and styling trends. "I tried to keep my eyes open for any new things that applied to the automobile industry," he recalled years later. He and Donaldson Brown created a Policy Group for Social and Economic Trends that monitored the effects of these conditions on present and future plans.

Alfred Sloan was among the first of America's corporate pillars to recognize that product appearance influenced sales. Sloan described the revelation in his autobiography. The Auburn Automobile Company introduced 1924 models with fully enclosed bodies (in contrast to Ford's still open Model Ts). The new Auburns, mechanically identical to the previous year, featured "advanced styling and coloring. A sweeping belt line . . . often painted in contrasting colors [that] gave a striking impression." Sloan and Brown took note when Auburn's revenue losses from 1923 turned to gains before 1925.

(left) The second-generation Corvette featured optional big-block engines, moving Corvette to the forefront of the muscle car movement.

GM chairman Alfred Sloan hired Harley Earl in 1927 from his Hollywood family car-body business to create the "Art and Colour Section," the world's first styling department. By dictating that Earl's department restyle GM cars each year, Sloan is credited for introducing planned obsolescence. 2002 General Motors Corporation. Used with permission of GM Media Archives.

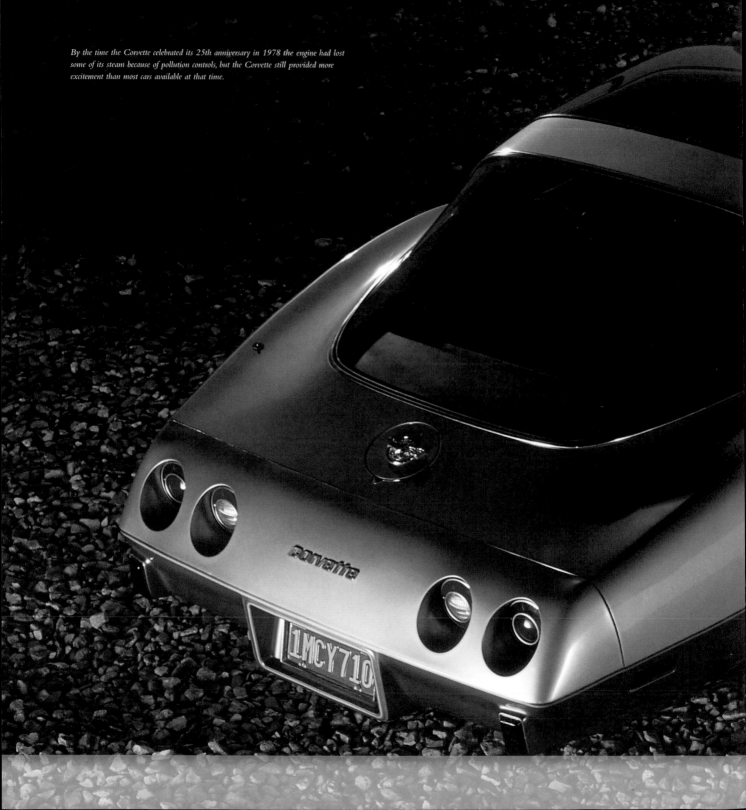

By the time the Corvette celebrated its 25th anniversary in 1978 the engine had lost some of its steam because of pollution controls, but the Corvette still provided more excitement than most cars available at that time.

Lawrence P. Fisher, general manager of Cadillac division and one of the founding brothers of Fisher Body (the corporation's body maker but still outside GM at this point), agreed with Sloan that GM would benefit by paying more attention to the cars' appearance. Cadillac still sold bare chassis to wealthy clients who wanted to be seen in personalized custom vehicles. One of Cadillac's Los Angeles dealers, Don Lee, had acquired J. W. Earl Automobile Works, a custom coach-building firm, eight years earlier. Many of Lee's customers were Hollywood stars, flashy, trend-setting people who wanted cars that reflected their screen images and, more important, were different from anyone else's.

J. W. Earl had started in 1911 making custom car and truck bodies as service vehicles and props for the emerging talking-film industry. By 1918, when it showed its first complete automobiles at the L.A. Auto Show, Earl occupied its own three-story, block-long building south of downtown Los Angeles. Earl's Stanford University–educated son, Harley, had designed not only car bodies but also airplane fuselages for the Glen L. Martin Company, one of southern California's earliest aircraft manufacturers. Airplane lines and contours were part of Harley Earl's post-Stanford education.

Fisher first visited Harley Earl in early 1925. He watched the 32-year-old designer forming scale models of cars in clay. This technique let Earl experiment with lines, shapes, and reflections of light before committing to large-scale wood mock-ups. Earl blended fender lines into running

Cadillac boss Lawrence Fisher hired Earl to create the 1927 LaSalle, the industry's first car designed by a stylist instead of an engineer.

Harley Earl initiated and ran the styling department at GM until he retired in 1959. His credits include tail fins and the original Corvette. 2002 General Motors Corporation. Used with permission of GM Media Archives.

The Corvette recaptured its lost performance when
the fourth-generation car was introduced for the
1984 model year.

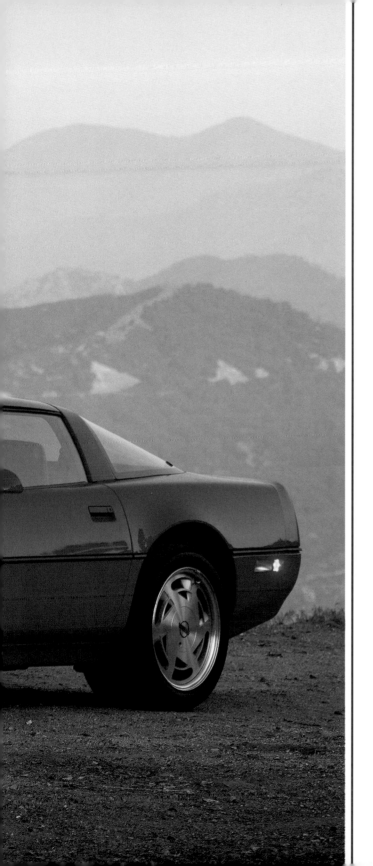

boards, hoods into windshields, engine compartment sheet metal into body side panels. For Fisher this was a revelation. At most American car makers, the chassis engineering division designed and delivered its frame complete with the engine, hood, radiator, running gear, suspension, wheels, tires, and fenders to each body division, which bolted on its own passenger compartment, each element conceived independently. Fisher saw Earl with shapes that appeared molded from one piece and cast from one mind.

Fisher brought Sloan photographs. They had a new entry-level Cadillac for spring 1927 called the LaSalle, part of Sloan's effort to fill holes in GM's price range. They hired Earl as a consultant to design a car as beautiful as his customs. While he was in Detroit, Fisher showed him working drawings of the 1927 Cadillacs. Fisher and Sloan now feared these would be overshadowed by Earl's LaSalle. Harley pronounced the Cadillacs drab but thought that fitting wire wheels would at least lower them, making them appear longer and more dramatic. He suggested using bright paint. Cadillac in 1924 had offered three colors for its model range. "Hollywood Harley" recommended they offer cars in any of 500 color and interior options.

The LaSalle turned heads and brought the buyers into showrooms. Sales of the Cadillacs brought Earl back to General Motors to head Sloan's newest creation, the Art and Colour Section, starting on July 27, 1927. Answering only to Sloan, he was to direct the design of general production cars and do research and development work by creating additional special car designs.

Not until September 1940 did his promotion to vice president of a renamed styling section give him the title to match his impact. This came partially as the result of a highly visible failure in 1929. Earl designed a car for Buick, GM's most profitable division since 1918. He intended for the car body to fit down inside the chassis, but the engineering department "redesigned" it so it would mount onto its existing chassis without any additional work. Preoccupied by design assignments that followed the Buick, Earl never saw the car after its designs left his studio in late 1927.

The design would have been a gorgeous and bold leap from the previous model. With engineering's revisions, it was a disaster, quickly dubbed the "pregnant Buick." Division sales plummeted and Sloan pulled it from production after only one year. The damage was brutal; the Depression, which began in October 1929, hit Buick the hardest of any GM division, turning the once profitable nameplate into a money-losing division.

Earl escaped unscathed. Sloan reacted decisively. He tightened his authority over manufacturing and production engineers. The Buick clarified for everyone the impact of successful and awful design. It fathered another GM innovation: the annual model change. Previously, successful car builders updated their models whenever improvements were ready, generally shutting down production to instigate the changes. Sloan first observed this new effect in 1924 among weaker competitors Hudson, Dodge, and Chrysler, who, in that year's shrinking market, brought out new models with heavy promotion and experienced a healthy and enduring surge in sales. Sloan's sales department began to capitalize on this phenomenon. "Each year," he wrote in his autobiography, "we build the best car we possibly can to satisfy our customer, and then the next year we build another to make him dissatisfied." There was sound Sloan-Brown business sense to this. "The primary object of the corporation," he wrote, "was to make money, not just to make motor cars."

When Earl's 1933 Chevrolets were introduced, the public, startled by the bulging curves and uneasy proportions of the 1929 Buick, loved them. People called the cars stylish, judging the overall design unified. The success of these cars led the public to label their creators "stylists."

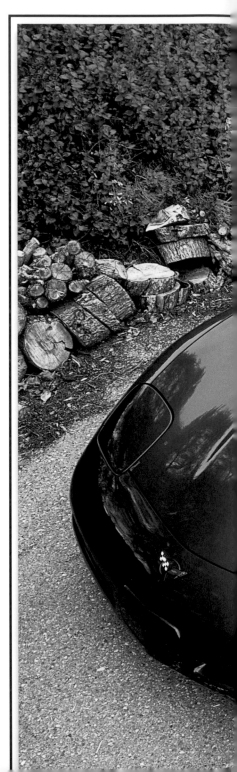

Over the years Chevrolet has produced several limited edition cars to celebrate the Corvette's being chosen as the official pace car for the Indianapolis 500. This is a 1998 example.

Mitchell's Sting Ray was somewhat street legal, and he used it as a daily driver to commute to work. 2002 General Motors Corporation. Used with permission of GM Media Archives.

Some within GM called Earl's department "the beauty parlor," but their opinions changed as year-end reports tallied each division's performance. Sloan was an advocate from the start, and Earl's influence grew.

"For a long while," Sloan wrote, "the Art and Colour Section occupied quarters in the General Motors Building Annex in Detroit. The focal point of the work area was the blackboard room. To this room came executives from Fisher Body and every car division. We were all window-shoppers in the Art and Colour 'sales' rooms," he continued. "Art and Colour was proposing new designs, presenting new idea sketches, selling progress. As time went by more and more of these ideas appeared to be feasible."

Earl first visited Europe for GM in 1927 with Lawrence Fisher, calling on every car manufacturer and car body maker they could get in to see. They learned that what worked in one part of the world would not be appropriate in another. Some ideas would succeed only if they were adapted and modified to match GM's assessment of what was good for America and good for GM customers.

World War II ended in Europe in May 1945 and in Japan in August. Years of hard work and good wages with few goods available for consumers had left Americans with pent-up desires, especially for products using steel or rubber, two materials critical to war efforts. When North Korea invaded South Korea on June 25, 1950, it seemed worrying but distant. Americans went to fight because it became clear that communism was the real enemy, but it was another war thousands of miles away. It need not interrupt the return to American life that many had begun anxiously.

In 1950, there were 1.5 million television sets in America. A year later there would be 15 million sets. In November 1952, Americans elected General Dwight David "Ike" Eisenhower their next president. Eisenhower represented the battle against the Red Menace, the political code name for the threat of communism taking over the world. He quickly authorized an interstate highway system, similar to the auto routes, autobahns, and autostradi of Europe. The long, smooth American roads, meant for efficient movement of U.S. armed forces, fueled a hunger for automobiles. The country was developing a middle class that had enough money to pay its bills with some left over. Leisure time became a concept and then a reality, and the automobile helped. By December 1, 1950, the United States had 2,200 drive-in theaters, double the year before. Magazines and newspapers questioned whether or not automobiles would kill movie theaters.

By the early 1950s, air conditioning, radios, and automatic transmissions were primary options that General Motors intended to fit as standard equipment on all but its lowest priced products. GM felt these were what Americans wanted most in their cars. With some 80 models in their production line-up in the early 1950s, the central office fulfilled Alfred Sloan's promise to offer a car for every purse and purpose. Earl's blackboards revealed a new car Harley hoped one of the divisions would buy, one he knew needed GM's touch. It was a sports car that he felt sure Mr. Sloan's successor, the corporation's new chairman, Charles E. Wilson, would see as "exclusive in design, possessing superior engineering qualities and carrying with it a peculiar appeal to fashion [that] afforded the opportunity for a favorable rate of return."

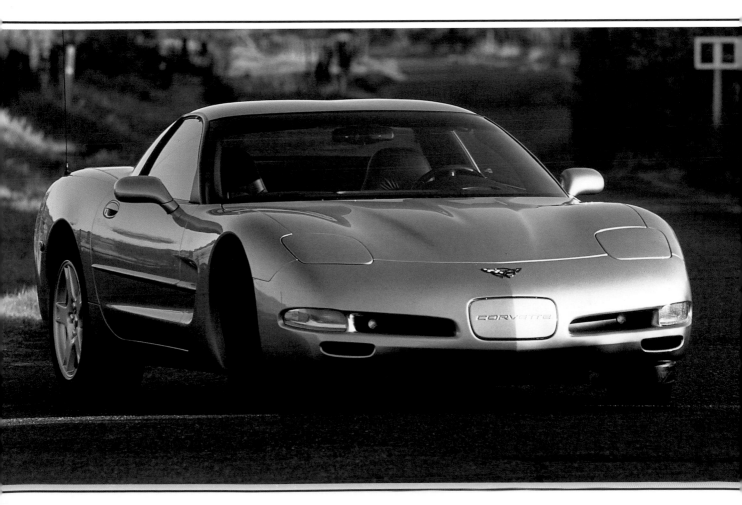

Corvette's C5 generation appeared first as a fastback coupe in 1997, then in 1998 as a convertible. In 1999, this notchback, or hardtop, model appeared as the third variation of the series.

1950-1952

CHAPTER TWO

COMPETITION
CREATES A WATERSHED

ebster's New World Dictionary defines a watershed as "a ridge or stretch of land dividing the areas drained by different rivers or river systems." It also says it's "a crucial turning point affecting action, opinion, etc." Chevrolet's sports car was both of these. Several independent events, forces outside Chevrolet and General Motors, flowing like separate rivers, moved toward one single point in the early 1950s. They gathered speed, power, and mass as they tumbled toward Chevrolet's crucial turning point.

The first of these forces was organized labor. Motivated by patriotism, its members had worked hard during World War II, but by 1950 workers had grown restive. When the government lifted wartime wage and price controls, the United Auto Workers (UAW) sought pay raises. Unhappy with Chrysler's offer, they struck the number three automaker on January 24, 1950, and stayed out for 100 days. GM's President Charlie Wilson would not risk his corporation. Chevrolet had just passed Ford sales for the first time since 1927, selling more than one million cars in 1949. These had been restyled with Harley Earl's supervision under new Chevrolet studio chief Ed Glowacke. GM settled a five-year benchmark contract with autoworkers on May 23. A month later, on June 25, North Korea invaded South Korea, and a world that had seemed safe and secure for automakers and their workers began to change.

Within a year the United States had committed 2.9 million troops and Chevrolet was occupied with its largest military contract ever, manufacturing Allison J-35 turbojet engines at its Tonawanda, New York, plant. This consumed factory floor space and its labor force. In its automobile line, Chevrolet lagged behind Ford sales in convertibles and station wagons, a fact that told division general manager Thomas H. Keating that Chevrolet held little interest among younger buyers, with families and without. Yet Chevrolet, despite outselling Ford again in 1950, was tapped out from jet engine production and a slowing *(previous pages) This was the optimist's view of the future, deeply ingrained in the minds and hearts of U.S. industrialists: Americans, flush with post war self-confidence, zooming toward tomorrow in a car like none of them had seen before.*

Within months Jaguar knew it had a winner and re-engineered the car to accept a steel body, ultimately producing 12,078 examples between 1949 and 1954. They introduced a coupe in 1951 and a convertible in 1953. The car's 10-second 0–60 miles-per-hour time and 120 miles-per-hour top speed (hence its "XK-120" designation) inspired Harley Earl.

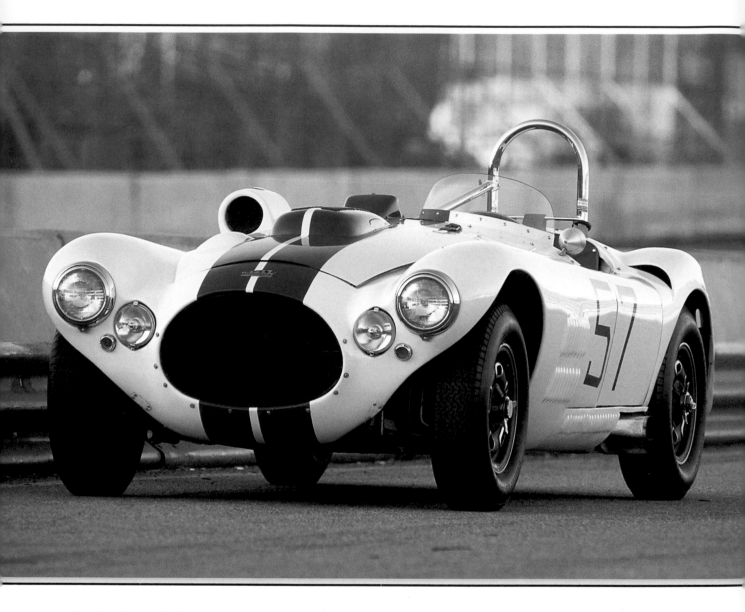

Briggs Weaver designed two identical roadsters and a coupe for Cunningham. They weighed 2,400 pounds, nearly 900 pounds less than Cunningham's previous racing models, and these new cars were slightly smaller as well.

economy. It couldn't afford to restyle its cars for 1953, although Ford would have new models in 1952. Keating approached GM's engineering policy committee (another Sloan/Brown instigation) and convinced committee members that Chevrolet's conservatism was hurting its sales. He felt its reliance on six-cylinder engines exemplified the condition, particularly when Detroit's best-kept secret was Ford's eminent overhead-valve V-8 (which would arrive for the 1954 model year). After seeing Ford's smart new 1952 models in late December 1951, Wilson agreed to help Keating turn Chevrolet around. In early January 1952, he told the Chevrolet chief he could have anything, or anyone, he needed to improve Chevrolet. Keating identified Ed Cole, the Cadillac engineer who had managed the development team responsible for Cadillac's 331-cubic-inch displacement, 210-horsepower, short-stroke high-compression, overhead-valve V-8 in 1949.

Ed Cole graduated from the GM Institute in December 1932 and promptly joined the Cadillac division as an engineer. Eighteen years later, racer Briggs Cunningham entered the 1950 Le Mans race with a Cadillac-V-8-engined Ford, the Fordillac. Then he learned from race organizers he could only race production-based cars or pure prototypes. Stymied, he contacted Cadillac's chief engineer, Cole, who suggested Cunningham run Cadillac Coupe de Villes. Cole tested Cunningham's Fordillac on the chassis dynamometer, and from what he learned, he designed a five-carburetor manifold for the GM cars. He also helped Cunningham prepare an ungainly prototype dubbed "Le Monstre." Finally, he loaned him a Cadillac engineer, Frank Burrell, who went along to the race. (The coupe finished the race in 10th place; Le Monstre came in 11th.) In early 1952, Cole was supervising Cadillac's production of the army's T-41 tank at GM's plant in Cleveland. In the spring, Wilson asked Harlow Curtice, his executive vice president, to supervise Chevrolet's turnaround. Curtice summoned Cole home immediately. Soon after Cole arrived, after his promotion to chief engineer at Chevrolet division in May 1952, he brought in chassis expert Maurice Olley. Early in his career, Olley had worked for Rolls-Royce in England and in America before joining Cadillac and Cole. Now Keating had the engineers he needed to transform Chevrolet into a younger buyer's car company. What he needed next was a product.

STEEL, THE ESSENTIAL ELEMENT

Steel was the second pivotal element in this story. It was crucial for manufacturing automobiles. It also was essential for making the tanks, ships, and shells bound for Korea. The war there made things complicated. U.S. President Harry Truman re-imposed wage and price controls on January 26, 1951, six months after the United States joined the fight in Korea and about four years after lifting the controls placed during World War II. Yet Truman's new Wage Stabilization Board authorized pay increases for steelworkers. The steel companies, believing they were unable to raise prices to cover the elevated costs, refused to pay the new rates. Intending to avert a strike, Truman seized the steel mills on April 8, 1952, using the existing employees and management to produce steel. Answering a suit by the mill owners, a lower court judge ruled Truman's seizures illegal. In response, 600,000 steelworkers walked out, dropping steel production from 300,000 tons a day to 20,000. At the end of May, a higher court transferred

By this time, Briggs had found better power and easier access to engines and accessories through Chrysler Corporation. He fitted his cars with Chrysler's 331, cubic-inch V-8s, topped with four dual-throat Weber carburetors.

the mills back to government control and workers returned. Then on June 2, the Supreme Court ruled Truman had usurped powers that belonged to Congress in a time of war. Workers went back out and remained outside for 53 days. In sympathy, Great Lakes iron-ore shippers remained in port, interrupting movement of this critical raw material. Because of the wartime need for steel, the government's National Production Authority halted all steel delivery to consumer goods producers. Workers returned on July 24, 1952, with a smaller wage increase than first approved while steel was allowed to raise its rates $4 per ton. For the auto industry, the Korean War had invaded Detroit. Only Ford Motor Company's own River Rouge plant, fed with Ford iron-ore delivered by Ford's own shipping line, ensured them steel output during the strike. For GM and others, even when the huge ore ships returned to the Great Lakes, steel producers and the auto industry had to face a threatened coal miner's strike in the fall of 1952 that would again shut down the steel-making furnaces. The seed of doubt this episode had planted among all auto makers required alternative thinking about materials.

Fiberglass was the most appealing, and this was the third element of the inevitable flow toward the Chevrolet sports car. By 1952, however, GM and the entire industry had known about this material—also called glass reinforced plastic (GRP)—for 20 years. Its uses went back even further.

Plastic itself dates back to 1868 when chemist John Wesley Hyatt produced the first cellulose nitrate compound. He called it "celluloid" and found commercial applications for it in billiard balls, dentures,

Between World War I and II, Howard "Dutch" Darrin created some of America's most memorable and stylish car bodies for luxury car builders such as Packard and Lincoln. For his "own" two-seat sports car, he carried over classic features such as the half-convertible roof with exposed landau bars. It was car styling out of another time, and it never caught on.

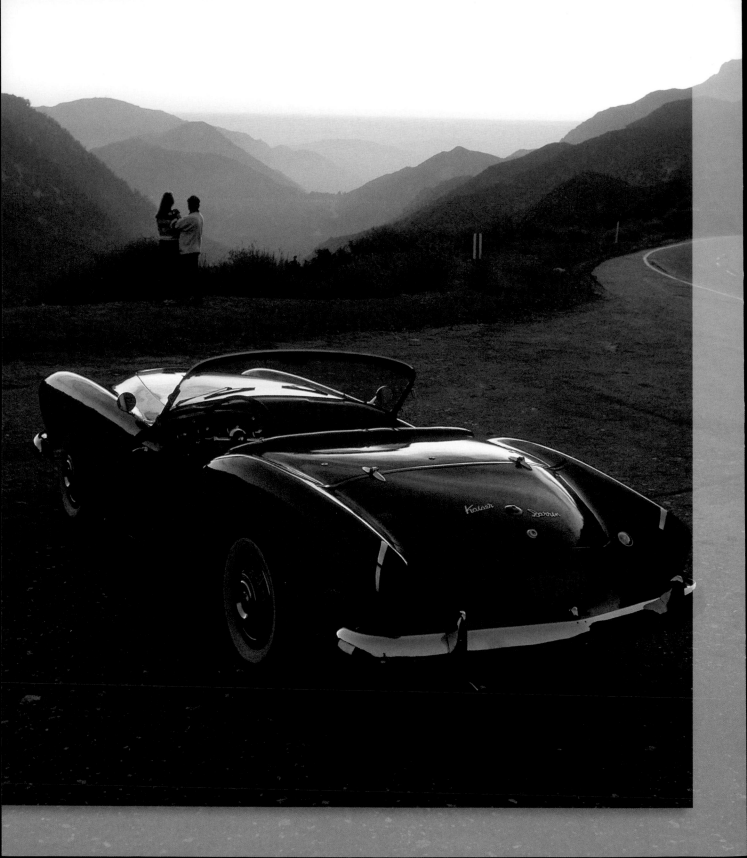

men's shirt collars, and side windows in automobiles; however, the sun's ultraviolet rays rapidly yellowed and dried out the material in windows.

Dr. Leo Henrik Baekelund first formed phenolformaldehyde in 1909. He named the resin he developed from his compound "Bakelite." Electrical appliance makers used it for decades to save hands from heat and isolate metal components from electric current.

Through the next 35 years, plastic development continued. While there were only two basic resin compounds offered commercially at the end of World War I, there were dozens by the outbreak of World War II. By 1929 in Germany, Daimler-Benz and Bayer Chemical had begun to mold body panels, rear decks, and fenders; however, they dropped the project after completing only a few prototypes.

Henry Ford first got interested in industrial uses for soybeans and their by-products in 1931. These included phenolformaldehyde, which Henry learned could be mixed with various wood fibers to make a strong, reinforced plastic. Ford's engineers could mold or press it into compound curves or straight, flat panels. By 1941, his staff scientists constructed an entire car body out of the soybean plastic.

By 1940, General Motors, working with Dr. R. Games Slater, produced dashboard trim and even steering wheels out of plastic. Slater was a research chemist with Owens-Corning, and in 1944 he and others experimented with fibers of fine glass woven into a mat and bonded with polyester resins. O-C marketed this substance under the trade name Fiberglas, and while it was different from GRP, the two materials became universally known as fiberglass.

Out in southern California, boat builders recognized that fiberglass yielded an easily shaped, low-maintenance hull. Bill Tritt, a boat maker in Montecito near Santa Barbara, started the Glasspar Company in 1950. He and his partners got a call from an air force major, Kenneth Brooks, who had another use in mind. He wanted to give his wife a Jeep for her personal use, but he wanted it to look better than a boxy Jeep.

Tritt took the job and completed the car body early in 1951. He named it the Boxer. It was smart looking and its light green color attracted attention. One very interested individual was the local sales engineer from U.S. Rubber. The company's Naugatuck, Connecticut, chemical division produced Vibrin, a polyester plastic that Tritt used as a key ingredient in the mix of his GRP. Naugatuck's Vibrin sales director, Dr. Earl Ebers, became a vigorous supporter of the Boxer project. He had long wanted to get into a Detroit design studio, but he'd had no luck. (Naugatuck had another compound, a cloth it also wanted to see in automobiles, called Naugahyde.)

Glasspar and Naugatuck collaborated on making four more Boxer bodies in mid-February 1952.

Darrin first experimented with fiberglass car bodies in 1946. He recognized the economy and creative flexibility it offered. By 1952, he had convinced Henry J. Kaiser to enter the sports car market, and in 1953 Kaiser introduced this two-seater. Through 1953 and 1954, he sold only 435 examples.

Darrin devised sliding doors that disappeared into unused space in the front fenders behind the front tires. It offered a less cramped interior than Jaguar's XK-120, but it was still far from spacious. Sadly, it cost nearly $5,000, as much as a Cadillac or Lincoln sedan.

In a fluke of timing, days later, *Life* magazine published a lengthy illustrated story called "Plastic Bodies for Autos" just as newspapers and trade magazines carried stories of continuing steel shortages. Ebers' phone began to ring. One call came from another southern Californian, a Chrysler and Willys dealer in Downey, south of Los Angeles, named Blanchard "Woody" Woodill. Friends had talked him into making his own sports car. He eventually bought something like 90 bodies from Glasspar. He manufactured a car he called the Wildfire, his version of the Brooks Boxer that he built on an angle-iron chassis made for him by Harold Post in Orange, California. Woodill sold his Wildfire either as a kit for about $1,200, or complete with a Willys 90-horsepower six-cylinder or Ford 135-horsepower flathead V-8 engine for about $3,200.

More significantly, Chevrolet engineering called Ebers. (GM already had some experience with fiberglass. During World War II, Cadillac scrapped the tooling for its body fenders. After the war ended, Ed Cole, who knew of the material from various wartime applications, found it was a quick way to

While its side view appropriated sweeps and curves from Jaguar, the front end was unique to Darrin, and many feel that was part of the car's downfall. The "puckered kiss" grille was not widely admired. Behind it labored a standard Kaiser 90-horsepower six-cylinder mated to a three-speed automatic that yielded only 98 miles-per-hour top speed and 0–60 miles-per-hour acceleration in 15 seconds.

make replacement fenders.) Ebers acquired the Brooks Boxer and showed it at the National Plastics Exposition in mid-March 1952. He met other Chevy engineers during the shows, and from their reactions, he decided to drive the car directly to GM's styling auditorium. Ebers and his staff showed engineers they could take a mold from a fender and produce an exact duplicate out of fiberglass.

Chevrolet engineering and GM styling quickly adopted the material for experimental car bodies and dream cars. They also used it on these prototype and show cars to replace conventional plaster of Paris–over–wood forms that previously they had covered with hand-hammered steel.

There in his own styling auditorium in March 1952, Harley Earl could see this vehicle itself, not just magazine and newspaper pictures and stories. He saw materials that were the next advance in his car design/model-making process, a substance that could make something happen, in prototype form, quickly and easily. He also saw before him a type of automobile that had been in his head for some time.

THE FOURTH ELEMENT

The fourth element was the sports car itself. While these two-seaters raised little interest among many American customers, they already had captivated America's most innovative car designers, engineers, and builders. As early as April 1944, Maurice Olley, Ed Cole's chassis design engineer at Cadillac but on loan to the British Ministry of Supply at the time, spoke to the Society of Automotive Engineers. He speculated on the types of cars consumers would see after World War II. As a veteran of automaking in the United Kingdom and the United States, he bemoaned Detroit's devotion to chrome and sheet metal excesses. He enthused over small, fun-to-drive cars, hoping to see new vehicles patterned after European models but possessing American engineering.

In 1952, U.S. buyers registered more than four million new automobiles. More than three million of these were four-door and two-door sedans, but only 11,199 of them were sports cars. Some of the difference came from Americans' need for family cars that were unavailable in the 1940s due to World War II. Still, by 1950 many young people, including Earl's own sons, Jerry and Jim, found sports cars intriguing. (The boys came by their interest hereditarily. In 1911, when Harley was 18, he entered and won a car race driving his father's sporty Mercer roadster.) Few models were available in the early 1950s, however; tiny Crosleys and curvaceous Kurtis-Krafts were built in the United States. The new Cunningham Cadillac–engined C-1 or the Anglo-American Nash-Healey was far too costly for even Jerry Earl's college student budget. England produced the sensuous Jaguar

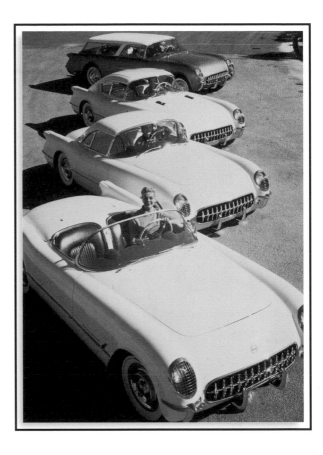

In addition to the roadster version (bottom), Chevrolet experimented with other variations of the Corvette, such as a version with a removable hardtop (second from bottom), the fastback Corvair (third from bottom), which was shown at the 1954 Motorama show, and the Nomad version (top), which later appeared in production form using Chevrolet's full-sized sedan frame. 2002 General Motors Corporation. Used with permission of GM Media Archives.

This was the 33rd car produced, now restored to NCRS (National Corvette Restorers' Society) highest standards. While GM design chief Harley Earl supervised its appearance, he assigned Bob McLean to create its specifications, and Duane "Sparky" Bohnstedt to style its appearance.

XK-120, the spindly MG-TC, the Aston-Martins, and Triumphs. These were primarily intended for export sale in North America (nearly 60 percent of the 12,000 XK-120s produced ended up here). They sold to so few Americans, however, that the domestic makers paid little attention to them publicly.

Harley Earl noticed. As GM's vice president of styling, his budget was generous and his expenses were never challenged. His department produced automobiles for the major annual European shows, taking cars to Paris, Geneva, London, and Milan. Earl and GM officers and designers often stayed for weeks, visiting car makers and watching international races. Earl appreciated the cars he saw overseas,

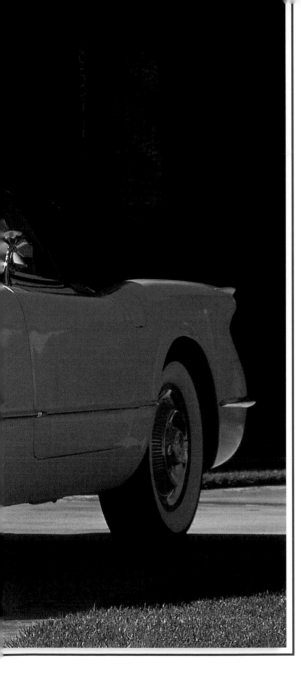

and he admired the lines and the performance of the Jaguars, though he knew European sports cars might not translate directly to GM's audiences.

Earl was well acquainted with international sportsman Briggs Cunningham who had raced yachts for the America's Cup and Cadillacs at Le Mans. In June 1950, Earl watched the 24-hour race alongside Ed Cole with a guest pass from the Cunningham team. Later that year when Cunningham competed in an endurance race at Watkins Glen, New York, Earl arrived in his 20-foot-long, two-seat Buick Y-job. Cunningham, who was near to completing his prototype C-1 production road car, teased him, asking Earl why GM couldn't build a "proper" sports car, something Cunningham could race. A year later, after Cunningham ran four of his 1951 C-2R models at Le Mans, Earl arrived at Watkins Glen in his new, smaller 16 1/2-foot Buick LeSabre. This still was no sports car from General Motors. So Cunningham built his C-3, completing the first in 1953, but now using Chrysler's new hemispherical head

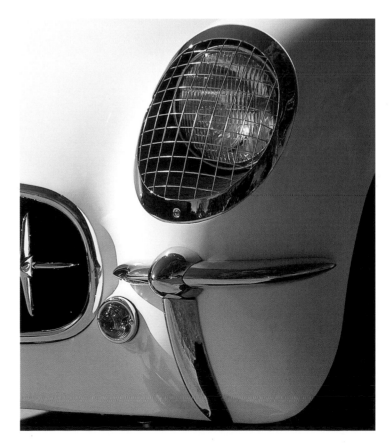

Harley Earl designed countless custom bodies for his father's Cadillac customers, always favoring long hood and short rear deck proportions. Earl noticed sports cars he saw from Europe copied this style and he specified the same for his new creation: the Corvette. European race cars covered their lights to protect the glass from flying stones.

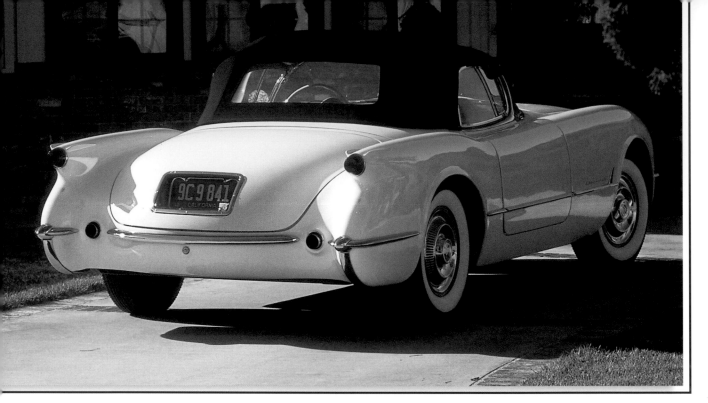

Harley Earl loved to make cars look longer, lower, and wider than they really were. Bob McLean, working from Jaguar XK-120 dimensions, stretched, squashed, and pulled those dimensions to create the new Corvette. To make sure the passenger cockpit and engine fit within its 102-inch wheelbase, McLean began his design work at the rear axle and worked forward, setting dimensions as he went.

Molding the plastic body to "Sparky" Bohnstedt's bullet taillights caused fiberglass body makers terrible problems. Restorers now moan about the delicate multi piece rear bumper assemblies. Airflow over the rear stalled exhaust fumes, and early cars often discolored around the protruding pipes.

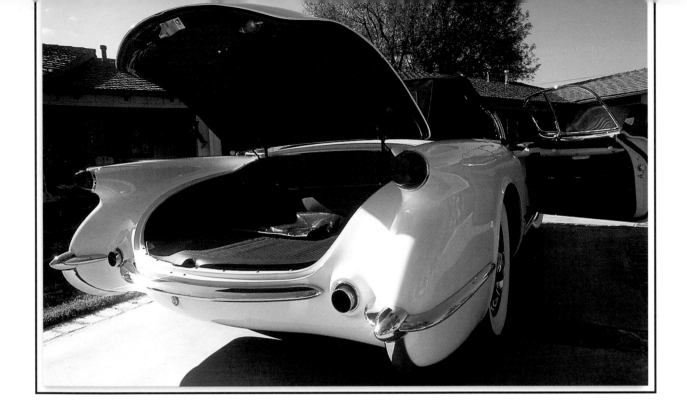

high-performance, 310-horsepower V-8s. His cars had brought attention to America's modest efforts at sports car production wherever they competed overseas during the early 1950s, but Cunningham continued to chide his friend Harley.

Several English-American hybrids appeared. A Belgian engineer of Russian parentage, Zora Arkus-Duntov, helped other racers stuff Ford, Mercury, and then Cadillac V-8s into Sydney Allard's unsophisticated English roadsters in the late 1940s. (Listing his hometown as New York, Duntov raced an Allard J2 with a Ford V-8 fitted with cylinder heads of his own design in the inaugural Palm Beach Shores road race, January 3, 1950. He helped another New Yorker, Tom Cole, prepare his Cadillac-engined Allard as well.) On the West Coast, Frank Kurtis produced 36 of his Sports model in 1949 before television super-salesman Earl "Mad Man" Muntz acquired the rights. He renamed the car the Muntz Jet and eventually built 394 of them, using Cadillac V-8s in 1949 and Lincoln engines from 1950 through 1954. Englishman Donald Healey made a deal in 1951 to use 3.8-liter, six-cylinder Nash engines in his Pininfarina-bodied coupes and roadsters. He shipped all 506 to the United States.

American industrialist Henry J. Kaiser entered the small market for compact, sporty cars with his Henry J in late 1950. He had collaborated with Joseph W. Frazer, a former Chrysler vice president of sales, to form Kaiser-Frazer. They hired two exceptional designers, Howard "Dutch" Darrin and Bill Stout. Darrin had created stunning bodies for Packards, Lincolns, and others; one of Stout's more significant projects was his own Scarabs, design-study vehicles, some of them fabricated in fiberglass.

In Milwaukee, industrial designer Brooks Stevens used the Henry J 100-inch wheelbase chassis and installed Willys 2.8-liter, in-line six-cylinder engines. He created bodywork resembling the fearsome 1930s Mercedes-Benz SSK two-seat racers. Stevens called his car the Excalibur J, and he built

True to sports cars of the era, luggage capacity in the trunk was severely limited. As Chevrolet hurried the car into production, it could only offer it in white with a red interior. Chevrolet offered two options, a heater and an AM radio, though all 300 first-year cars were produced with the options as standard equipment.

Postwar steel shortages in the United Kingdom delayed development of Jaguar's new Mk. VII sedan, but the firm had completed development of its new XK engine. Jaguar decided to build a two-seat aluminum-body roadster to show off the engine and create a demand for the new sedan. They only planned to produce 240 roadsters.

three prototypes that ran successfully in Sports Car Club of America (SCCA) D-modified class races. Stevens wanted Kaiser-Frazer to put into production a road-going version of his Excalibur, but Henry Kaiser wasn't yet convinced that America was ready for a sports car.

Dutch Darrin worked for Kaiser out of his own studio in California. On his own time with expenses coming from his own pocket, Darrin created a low, sleek two-seater hoping, like Stevens, that Kaiser would produce it. As with Stevens' car, Darrin based his roadster on the Henry J chassis, using the same Willys six. He fabricated its body out of fiberglass. In August 1952, he showed the car to Kaiser, who didn't like it until his new young wife fell in love with it. When Kaiser asked Darrin why he'd done it, the designer told him he'd heard that Chevrolet and Ford were already working on similar projects. This car, Darrin explained, would be the Kaiser-Frazer answer to the others' challenges.

WHAT THE CUSTOMER WANTS

Nearly every element was in place, each ingredient flowing steadily toward the confluence, the next turning point in Chevrolet's auto-making history. By the early 1950s, Alfred Sloan's faith in Harley Earl had moved the designer into the as-yet undefined realm of product planner. Earl used carefully controlled environments to monitor public response to his ideas.

GM had begun hosting "Industrialists' Luncheons" in the early 1930s at the Waldorf Astoria Hotel grand ballroom in New York City. It was clever psychology; GM showed the future to these men (and it was men only; their wives were not invited). By taking these influential customers into its confidence, the corporation educated them at the same time it gauged what these conservative individuals liked. When these men left the Waldorf, they knew where GM was headed. They could knowledgeably advise their clients to invest in GM. At the same time, Harley Earl and other GM officers knew better what kind of automobile these most influential—and wealthy—customers might buy for themselves.

GM's challenge to Darrin and Kaiser was a not-so-well-kept secret by mid-1952. In Chevrolet studios, now directed by Clare MacKichan, designers frantically worked toward a show opening January 17 at the Waldorf Astoria. Corporate accountants had balanced the cost-per-luncheon-invitee of the earlier events against possible sales revenues. They calculated the luncheons as losses, giving no value to the information gained or goodwill spent. Executive vice president Harlow Curtice had a business background, yet he understood the Sloan/Brown theory of giving an idea time to pay off. Under his influence (he would become president of GM in February 1953 when Charlie Wilson went to Eisenhower's Pentagon as secretary of defense), the luncheons became broader and more public. Renamed *Transportation Unlimited,* these shows ran several days. Wives were definitely invited. These programs in 1949 and 1950 met with so much success that the sales staff considered taking the show beyond New York. With strained finances and few new products to show off, however, Curtice canceled the 1951 and 1952 series. (Earl was forced to debut his LeSabre dream car at the Paris auto show in 1952.)

For 1953, Curtice approved adding Miami in February, then Chicago, Los Angeles, San Francisco, Dallas, and concluding in Kansas City in June. Looking for a more evocative title, they appropriated the term *Motorama* from a fledgling car display that had begun in Los Angeles three years earlier. For 1953, Harley Earl would introduce the Cadillac El Dorado, the Oldsmobile Fiesta, Wildfire, and Starfire, the Buick Skylark and Wildcat, the Pontiac Parisienne, and another model from Cadillac, the

Seat movement, which was limited by frame rails rising over the rear axle, cramped the car's interior, yet many fans, seduced by the sweeping exterior lines of what they argued was the most beautiful car in the world, accepted the tight fit. In England, the car sold for £998, slightly less than $3,500.

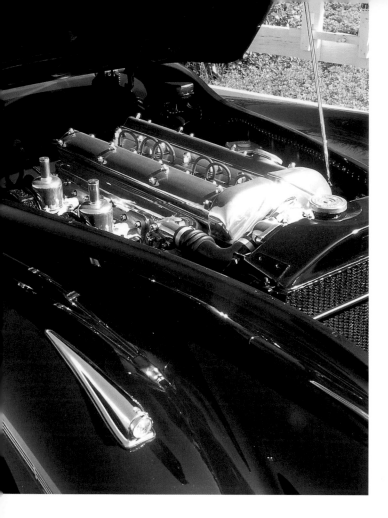

LeMans. Oldsmobile's Starfire and Wildfire and the Cadillac LeMans were fiberglass. Wilson and Curtice had excluded Chevrolet from the 1949 and 1950 shows, believing that a division producing cars for the masses didn't project the right image for dream cars. Tom Keating asked for a new vote for 1953.

Between 1950 and 1952, Chevrolet division sales dropped almost 40 percent, prompting Wilson's offer of anyone or anything. Keating now had Ed Cole and the board of directors' support. Now he and Cole needed something novel to excite customers, to draw them into the showrooms. Keating made it clear that the 1953 Motorama would have at least one Chevrolet. Soon after Cole got to Detroit from Cleveland in late May 1952, he and Keating went shopping at Earl's studio.

Earl drew his sports car idea from an existing pattern: Fit a unique, stylish two-seat body around a production engine and frame. He first envisioned this car in the late fall of 1951 as something GM could sell for about $1,800, close to Triumphs or MGs and about half the price of Jaguar's $3,345 XK-120. He even moved a Jaguar into the Body Development Studio so his staff had a design target. He assigned Bob McLean, a young California Institute of Technology graduate of both engineering and industrial design, to create a car. He tagged a recent hire, Duane "Sparky" Bohnstedt, to style the body for the project.

(bottom opposite) While beauty is subjective, performance is measurable, and the Jaguar XK engine yielded the fastest production automobile in the world. Its 160 horsepower provided a top speed of 120 miles per hour. A later XK-120 version, the XK-120M, offered 180 horsepower and achieved better than 130 miles per hour from its in-line six-cylinder engine.

Earl wanted to use a V-8 engine, but only Cadillac, Buick (with a 322-cubic inch displacement 188-horsepower engine), and Oldsmobile (with its 304-cubic inch displacement 165-horsepower version) produced them, and the upper division's jealously guarded their technological advances as part of their marketing advantage. He'd have to use Chevrolet's six. Earl's other objectives, including adopting the Jaguar as inspiration, set McLean's direction. Virtually every sports car of the period emulated the long hood/short rear deck parameters of the classic 1930s cars. McLean and Bohnstedt followed convention. McLean penciled in the in-line six-cylinder engine. He designed a new 102-inch wheelbase frame. To make everything fit, he began his design work at the rear axle of his chassis, drawing in the passenger/driver compartment and working forward. He set the engine well back, matching the Jaguar and allowing him to keep the car balanced. The car had nearly equal weight on the front and rear axles when it was loaded. McLean drew a 57-inch front track and 59-inch rear, some 6 inches wider at front and 9 inches wider at the rear than the Jaguar. This followed Earl's standards of making cars appear lower, longer, and wider.

Time passed rapidly. Near the end of spring, on June 2, 1952, Earl finally showed Bohnstedt's finished full-size clay model to a small group, including GM chairman Harlow Curtice, who had enjoyed a private showing earlier. For this show, Curtice brought along Tom Keating and Ed Cole.

Cole and Keating were thrilled, Cole, by some accounts, almost jumping in excitement. They made it clear to Earl that this was the car they wanted for Motorama. Earl was equally pleased. Without their enthusiasm, the sports car would have languished in the studio. No other division had expressed any interest in adopting the project. Only one feature remained to power this new car into the market place. The fifth and final element that made the sports car real was the issue of competition, not in racing, but in production.

BECOMING A SPORTS CAR ENTHUSIAST

Ford's styling chief, Franklin Q. Hershey, had worked for GM, reaching the position of Cadillac's chief of design before he was terminated in 1948 for running a side business making ashtrays. Unlike his boss at GM, Hershey didn't much care for sports cars or European cars. He loved American classics, having worked at Walter Murphy Body Company in Pasadena, California, in his first job making custom bodies for Duesenbergs, Packards, and other cars. So in late 1951 when a group of Ford designers and engineers formed the Ford Motorsports Club, Hershey passed on the invitation to join. A few months later, in early 1952, his attitude changed as Jim and Cheryl Farrell reported in their book, *Ford Design Department—Concept & Show Cars, 1932–1961.* Just after Hershey had been hired away from Packard to head Ford's styling, club member J. R. "Dick" Samsen, one of his designers, asked him why Ford didn't build a sports car.

The stubby two-speed automatic transmission shift lever protruded from the carpeted tunnel between the seats. Side windows did not roll up or down but were completely removable. With windows fitted, owners had to slip their hands inside through the opening vent windows to reach the round white door knob to open the doors.

Hershey told him the company knew it could not make money on a sports car. That is, until one late winter evening when a close friend and dinner guest at Hershey's home, a designer working for GM, showed his host a photograph. It was Chevrolet's new sports car, and Hershey knew immediately what he and Ford division must do. Overnight he became a sports car enthusiast, buying himself a Jaguar XK-120 and studying every other sports car available. In March 1952, he hired a GM designer, Bill Boyer, right from under Harley Earl's nose to design Ford's response to Chevrolet's new sports car. Boyer worked feverishly in a small secure studio with Dick Samsen and Allan Kornmiller and a few engineers and fabricators, basing their car, as Bob McLean had based his Chevrolet, on Jaguar's XK-120. Boyer, Samsen, and Kornmiller had a full-size clay model ready for Ford management to see in the Dearborn design studio as the doors opened on GM's Motorama in New York City's Waldorf Astoria Hotel on January 17, 1953.

Harley Earl had hoped for V-8 power for his sports car, but only Cadillac, Buick, and Oldsmobile produced them, and none of them would loan their engines to lowly Chevrolet. Earl and McLean had to live with a tuned version of Chevy's venerable 235-cubic-inch in-line six that offered buyers 150 horsepower.

THE BIRTH OF A TREND

Within weeks of Keating and Cole seeing McLean's sports car, they sensed they had been present at the birth of a trend. They had no idea Ford knew about what they were seeing. That factor would come into play a few short months later, about the time more than 125,000 sports car and performance enthusiasts gathered in southern California. At the fourth annual International Motorama, the independent show held in Los Angeles each June, a record-breaking crowd wandered through exhibition halls filled with dozens of custom and sports cars. The review in *Automotive Industries* the most

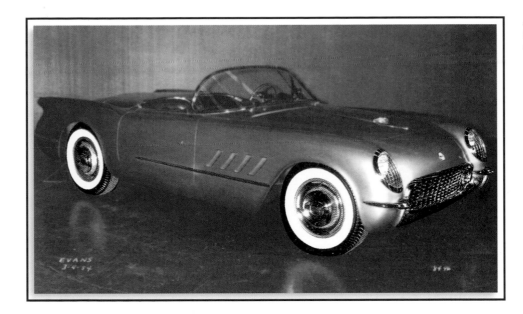

influential monitor of business and technical developments for car makers, reported that "more than $2 million worth of hot rods, custom built and European cars were on display. . . a dozen different models feature glass reinforced plastic bodies." The accompanying page of pictures showed a Glasspar coupe, a Hudson Italia, and a Ferrari-like open two-seater built on a Ford chassis with a Cadillac engine, the Fordillac. Through the summer and fall, major automakers from Packard (with its Pan American) to Ford of France (with its Comette) announced or introduced sports cars for the coming year. Ford hinted it might bring the rounded Comette to the United States to cater to the growing sports car market, and Ford and other makers promoted their own growing uses of fiberglass in prototype and show cars as well as production applications.

Chevrolet had endured a two-year-long cold spell in consumer enthusiasm. Now the climate was improving. Just as in any watershed, various streams run with an increasing sense of destiny and urgency toward the ocean. The elements here were flowing: Better-paid laborers made a growing middle class; a shortage of steel proved the potential of fiberglass; a hungry division needed to bring younger ideas to younger buyers. A fierce rival, propelled by two former employees, moved stealthily toward direct competition.

When the crowds saw GM's Motorama in New York City on January 17, 1953, they glimpsed the best idea of a powerful and influential designer whose work had almost fallen on blind eyes. The public's response in years to come finally would be judged a watershed for Chevrolet, General Motors, and the American auto industry.

1953–1955

CHAPTER THREE

A FUTURE CLASSIC STRUGGLES TO LIFE

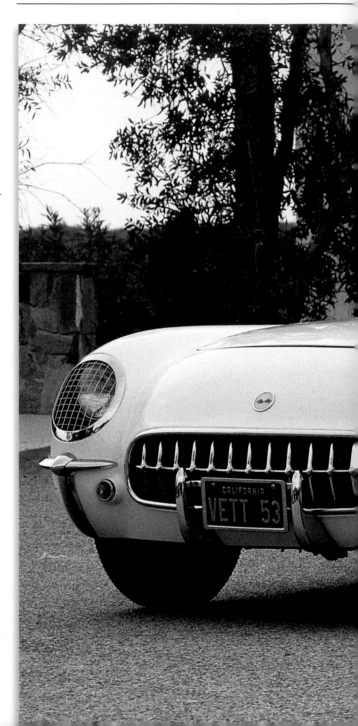

o mislead curious corporate insiders, Keating approved disguising the sports car with the code name Project Opel since Earl's styling department did work for GM's German subsidiary. Cole ordered one car, which was completed to show standards for the 1953 Motorama event. Provided it didn't bomb, Keating agreed to start production of the car the following summer for presentation as a 1954 model.

Cole's staff worked on the performance of the standard "Blue Flame Six" to get closer to sports car proportions, and Maurice Olley began to engineer the hastily drawn chassis to meet GM production procedures. It was a challenge.

Olley had to revise the 1949 sedan-configuration front suspension to fit inside McLean's slim body. The final drive was a Hotchkiss rear end that Olley secured with four-leaf springs sloping upward at the rear and attached to the frame by tension shackles. This angle induced understeer, the plow steering that engineers liked for sedans. Olley quickened Chevrolet's regular worm-and-sector steering system to achieve a more sports car–like response. He could only use production brakes as well, but he enlarged the master cylinder and adjusted front-to-rear bias to give slightly more to the rear.

The low rearward engine placement finally forced Olley to design a new frame formed of steel boxed-section side members that he tied together with a central crossing X-member. His X-frame swooped low enough that he set the driveshaft above it, avoiding the more conventional technique that drilled holes for the shaft, weakening the torsional strength of the chassis. The new frame represented a huge expense in the car's development. Although Olley saved money using stock or mostly stock pieces elsewhere, the financially strapped division had to make other compromises.

In the end, Earl and Cole accepted Chevrolet's six-cylinder engine. Cole's colleague on the Cadillac V-8 development, Harry Barr, had joined him at Chevrolet. In stock trim in sedans, the Blue

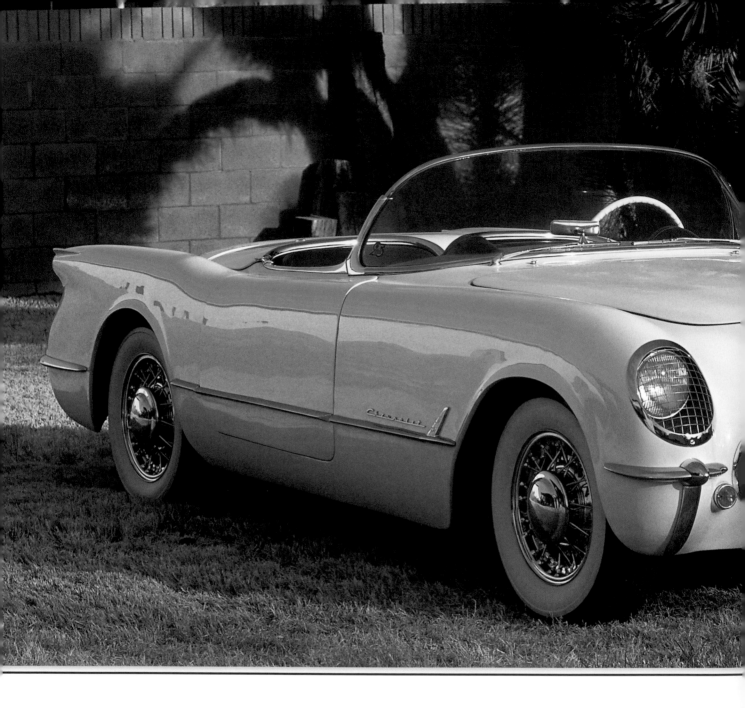

Flame Six, first offered in 1941, produced 115 horsepower. Barr added mechanical valve lifters, a new aluminum intake manifold for three Carter carburetors, and a split exhaust manifold leading to separate exhaust mufflers and pipes on each side at the rear. Then, by increasing compression from the stock 7.5:1 to 8.0:1, Barr raised output to 150 horsepower. Olley examined mufflers and later wrote, "Sports car enthusiasts [agree] the exhaust should have the right note. They don't agree what this is. Some prefer 'foo-blap' while others go for 'foo-gobble.' It is impossible to please them all." Olley chose the latter.

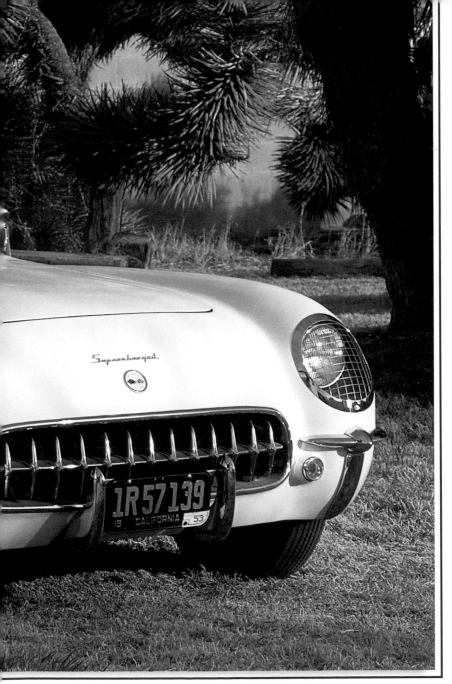

By the time this car rolled out of the Flint plant, creative minds already were devising ways to make the sports car more sporty. While Chevrolet's Tom Keating and Ed Cole had been given the go-ahead to produce a Chevrolet V-8, few outside GM engineering knew it.

Art Oberly at McCullough Supercharger Company in Venice, California, offered to develop his product to work on Corvette's Blue Flame Six to improve performance. General Motors agreed, but it had promised early production cars to VIPs. This one, #24, was meant for the president of Standard Oil Company. History is vague, but it seems the oil man got this car to Venice where Oberly and Erik Kaughman installed the first supercharger and gave the car its distinctive hood badge.

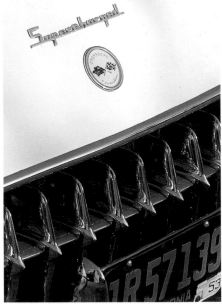

Barr's 150 horsepower came up short against Jaguar's 180 horsepower, but it was better than anything else quickly available. Earl and Cole wanted a manual transmission for their sports car, just as in the Jaguar, but no four-speed existed in America. It was another matter of time and cost. The well-developed two-speed Powerglide automatic transmission (Chevrolet had delivered nearly 6 million of them by now) mated perfectly with the engine that fit the Olley-McLean

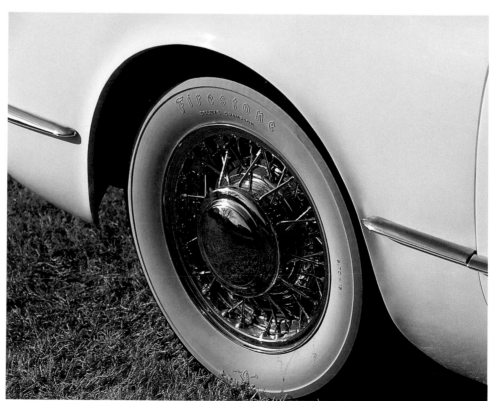

(above) The only visible differences between a normal early production 1953 model and this supercharged car are the script badge on the nose and replacement of Chevrolet's steel wheels with 1953 Buick Skylark wire wheels. Otherwise, nothing gives away the substantial improvement in performance offered by the McCullough blower.

Some of the history of this nearly unique car is still unclear. It seems that McCullough not only fitted the supercharger to improve performance but Art Oberly also may have added the Buick Skylark wire wheels to render a more sports car–like appearance. It was not a simple conversion, and very few other cars have appeared with the wire wheels.

package. Olley defended the decision, sounding more like Alfred Sloan than Ed Cole when he presented a paper to the Society of Automotive Engineers (SAE) on January 14, 1953, three days before the world first saw the car. Americans, Olley concluded with foresight, were less willing to trade the luxury that was increasingly available in American sedans for the austerity common to sports cars.

As the end of the year approached, Keating and Earl agreed to build the Motorama show car out of fiberglass. If the car went into production, Chevrolet would make it in steel.

Appearing in brilliant white fiberglass in the Waldorf Grand ballroom, the car now bore the name *Corvette* written in a simple script across its nose. Myron Scott, Campbell-Ewald ad agency's chief photographer, came up with the name. He admired the fast naval vessels of that name that performed patrol duties during World War II as destroyer escorts in North Atlantic convoys.

After Motorama, Chevrolet and GM management felt confident about the two-seater. The enthusiastic response of New York City's 306,000 Motorama guests (and ultimately 1.7 million in all six cities) suggested they start production before 1954.

Art Oberly and Erik Kaughman added twin vacuum-pressure gauges, mounting them on a production-looking bracket. Because of the length of tubing required to move the compressed supercharged air around the engine, one gauge monitors pressure out of the supercharger and the other checks it as it enters the carburetors.

The new Corvette project caught some suppliers unaware. The car had been in Earl's mind for nearly two years and in Cole's imagination for six months; however, getting production approved required work beyond design and chassis engineering. Chevrolet had to find someone to make the car body.

MOLDING FIBERGLASS

On February 5, 1953, Robert Morrison was back in Detroit to see Carl Klein, a junior Chevrolet division purchasing agent. Morrison had sold Fords until the early 1950s when he and his partners inherited an ailing, undercapitalized molded glass–reinforced plastics operation. Morrison had turned things around, and by late 1952 he was producing thousands of molded fiberglass bread palettes for Wonder Bread's Continental Baking division. He spun off that business into a tray division. With 12 presses in Ashtabula, Ohio, and 10 more in a satellite operation in nearby Linesville, across the Pennsylvania state line, he was busy. He and his partners still talked about the auto industry, but they

McCullough's supercharger is visible at the right front corner of the engine compartment. A flexible hose links it to the three stock Carter carburetors connected by another solid red-painted tube dubbed the "log." Because the supercharger was large, Oberly and Kaughman repositioned the factory air cleaner out of the engine compartment and into the upper rear of the right front fender, a kind of early "cold box" intake.

concluded that it was too big, and with their 30,000 square feet of manufacturing space, they were too small.

Yet in late fall 1952, some body engineers came to visit from General Motors' Fisher Body Fabrication and Assembly division. They carried drawings for more than 100 parts. Could Morrison's Molded Fiber Glass Company (MFG) produce them? How long might it take? What about cost? What kind of quantities?

Morrison told them MFG could do the work, but then the project seemed to die. He heard nothing for weeks. Then in mid-January a supplier sent him a telegram: "Go to the Waldorf Astoria Hotel in New York City this coming weekend," it said. "Go see the display."

Money was tight, not only for Chevrolet but also for Morrison. He didn't go. He recalled years later what he missed: "In that ballroom was Chevrolet's new fiberglass two-seat sports car. GM had planted the car with microphones, to eavesdrop on the guests they had invited in to see it and some other prototypes. They heard 'It's lovely. It's cute.' They heard people say they wished they had one."

The Corvette on one of its early trips to the fabled Brickyard, the Indianapolis Motor Speedway. 2002 General Motors Corporation. Used with permission of GM Media Archives.

McCullough's promotional literature produced in early 1954 in cooperation with the Ethyl Corporation of San Francisco reported that 0–60 miles-per-hour times dropped from 12 seconds to 9 seconds. Horsepower at the rear wheels increased from 87 with the standard three Carters, to 117, a 35-percent jump. Oberly and Kaughman ran acceleration tests at Fontana Raceway in Fontana, California, and produced high 13-second quarter-mile times.

Both 1953 and 1954 models operated on 6-volt electrical systems. Turn signals were a $16.75 option, though like all 1953 and 1954 Corvette options, both cars were built with all the options included. Wide whitewall tires—6.70x15—were another standard option.

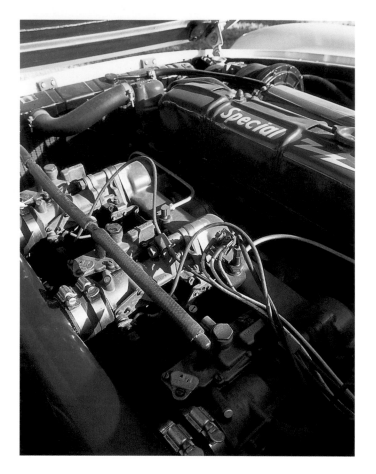

Historians believe that fewer than two dozen McCullough supercharged engines were produced in 1953 and 1954.

(opposite) The Blue Flame Six persevered, still offering 150 horsepower (87 at the rear wheels) as it had through 1953. Sometime during the model year, Chevrolet revised camshaft lobes, increasing gross output to 155 horsepower. The Blue Flame and 150 decals were fitted only to painted valve covers. Some cars were delivered with chrome-plated covers, and these got no decals.

On Monday, January 24, Morrison heard from Chevrolet. Could some men come down to see the plant the next day? Project engineer Carl Jakust and his boss, E. J. "Jim" Premo, chief body engineer for Chevrolet division, arrived the next day. Though the Fisher Body engineers had shown plans to Morrison before, the Chevrolet body engineers took new measurements of each fiberglass press. They planned to redesign their parts to fit Morrison's machinery. Morrison told them his presses were in use; he'd buy new ones, and he offered to help redesign the parts himself so that they not only would mold well but also would be strong.

Jakust and Premo were still nervous. Did MFG have the capacity to meet Chevrolet's need? This was crucial. Chevrolet had lost the youth market to Ford. Ford's postwar cars had V-8s and had convertible tops. Chevrolet needed to get this two-seat sports car out as fast as possible. It wanted to produce 50 each day.

So on Tuesday, February 5, two weeks after Jakust and Premo's visit, Morrison drove over to Detroit to meet Klein at 9 A.M. to plan production of 12,300 sets of the 103 body parts that made the Corvette. General Motors needed delivery spread over 18 months.

Signals got crossed. Klein was gone for the day. Morrison asked to see his boss, Ed Furbacher, Chevrolet's senior purchasing agent. Furbacher was also gone for the day. Morrison felt that he'd been stood up. He headed for the elevator. When the door opened, Elmer Gormsen stepped out. Gormsen was chief purchasing agent for Chevrolet division and boss of the two missing buyers. He had met Morrison on his last visit to GM. Gormsen was direct, telling Morrison that Chevrolet had decided to build the Corvette in steel. No one in that industry had the capacity to produce 50 bodies a day, he said.

But Morrison hadn't had his say. Harold Boeschenstein, chairman of Owens-Corning, was a friend and an ardent supporter of Morrison and of MFG. Boeschenstein had personally promised help. Morrison had located a large building near Ashtabula that was immediately available.

Gormsen walked Morrison to the door, telling him vaguely that if anything changed, he'd get in touch. Morrison had an afternoon appointment with Kaiser-Frazer engineers and drove across town figuring the Chevrolet deal was dead. His afternoon stretched into evening, checking fits and finish of each piece. He took Kaiser's engineers to dinner. That long session with Kaiser was scarcely fruitful. Kaiser ordered 500 sets, but Morrison warned his people "to go easy on this, make a hundred parts and then stub your toe. Don't make any more.' I had a feeling they weren't too solid by that time," he recalled.

It had been a long, bad day. He left Detroit around 8:30 P.M., driving steadily but unhurriedly back to Ashtabula. *Why race home with bad news,* he thought.

"I got home about 1:30 the next morning. My wife got up and told me, 'There's a man calling you from Detroit. Wants you to call him no matter how late you get in.' So I called the number and it's Elmer Gormsen. He kind of laughed and said I didn't need to call him so late. But since I did, he said to go ahead and get that building. 'Because we've decided we're going to do the Corvette with a fiberglass body.'"

Robert S. Morrison was back in the automobile business. MFG had a $4 million contract. Chevrolet wanted the first of the 300 complete sets of body panels before June 1. It was a night Morrison's children would remember all their lives. His son, Robert Jr., recalled that the early morning of February 6, 1953, was the first time that he and his sister had ever tasted champagne.

Sportsman Red, Polo White, and black exterior cars got red interiors, and all models for 1954 got beige convertible tops. (Chevrolet fitted Pennant Blue cars with beige interiors.) The cars still used only removable windows (Chevrolet provided a bag in the trunk for storage), and door opening could only be accomplished by reaching in through the pivoting front quarter window.

On February 6, hours after Elmer Gormsen hired Robert Morrison (and as show staff prepped the prototype car for the Miami Motorama opening), Morrison and his partners left after inspecting the empty building nearby. It was an old railroad structure laced with tracks and totally unusable. Morrison called Harold Boeschenstein, and Owens-Corning came through. Then he called Gormsen to tell him MFG would be constructing a new building just for the Corvette.

When MFG got the order, the whole young fiberglass industry knew about it. Morrison only had four of his key people left after spinning off his tray-making operation. When the new 167,000-square-foot Corvette building was complete, his organization was stretched thin.

While Chevrolet introduced the Corvette at $3,733 fully equipped in 1953, it listed the base price at $3,498. For 1954, it reduced the base price to $2,774, but it did so by listing the automatic transmission, tires, and other previous standard equipment as options. This led some to believe that Chevrolet also offered a manual gearbox.

"Chevrolet was quite cooperative with man power," Morrison recalled. "And resin suppliers and Owens-Corning sent people in. Paid their expenses. Didn't cost us a penny. You'd see a salesman from one company and a salesman from another working on the same press. Competitors working alongside each other helping us get the work out." Chevrolet body engineers quickly learned from the suppliers the techniques for producing bodies.

By midyear, Chevrolet had remedied the exhaust staining problem by fitting exhaust pipe extensions. These moved the gases out into the airstream coming over the rear of the car and out away from the body. These were stainless steel.

One method was called hand lay-up. GM engineering parts fabrication department already used this slow, exact process to create Motorama Dream Cars and Earl's prototypes, including the Corvette. The "matched-metal die method" was similar to steel body production and offered many benefits. Large presses used either cast iron or plate-steel molds that were mated to each other. Morrison's 15 new hydraulic presses compressed these molds together like steel-stamping dies to form the fiberglass panels under as much as 500 tons of pressure. MFG also established a recipe for Corvette fiberglass that has changed little over time. Roughly 30 percent of the mix is glass fiber, 29 percent is aluminum silicate filler, and the remaining 41 percent is isothalic resin. In the 340-pound 1953 car body, this broke down

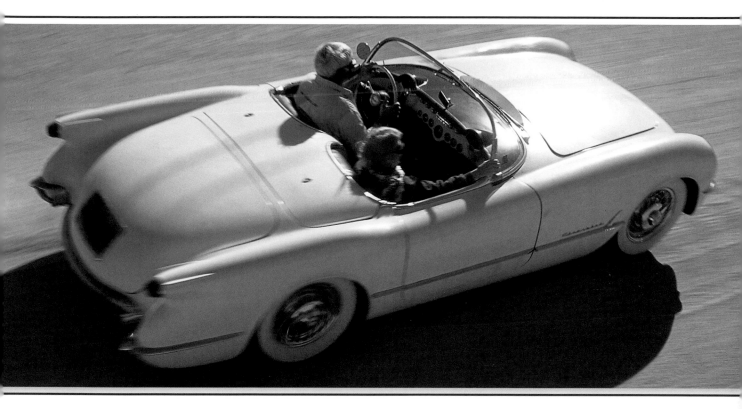

This was a car engineered in Harley Earl's styling department. Chevrolet's General Manager Tom Keating and others agreed it could greatly help Chevrolet regain its shrinking audience, so the car was hurried into production. Engineers took just enough time to change fanciful ideas into an automobile that could come off an assembly line and go around a corner. The 1953 and 1954 Corvettes represented a remarkable achievement. 2002 General Motors Corporation. Used with permission of GM Media Archives.

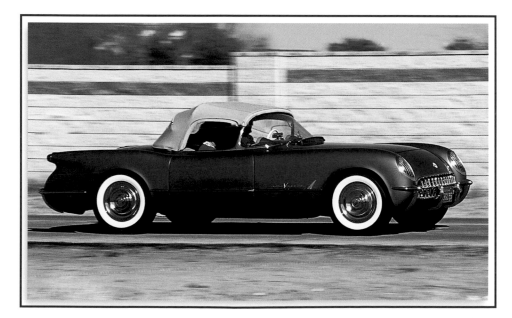

With 195 horsepower now on tap and a three-speed manual transmission available to manage it, performance and driving excitement improved greatly.

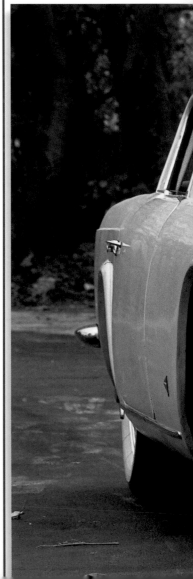

to about 136 pounds of fiberglass, 153 pounds of resin, and 51 pounds of the inert filler. This formula and the matched-metal die method provided the greatest quality and consistency of pieces, something critically important for an interchangeable parts–oriented business like auto making. In addition, matched-metal was the fastest process, and its molds offered the benefit of a production life of as many as 20,000 impressions.

Gormsen told Morrison that Chevrolet rejected steel, in the end, because tooling costs would have been four or five times higher for steel than for fiberglass. Worse, it would have taken much longer to produce steel-stamping dies than MFG needed to make its molds. Chevrolet had learned from Morrison that they could consolidate parts, which meant fewer dies. Still, Chevrolet had concerns.

"There was a sort of betting going on up in Detroit," Morrison explained, "that we wouldn't be able to make the underbody; there *was* some trouble. In early June 1953, the foreman in charge of repairing the underbodies said he needed 40 more people.

"The underbody was breaking right at the junction of the driveshaft tube and the kick-up right before the rear axle. There were two sharp angles and no way for it to give at all. Every damned one of them was breaking."

Morrison graduated from college with a degree in economics and a minor in chemistry; he learned his engineering by doing it. MFG's Corvette presses were huge compared to the 42 x 48-inch

The motivation for this car remains a mystery. The long-established Ghia Carrozzerie in Italy operated a subsidiary in Switzerland, Ghia Aigle. What can be determined is that a buyer took delivery of a 1954 Corvette roadster for use in Europe. Sometime after delivery, he presented it to Ghia of Switzerland, who, some now say, turned it into a replica of a Ferrari 250GT coupe.

platens Fisher Body saw when it first came to Ashtabula. The underbody piece for the 1953 car was 10 feet long, 6 feet wide, and 26 inches deep from the lowest spot to the highest. Morrison saw the break and knew the cure.

" 'Get a big bucket of water and get some cloths,' I said. 'When the press opens, put the cool wet cloths right over that spot that breaks. And leave it there for a few seconds.'

"It eliminated all the breakage. Most any resin is weak when it's hot. Cooling it down with the wet cloth, we got it strong enough quickly so we could lift it out without breaking."

Ghia designed its version of the Corvette with a fixed roof, roll-up windows, reclining leather seats, and a four-speed transmission. Its curious multinational personality is reinforced by a Veliga-instrumented Ferrari dashboard.

HITTING THE STREETS

When the new Corvette hit the streets in September 1953, it landed more with a dull thud than a big splash. Its price, fully equipped and in white only, came in at $3,513, not Earl's target, $1,800. The Blue Flame Special and Powerglide transmission moved the car from 0 to 60 miles per hour in 11 seconds and gave it a top speed of 105 miles per hour. The target Jaguar XK-120 cost $268 less, hit 60 miles per hour a second quicker, and went 25 miles per hour faster. Jaguar and even the fiberglass Kaiser-Darrin, with its odd, slide-open doors, were available in a variety of colors. Corvette side windows were sunlight-yellowing plastic and tops were only black. Build quality was inconsistent. Assembly line workers struggled to get machine-made bits to fit handmade bodies. The car suffered teething problems.

Corvette's biggest gamble was simple economics: supply versus demand. Tom Keating hedged his bets when he authorized first-year production of just 300 cars. The only news of the car following its debut appeared in automotive trade journals and plastics industry reports. By September, the 1.7 million people who attended the Motoramas had nearly forgotten about it. A small story in *Automotive Industries* magazine reviewing the Motorama shows informed readers that while Chevrolet planned to sell the Corvette for around $3,000, this price represented a net loss to the division of nearly $2,000 per car. Keating's gamble was taking on serious proportions. The news intended to make the car seem like a bargain; to the business community, the Corvette sounded like a mistake. Keating needed to rekindle the momentum developed at the Motorama shows. He had to gauge customer reaction, monitor factory production glitches, and watch assembly costs. The cars manufactured in Flint through July were still prototypes in many ways. Workers fitted hand-formed stainless steel trim and cast bronze pieces, while cars built in August had used pot metal. A. O. Smith Corporation, the outside contractor making Corvette's frames, fabricated hand-formed gussets to reinforce rear spring mounts. Technicians were revising these from one frame to the next until Cole and Olley settled on a final design.

Chevrolet held a press introduction on September 29. Fifty journalists shared eight cars, and each drove a seven-mile course at GM's Milford Proving Ground. The Flint factory delivered a few more cars before October 1. Some of these stayed within GM, going straight to engineers who used them for further development, or to executives. Dealers learned in early July that they should not accept orders promising delivery in 1953. The division then delivered another 50 cars through its highest-volume dealers to an A-list of handpicked, carefully selected, highly visible entertainers, prominent athletes, and executives from other major companies. Briggs Cunningham and his father-in-law each ordered one during the New York auto show, but when Briggs got his, he kept it only a week, judging it "not much of a car." Normal customers found that Chevrolet was circulating a few Corvettes from one dealer to the next, staying two or three days as display models. The 306,000 New Yorkers

Even if the performance may have deteriorated slightly from the heavier steel body, the car benefited from true dual exhausts. This car makes a delightful sound. Its resemblance to mid-1950s Ferraris, especially from this rear view, is uncanny if not intentional.

The evolution here would have Harley Earl either grinning or spinning in his grave. Earl's Chevrolet stylist Carl Renner produced the car for the 1954 Motorama, giving the public an advanced view of another car already approved for production. Earl based the station wagon on a production-standard Chevrolet chassis; the current owner, however, chose something much wilder.

who spoke unwittingly into the styling department's concealed microphones said if General Motors would build it, they would come. Some 20,000 went to their local dealers hoping to order cars. They never had a chance.

It got worse. Once the other 250 cars became available, there weren't another 250 celebrities, authorities, and athletes anxious to pay a high price for a crude car. Corvettes leaked water at the windshield and the top. It wasn't an inexpensive car, but it acted like one.

The car sent mixed signals. Tom Keating, sensitive to public perceptions, attempted to direct their interpretation. In a statement released after the introduction, he said, "In the Corvette, we have built

Carl Renner mated the front end of the Corvette to a station wagon chassis, adding in the distinctive round rear end profile and rocket taillights. The original car created a great deal of enthusiasm and demand that Chevrolet hoped would translate directly to sports car sales. Then, like almost all prototypes, Chevrolet ordered the original show car cut up and destroyed in July 1955. The car died but not the idea.

a sports car in the American tradition . . . to satisfy the American public's conception of beauty, comfort, convenience plus performance."

While Keating directed its exclusivity toward the country club set, it was too unsophisticated for them. On the other hand, sports car enthusiasts cried for more power and a transmission they could shift themselves. While Chevrolet, as a division, sold 1,342,480 cars in 1953, only 183 of them were Corvettes.

The Flint assembly plant, actually the former customer delivery garage on Van Slyke Avenue and Atherton, was small; its line was long enough for only six chassis. It gave engineers and manufacturing personnel the chance to get the bugs out of the system while the line in St. Louis was being converted to Corvette's permanent home. There were bugs. Start-up was slow, grueling, and exhausting. It took work crews three 16-hour days to assemble the first car, completed on June 30. Through July, they were satisfied to finish a car a day. By August, three cars a day rolled off the line.

Chevrolet got the plant running smoothly enough to open for tours, to show off not only the completely fiberglass car but also the somewhat unusual assembly system. Throughout October and November, members of the Michigan Education Association visited the plant. Their tour lasted four hours, long enough that Chevrolet fed them a box lunch. They moved through the structure on a kind of trolley. Retired teachers Jean and John Anderson remember that the pace was frantic. "The workers appeared to be under great pressure," Jean said. "They were working like crazy. We saw everything. I mean *everything*. They had what may have been the first robots in the auto industry, and these things would just pick up the engine block and turn it every which way. The tour guide stressed that the assembly line procedure at this plant brought all the parts together for various subassemblies and then all of those to final assembly." Parts came from outside the plant and outside Flint. Engines arrived from Chevrolet's Tonawanda plant, and A. O. Smith, in Granite City, Illinois, assembled the bare frames. Both body panels and tires came from eastern Ohio.

On December 24, Chevrolet ended production at Flint, having completed 301 cars. Four days later, production started in St. Louis at the old millwork building for buggies and early automobiles. Before the new year, the St. Louis factory completed its first 14 cars. Total production for 1953 ended at 315 cars, according to *Automotive Industries* in February 1954. By June, when the first magazine reviews appeared, production was up to 50 per day in St. Louis (it had reached 50 a month in Flint).

In May 1953, a month before production began, Chevrolet hired an ambitious, inventive engineer who first saw the Corvette as one of the crowd visiting New York's Motorama. Zora Arkus-Duntov

Hot Rod Enterprises (HRE), based in Auburn, Washington, had a customer who had hoped to create the replica, but he died before realizing his dream. He had acquired a 1955 Bel Air Nomad wagon along with more modern running gear—the ZR-1 LT5 V-8 and ZF six-speed transaxle—and much of its suspension. Successful businessman and long-time Corvette enthusiast Tom Armstrong adopted the concept, and HRE returned to work. It was a project of epic proportions and challenges.

came in with good credentials. He was born Zachary Arkus on Christmas Day 1909 in Brussels. Writer George Damon Levy interviewed Duntov in 1988 for *Corvette Quarterly* and learned his story. When he was in his teens, his mother, a Russian physician, divorced her engineer husband. She later married Josef Duntov, another engineer, and "Zora," the Russian diminutive nickname for Zachary, began hyphenating his last names. Schooled in Germany, he loved cars and gained considerable racing and engineering experience throughout Europe. He helped several owners tame the handling of their early V-8-powered Allards. He joined Cole's staff when he was 44 and went straight to work for Olley. He got into the first engineering Corvette as soon as he could. Pressing it to its limit, he found, as he told Levy, "a car in which the two ends were fighting each other." While the rear end's canted springs did achieve Olley's goal of inducing understeer, the front end that Olley had made from modified sedan parts caused oversteer, from which it was difficult to recover. It was too late to help the 1953 production cars. Still, Duntov performed the first of countless surgeries he would undertake over the next 22 years.

Sales improved in 1954, aided by the start of major advertising for the car. (The first Detroit-area newspaper ad appeared in late May 1953. It announced a chance to see "America's Sensational Sports Car!" at the Michigan Motor Show in early June.) One 1954 series was image-oriented. It ran several times in the *New Yorker* magazine, each time using the tag line "First of the dream cars to come true." These emphasized Corvette's styling, handling, and unique appeal.

Corvette made its first international racing appearance entering the third annual 12 Hours of Sebring on March 7, with one car from A. F. Young, to be co-driven by Jack Morton. Before the race began Saturday afternoon, Young withdrew the car.

Engineering modified the camshaft, boosting horsepower by 5 to 155. Chevrolet added two paint colors, black and Sportsman Red, all with red interiors. Toward the end of the year, cars began to appear in Pennant Blue with beige interiors. Chevrolet changed the black top for 1953 into tan for 1954. While St. Louis had the capacity to produce 10,000 Corvettes a year, they manufactured just 3,640, and Chevrolet sold only 2,780. *Automotive Industries* magazine reported on November 15, 1953, that, anticipating a slowdown in production, Chevrolet would cut its St. Louis workforce from 2,900 to 1,400. Between 1953 and 1954 sales, Chevrolet found itself with a surplus of nearly 1,100 unsold cars on January 1, 1955.

Ed Cole reflected on the dilemma surrounding the Corvette in an interview at the time. Quoted 18 years afterward in Karl Ludvigsen's 1973 book *Corvette: America's Star-Spangled Sports Car,* Cole lamented that Chevrolet "had no real feeling for the market. Was the Corvette for the boulevard driver or the sports-car tiger? We weren't quite sure." The inability to define their customer—*Road & Track* enthusiasts or *New Yorker* sophisticates—caused Keating and Cole a great deal of soul searching. They slowed St. Louis production to 16 cars a day and quietly worried if that was still too much.

While management wrestled with the Corvette's future, Clare MacKichan's Chevrolet studio and Ed Cole's engineers pressed ahead with revisions and updates. Styling wanted to use an egg-crate grille design similar to the 1955 Bel Air, and it proposed a functional hood air scoop and several dummy louvers along the body panel behind the front wheels. They wanted to rid the rear end of

(opposite top) Ahem. This ain't no Blue Flame Six. Owners Tom and Susan Armstrong had the ZR-1 LT5 engine installed, and HRE created custom headers that fed exhaust into flat-bottom collectors, then to 3-inch tubes into the muffler. While the Motorama Nomad exhausts ran out through the rear fenders, Armstrong voted to keep the body clean, and HRE routed the exhaust straight out the back.

(opposite bottom) To achieve 1954 Nomad proportions and appearances, HRE and Armstrong sectioned 3 inches out of the car body and lowered the floor 1.5 inches to provide adequate headroom before fitting four leather-and-tweed bucket seats, the full-length console, heating, air conditioning, a sound system, and even beverage holders. Armstrong had the 1955 Nomad wagon dashboard cleaned up, and he replaced the instruments with digital read-outs.

its troublesome taillight bullets. These required extensive hand-work from the beginning, because matched-metal molds had difficulty with the abruptness of the curves and the complexity of shapes projected out into space. But again there was no money. For 1955, colors could be changed; styling replaced Pennant Blue with Harvest Gold, and Sportsman Red became Gypsy Red. They could barely touch the body. Harley Earl and others began to hear that the car's future was in serious doubt.

Throughout 1954, the car still suffered from what reviewers and enthusiasts alike thought was insufficient horsepower. When Ed Cole arrived at the Chevrolet division, the engineering staff was already developing a new 231-cubic-inch displacement V-8 overhead-valve engine, a legacy that Ed Kelley, the previous chief engineer, left behind. Cole felt this needed immediate attention. He wanted to increase the V-8's displacement to 265-cubic-inch displacement, and Tom Keating agreed. It was an engine size Cole, Harry Barr, and a third engineer and racing enthusiast, Harry Burrell, had mused over while they were still at Cadillac. The 265 figure was a kind of genie-in-a-bottle displacement they felt offered them lots of room to grow and plenty of opportunity to play. According to Beverly Rae Kimes in *Chevrolet—A History from 1911,* Cole and Barr had designed that engine many times in their heads before Chevrolet offered them the opportunity to build the real thing. Keating's endorsement was all it took, and Alfred Sloan approved the project without ever seeing plans. Now Cole needed engineers, and he hired hundreds, taking his staff up to 2,900. He felt the need for this engine was urgent. His staff designed it and built a running model in 15 weeks. (Admittedly, for Cole and Barr, this design was old hat. They spent two years carefully and deliberately designing and developing Cadillac's 331.) Cole was so certain of the design that he ordered tooling and plant space before Barr and his engineers even fired the 265 for the first time.

Cole's engineers were anxious to see how it would affect the Corvette's performance, so they refitted the engineering

Even with 195 horsepower and an available three-speed manual transmission, a legacy of unsold 1954 models meant the production barely reached 700 in 1955, and poor sales threatened the car with extinction.

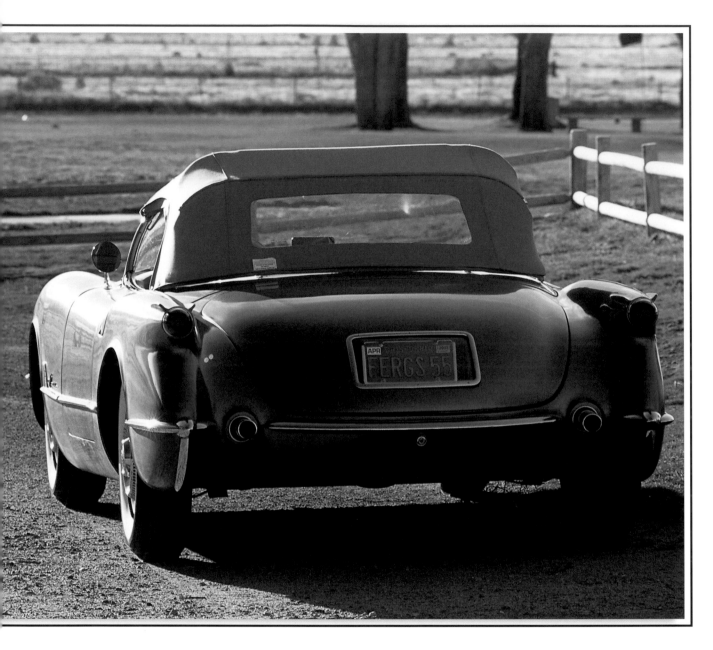

Physically, the 1955 model was identical to the previous two years although a new badge identified the optional V-8 engine. The "base" six-cylinder roadster held its price at $2,774, while the V-8 roadster started at $2,909 before the mandatory "options" were totaled in.

development car, 1953 number 002, with a prototype V-8. It ran flawlessly for 25,000 miles out at Milford, convincing Keating and Cole to offer it not only with the Powerglide but eventually with a three-speed manual gearbox for 1955.

The new engine pumped life into the ailing Corvette. Performance jumped as 0–60 miles per hour times dropped three full seconds to 8.0 in the late 1955 cars fitted with the three-speed. Top speed climbed to 120 miles per hour, and fuel economy improved from 17 to 20 miles per gallon. Chevrolet's timing was nearly miraculous. In March 1954, Ford announced its 160-horsepower, Y-block, V-8-engined Thunderbird with roll-up windows, to sell for $2,695. Production would begin in September. *Automotive Industries* reported the news: "A notable difference, however, is that it is being tooled for production in steel rather than plastic. The foregoing may be significant, since tooling cost is close to $5 million, compared to about $500,000 to tool the Corvette for plastic production. It could indicate that Ford expects to build more sports cars than Chevrolet does."

Motor Trend's Don MacDonald compared and contrasted the two, offering his perspective in the June 1955 issue: "The basic difference between the Corvette and Thunderbird is not so much the body material, but a conflicting analysis of the American market. The Corvette was patterned closely after the European concept of a competition car. Conversely, the designers of the Thunderbird aimed at and achieved a California custom flavor. This is why Corvette presently has an *almost* purist indifference to the problem of weather protection. It was easy for the come-lately Thunderbird to offer adequate coverage. . . ." MacDonald couldn't know it was cost, not "purism," that affected weather protection.

(previous pages) Of the 700 cars manufactured, production records are scarce. Historians guess that about 325 of these were Polo White, 180 were Gypsy Red, another 120 were Harvest Gold, and just 45 appeared in this Pennant Blue. The rarest color seems to be Corvette Copper, with perhaps only 15 manufactured.

Chevrolet Styling created the new designation for the optional V-8 engine by capitalizing the V in the side name badge, CheVrolet. As tire technology improved, GM and others switched to tubeless tires late in the 1954 model year. It is likely that nearly all 1955 models arrived on tubeless Firestone, Goodrich, or U.S. Royal tires.

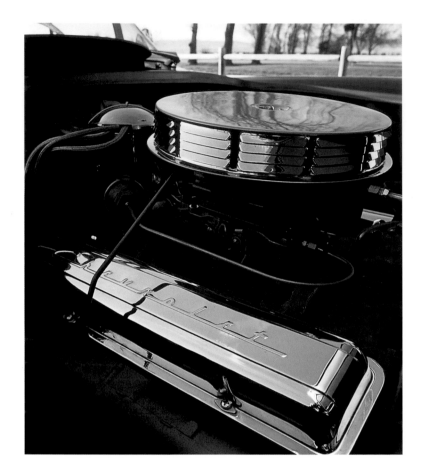

Ironically, despite MacDonald's assessment of the Corvette's competitive nature compared to the Ford, at Sebring on March 13, 1955, a single Thunderbird entry ran unchallenged by Corvettes. Fred Scherer of Skokie, Illinois, and co-driver Don Davis started 9th and finished 37th.

By the end of 1955, Ford sold 16,155 copies of its T-bird, while Chevrolet had halted production midyear, stopping after assembling 700 Corvettes. Chevrolet sold just 675 (a few dozen of which were fitted with the manual gearbox).

These kinds of numbers sent ordinary men to the showers, defeated and humiliated. But neither Earl nor Cole, Keating nor Curtice were ordinary men. Alfred Sloan was still chairman, and it was he who had already said, "The question is not simply one of maximizing the rate of return for a specific short period of time . . . [but] the fundamental consideration was an average return over a long period of time." With the sales figures his other cars produced, he would tell his board it could afford to be patient.

In 1953, General Motors sold 45 percent of the new automobiles and trucks in the United States. Chevrolet knew it had scored a home run with its V-8. The Corvette just had not yet caught the buyer's imaginations. After this, few people held much hope that Cole's new engine and a manual gearbox alone could save the car. "By the looks of it, the Corvette is on its way out," Duntov wrote privately to Cole and Olley in mid-October 1954. But, he argued, "dropping the car now will have adverse effects internally and externally. It is admission of failure: failure of aggressive thinking in the eyes of the organization, failure to develop a saleable product in the eyes of the outside world."

It was not Duntov's passionate eloquence that saved the Corvette. It wasn't even Cole's V-8. The final decision rested in the boardroom, and GM's board still did what Alfred Sloan felt was best for the company. Sloan looked across town and saw Thunderbird's success. It furthered his belief that the Corvette was the right car for GM and Chevrolet at the time, even if they didn't yet have the car "right." The Thunderbird sharpened GM's senses. Chevrolet Research, a group Sloan had created, reported that 17 percent of American households were two-car families. Chevrolet had once again outsold Ford, 1,646,681 cars to 1,573,276. Yet Ford had found 16,155 buyers where Chevrolet had not; Sloan knew GM had to recapture those individuals. He had no idea Ford was about to help.

Most production V-8 1955 models came with the automatic transmission, now improved to near perfection. Historians estimate perhaps only 75 cars appeared with the 3-speed manual. Even fewer were delivered with speedometers reading in kilometers, not miles. Export Corvettes sported few other modifications.

1956-1958

CHAPTER FOUR

ED COLE GETS SERIOUS

y the time Tom Keating approved Corvette production for two additional years, through 1957, designers and engineers had little time to make substantial changes to draw back buyers lost to the Thunderbird. Still, when the Motorama staff unveiled the 1956 Corvette in the Waldorf, Earl's stylists and Cole's engineers had transformed the car.

Mercedes-Benz had replaced Jaguar XK-120s as their target. Mercedes' 300SL racing coupes appeared in 1952 with raked head-lights like the first Corvettes. When production SLs appeared for 1954, Mercedes' designer Paul Bracq had mounted the lights vertically in the fenders. The engineers slightly tilted the in-line six-cylinder engine to lower the hood, which Bracq gave two gentle bulges for clearance. To Chevrolet's Clare MacKichan, those bulges said "power," the image everyone wanted for the V-8. When stylist Bob Cadaret finished the front of the 1956 Corvette, it resembled the 1954 SL. (Stylists commonly plagiarized each other. Jaguar's designers admitted duplicating a 1940 BMW race car for their XK-120.)

Another design element came from home. Cadillac's 1955 Motorama LaSalle II dream car introduced a long horizontal scallop in the body side. Now gracing the Corvette, it imparted a classic elegance to the side view, creating visual appeal yet breaking up the panel. Cadaret scalloped the taillights into the fenders. He achieved an economy of line by removing the excesses. The Corvette got roll-up windows (with power windowlifts available), outside door handles, and an optional power system for the convertible top. These things were impossible between Motorama and production start in 1953. Windows required forming curved glass and fabricating lift mechanisms and support rails. Harley Earl had wanted Bohnstedt's show car to remind everyone of sunny days. Purists took MG-TCs and Jaguar XK-120 roadsters with side curtains and without complaints, so his expectations seemed less scandalous at the time.

(previous pages) *It was supposed to look like the 1958 and 1959 models with four headlights and three front air intakes. Styling and engineering were nearly overwhelmed with big changes to the passenger car and pickup truck line, and they got swamped. Compounded by poor revenues from dismal 1954 sales, little time and no money meant only minor changes were possible for 1957.*

For 1958, Chevrolet gave the Corvette an extra pair of headlights. The chrome strip running back from between the paired headlights was a 1958-only feature.

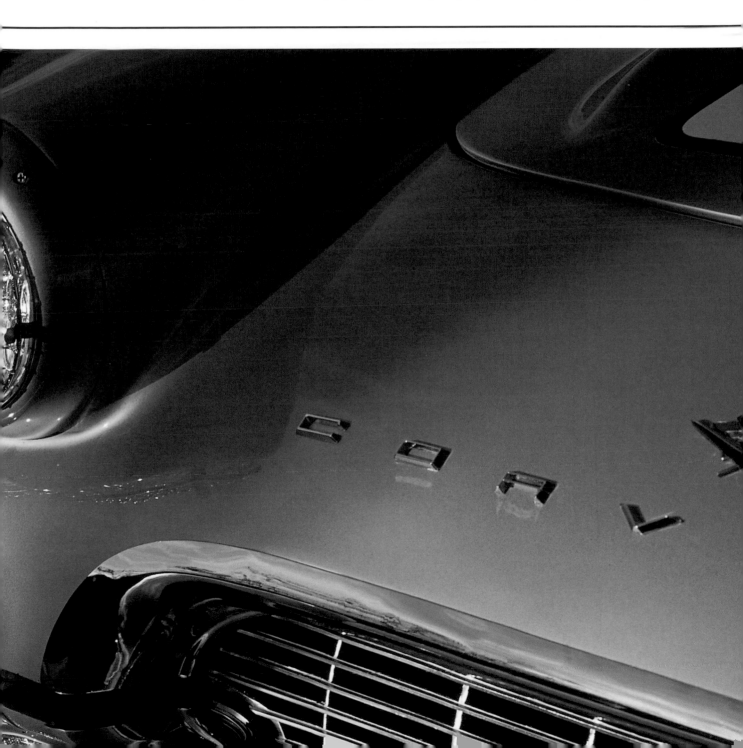

Mercedes-Benz developed the car in 1952 to evaluate its return to racing. After it won the 24 Hours of Le Mans and the Mexican Carrera Panamericana, American importer Max Hoffman quickly ordered 1,000. Because M-B had assembled it from production parts, like Chevrolet had done with its Corvette, it was easy to put into production starting in 1954.

Mercedes-Benz kept the car low by mounting its in-line three-liter six-cylinder engine on a slight angle. M-B had tamed fuel-injection so well that it introduced the system on this production sports car. With its four-speed transmission and the right final drive gearing, the 300SL could touch 150 miles per hour. Different gears let it accelerate to 60 miles per hour in less than eight seconds.

Tom Keating approved the 1956 styling changes in February 1955. The Motorama unveiling and production start were possible only by using fiberglass. (If the St. Louis plant used dies for steelstamping rather than for fiberglass molding, the 1956 car would have arrived closer to 1957.)

In mid-December 1953, Zora Duntov had written a memo that became a wake-up call to the Chevrolet division. He saw car enthusiast magazines filled up with stories about Ford. Would this exposure prompt readers to stay with Ford as their income grew? He believed Chevrolet could penetrate this market, but it would take time to get in. He proposed that Chevrolet produce engine and chassis performance parts and market them to the public.

"If the speed parts are carried as R.P.O. [regular production option] items for the Corvette," Duntov wrote in the memo, "they will be recognized by the hot-rodders as the very parts they were looking for to hop up the Chevy. . . . I do know that in 1954 sports car enthusiasts will get hold of

Chevrolet manufactured just six of these special versions, five in white and this one in Aztec Copper. This car also holds 35 national drag race victories and class records at El Mirage dry lake in California, where it was driven by Dean Moon. While exhaust exited through the rear bumper guards on production models, these six-cylinder cars ran it to the side just ahead of the rear wheels.

The exhaust pipes exited through the rear bumper on 1956–57 production Corvettes. Shown is a customized 1957 version.

the Corvette and whether we like it or not, will race it. [The] most frequent statement from this group is 'we will put a Cadillac [V-8] in it [for more power]. I think this is not good! Most likely they will meet with Allard trouble—that is, breaking, sooner or later, mostly sooner, everything between flywheel and road wheels. Since we cannot prevent people from racing Corvettes, maybe it is better to help them do a good job at it."

Duntov believed creating a sense of loyalty in Chevrolet buyers required faith that Chevrolet would produce what buyers wanted. He still had to prove himself before his ideas took on credibility, however.

His camshaft designs and the Ar-Dun cylinder heads he and his brother Yura had developed prior to joining Chevrolet earned them respect as creative development engineers. Duntov's work taming the handling of the 1956 production model established his chassis credentials within Chevrolet. The mark of Zora began to carry weight on his adopted car.

Corvettes came closer to realizing Duntov's handling goals since the new 265-cubic-inch displacement V-8 weighed 41 pounds less than the old Blue Flame Special. The V-8 was shorter and lower, which also helped handling. The engine with its single Carter four-barrel carburetor produced 210 horsepower; an optional second four-barrel raised

The redesigned body for 1956 eliminated Harley Earl's rocket taillights and introduced the cove styling motif that would remain through 1962. Body assembly quality improved for 1956 since the fiberglass panels now were pressed entirely by matched-metal molds, a much more precise method of panel forming. These six SR prototypes each were fitted with Halibrand magnesium alloy hubs and knock-off wheels.

output to 225 horsepower. Duntov ran a preproduction prototype 1956 Corvette up Pike's Peak in September 1955. Camouflaged as a full-sized passenger car, he set a new class record of 17 minutes, 24 seconds on the 12.5-mile climb to the top. Yet this meant little to average customers. Speed compared to other cars caught people's attention. The Jaguar XK-120 in hottest trim reached 130 miles per hour. Reports said Mercedes' coupe was capable of 146 miles per hour in standard trim. What if the engineers could coax 150 miles per hour out of the Corvette on Daytona Beach speed runs?

Cole gave Duntov clearance, and he moved to GM's Phoenix test track to determine how he could reach this speed. He needed another 30 horsepower, something possible with a wilder cam. Engineering cast several from his designs. Duntov could now run the engine to 6,300 rpm, producing enough power to reach, theoretically, 163 miles per hour.

This commitment to performance and publicizing the results was primarily the effort of one engineer, but not the one most people credit. While Zora Duntov could suggest changes or implement them, Ed Cole had the power to influence board chairman Harlow Curtice. A V-8 engine, new styling, Duntov's mountain record, and Daytona goals all were building blocks, raising the Corvette's foundation

(opposite lower right) While Chevrolet
extensively redesigned the car for 1956,
they hung on to the original dashboard
design. Gearshift knobs on the three-
speed manual were first white plastic
and later chrome except on these six
SR prototypes, which were among the
first 1956 models assembled.

The introduction of Corvette's Regular
Production Option (RPO) dual four-
barrel carburetor, RPO 469, provided
big news for 1956. Buyers felt the
improvement from 195 to 225
horsepower. These six SR models,
using RPO 449 with slightly higher-
lift camshafts (the so-called Duntov
cams), boasted 240 horsepower. SR
models featured a shorter steering
column to allow drivers more room to
move their arms while cornering.

higher and constructing a more stable structure for Cole's own aspirations for the car.

Cole had Duntov on his staff with road racing experience, and he had Mauri Rose, a three-time Indianapolis 500 winner working as coordinator with the private and dealer teams racing in NASCAR. Cole brought them to Milford Proving Grounds on December 13, 1955, to discuss racing Corvettes internationally starting in Sebring the next March. He invited his engine wizards Harry Barr and Walter Mackenzie (who became Chevrolet's racing manager-without-the-title), and other performance-oriented engineers, including Maurice "Rosey" Rosenberger, an engine and transmission problems troubleshooter, and Russell Sanders, chief of passenger-car chassis design, as well as outsiders Briggs Cunningham and John Fitch. Rose took notes that Corvette historians John Neas and Dick Robinson recently have unearthed and first published in *The Corvette Restorer,* the journal of the National Corvette Restorers' Society (NCRS). Chevrolet gave enthusiasts a sports car to race. Now Ed Cole wanted to know what Chevrolet should do so that they could win with it.

Fitch quickly offered constructive comments. Chevy needed to improve gear ratios in the three-speed transmission if no four-speeds were

Following successful speed record attempts on Daytona Beach in February, Ed Cole committed Chevrolet engineers to a four-car effort for the 12 Hours of Sebring in March 1956. John Fitch supervised the effort, run from a hangar at the airport circuit. For five weeks, from February 18 to race day March 26, engineers worked in Florida and in Michigan to prepare parts for the cars.

Chevrolet produced 3,467 convertibles throughout the model year, but it was these six that began to ensure the continued existence of the car. Unofficially dubbed the SRs, these cars, though largely stock in appearance, bore numerous modifications that made the cars race-ready for Sebring. They showed sports car enthusiasts what a Corvette—in street or race trim—could do.

possible. He worried about Corvette's oversteering tendencies and its 50/50 weight balance, though others present reminded him the Mercedes 300SL was 40 percent front/60 percent rear, and the new Aston-Martin DB3 was 50/50.

Cunningham found Corvette's steering too light and the wheel too close to his chest. He suggested revising the suspension since hard braking dropped the nose, dipping headlights uselessly low for night racing. He recommended doubling fuel capacity to run farther between pit stops.

Cole quickly committed his two 1956 engineering department development cars plus a third pre-production model to the Sebring event now barely 100 days away (He had already okayed Duntov's effort with one of the cars for the January Daytona Beach Flying and Standing Mile speed records.) He ordered a single four-speed German ZF gearbox for evaluation and tagged Frank Burrell, his engineer

All four of the racers received 37-gallon fuel tanks, limited slip differentials, Halibrand magnesium hubs, and knock-off wheels with Firestone Supersport 170 tires. Brakes were a challenge for racing. Fitch and Duntov tried four systems before settling on Bendix Cerametallix linings inside Chevrolet's heavily finned cast-iron drums.

who had aided Cunningham's Cadillacs at Le Mans, to run the project. After the Daytona runs, Burrell would get Duntov's Corvette at a rented garage in Sebring to supervise its conversion to a road-racing car.

At Daytona, the perfect mix of sand, low tides, and light winds never materialized. December slipped into early January 1956 before Duntov got a certified two-way run averaging 150.58 miles per hour. He met his goal using an engine that produced 240 horsepower from parts soon to be available over the counter. The crew went back to the official Daytona Speed Weeks in February with three cars, each engine with modified heads producing a 10.3:1 compression ratio and developing 255 horsepower. John Fitch, Duntov, and Betty Skelton, a veteran automobile and airplane racer, each had a car to run.

Ford showed up with its Thunderbirds, and competition was fierce. Officials measured times not only for top speed runs but also for standing-start mile runs. At the end of the week, suffering traction problems not solved even by running snow tires on the sand, John Fitch finished third (at 86.87 miles per hour) behind two Thunderbirds at the completion of the standing-start mile runs.

Racers don't need to know road speed, but they do need to know how fast their engine is turning, so John Fitch and his crew of Chevrolet engineers revised the sweeping speedometer to serve as an easily readable tachometer. This effort was Chevrolet's first factory attempt at road racing, and for Fitch, Duntov, and the others, every day meant new lessons learned and solutions invented.

Duntov averaged 147.3 miles per hour for the flying mile, beating all challengers, including the Thunderbirds.

In early January, Cole and Burrell learned that the Federation International de l'Automobile (FIA), Sebring's race-sanctioning body, required that all race car modifications had to be available to consumers for cars entered in production classes. They also needed to build at least 25 identical models for the racing version car to be classified as "production." They created a new model, the SR. Whether the initials meant "special racing" or "Sebring racer" remains uncertain, but the designation first appeared in print in a memo from Russ Sanders in engineering on January 6, 1956.

Rules allowed a small windscreen, and John Fitch, Zora Duntov, and Betty Skelton already had proven the value of this modification during their speed runs on the Daytona Beach. The curved plexiglass tipped the air up and over their drivers' helmets without pushing more air than necessary out of the way.

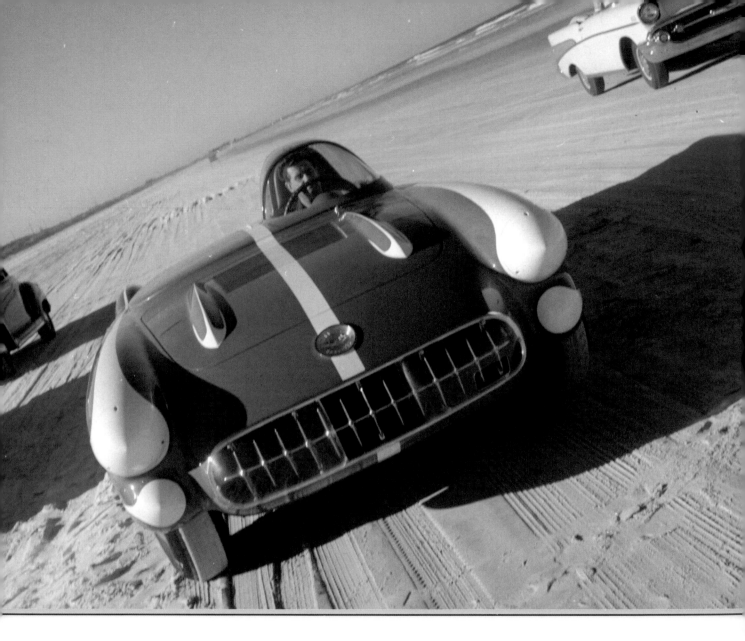

The Corvette SS proved its competitiveness on the sands of Daytona Beach back when racing took place on the beach itself. 2002 General Motors Corporation. Used with permission of GM Media Archives.

Engineering planned to equip the SR models with the Duntov camshaft, a semilocked differential, a 37-gallon fuel tank, seat belts, Auburn clutch, and Halibrand Spot disc brakes and quick change wheels. The memo confirmed that Walter Mackenzie would promote sales of complete cars through selected dealers.

Chevrolet was officially going racing. Well, not "officially." "It is particularly desirable to management," Walter Mackenzie wrote to Cole on February 6, "that dealers be used wherever possible as the parties who can own and enter the Corvettes in competition. This is more desirable even than outside private enterprises of any kind (at least in the initial stages of the new venture) because it must not be made to appear that such an outside firm or enterprise is merely being hired as a 'front' by Chevrolet." Industry critics already charged that car makers were obsessed with speed and horsepower without paying attention to safety improvements. The cries would get loud enough to reach GM chairman Harlow Curtice by 1957, with significant results for future racing efforts.

Meanwhile, Fitch added a fourth car to the team after Daytona ended. By late January, he and Burrell were in Sebring working on the team. Barr's engineers had no time to prep the fourth car, so Cole purchased items through Don Allen Chevrolet in Miami, Florida. Harry Burrell drove its break-in miles from the St. Louis factory back to Sebring. Back in Detroit, Duntov, Rosenberger, and Sanders were inventing and testing parts so they could catalog each one for eventual over-the-counter sales.

Halibrand's disc brakes were not ready. Fitch knew Sebring was hard on brakes, so he and Burrell settled on newly designed large drums. Burrell cut cooling ducts into the drum backing plates, fed by large air vents ducted from the front grille through inner fender wells. He also had to modify the Carter carburetors; these sloshed fuel in hard cornering, flooding the engine and slowing the car. Cole's engineers had studied the Mercedes 300SL. Fuel injection was something they wanted to bring to the Corvette. The Sebring carburetor tests strengthened their resolve.

Burrell and Fitch got one V-8 bored out to 307-cubic-inch displacement and fitted it with a prototype Rochester fuel injection and the ZF four-speed gearbox. The increased displacement shifted it to B-class while the other three cars remained in class C. Sixty cars started the race and, typically, 24 finished. Two of the Corvettes quit early. Class C car #5 quit after an hour with a broken rear axle. A second class C, #7, retired with a burnt piston after two hours. The fourth, #6, finished 15th overall, running with only top gear for hours. A virtually dealership-stock entry, #3, finished next to last. Fitch's B-class car, #1, worried him when its clutch began failing by the second lap, but his Le Mans experiences had taught him to nurse ailing race cars. He brought it in ninth overall, first in Class B. For anyone who knew racing, it was an impressive debut. The cars won respect from their competitors and the crowd.

Chevrolet's advertising agency, Campbell-Ewald, raced Corvette promotion into new territory. Agency writer and racing director Arthur "Barney" Clark prepared an ad for the April 1956 New York Auto Show program. He invited viewers to "Bring on the hay bales!" Clark pressed harder in the July issues of *Road & Track* and *Hot Rod*. The now-legendary ad

Engines for three of the four race cars started as stock RPO 449 models with the Duntov high-lift cam, modified to allow a 7,000 rpm redline. Engineers Harry Barr and Maurice Rosenberger bored out a fourth engine to 307 cubic inches to fit into Class B where the competition was less intense. It finished in 9th overall whereas this "production" C-class entry retired after just two hours with a burnt piston.

(above) Stylist Dave Wheeler created the shapes that became famous not with Jerry Earl at the wheel but with dentist Dr. Dick Thompson. Dubbed the SR-2, the car proved too much of a handful for the younger Earl at its debut at Road America's June Sprints in 1956. Thompson took over. He found it too slow and heavy to be seriously competitive.

Harley Earl loved European sports cars. Still, it annoyed him when his son Jerry purchased a Ferrari to go racing in SCCA events. Harley brought in a Sebring racer chassis and set his stylists to work building his son a better Corvette. Unfortunately, Harley's stylistic improvements to a pure production Corvette made it "modified" in SCCA's view, placing it against much tougher competition.

showed a stark black-and-white photo of Fitch's Corvette, headlights on, driving lights mounted below the grille, with co-driver Walt Hansgen running around the back of the car. It looked like a *Life* magazine photo. In the bleached white sky above the runner, Clark etched a new legend: "The Real McCoy." His text detailed "glove soft upholstery, roll-up windows, ample luggage space and a velvety ride." But then it hit: "Other people make a luxury car," Clark wrote with a none-too-subtle slam at Thunderbird, "that has much the same dimensions as this. That's not so tough. And the Europeans make some real rugged competition sports cars—and that's considerably tougher. But nobody but Chevrolet makes a luxury car that *also* is a genuine 100-proof sports car."

Cole and company performed postmortems. Brakes plagued them at Sebring. Production brakes were inadequate for even the six-cylinder engines with automatic transmissions. For competition with a 255 horsepower V-8, Burrell, Rosenberg, and Sanders had tried everything available on short notice. As Karl

Ludvigsen reported, "The only combination that proved it could stay the distance was that of Bendix Cerametallix linings inside heavily finned iron drums. . . . But [these brakes] were heavy, and they forced the Corvette to become heavier too."

Selecting the brakes was a decision with ramifications that went far beyond race day. It established ethics for future decisions in which someone balanced reduced weight against enhanced safety, comfort, or performance. Zora Duntov told Ludvigsen these brakes represented "a watershed decision that took the Corvette irrevocably in the direction of a larger, heavier car, barring any possible return to a lightweight design concept."

Before 1956 ended, Ed Cole succeeded Tom Keating as Chevrolet division general manager. Chevrolet division had produced only 3,467 Corvettes, while Ford *sold* more than 15,000 of its Thunderbirds. Harlow Curtice and his board members kept faith that Cole's efforts with the Corvette simply had not yet had enough time to prove themselves. Ford knew all along that Ed Cole and General Motors planned to keep the Corvette a sports car. So Chase Morsey, a Ford product planner, set the Thunderbird's direction, and design chief Frank Hershey concurred with Morsey's vision. Ford Thunderbird was to be a personal car, they agreed, something that buyers knew fit between a

While it first raced with the RPO 449 265-cubic-inch V-8 of the other Sebring racers, by February 1957, it was running a modified 283 cubic-inch V-8 tuned to 310 horsepower. Engineers continued to experiment with brakes, using most successfully a set of Chrysler 4 inch wide brake drums with flexible shoes that ensured a firm braking fit even if the drums went slightly out of round from overheating or wear.

sports car and a family passenger car. Chevrolet, they concluded, could keep trying with its poorly selling sports car.

THE "FUELIE" SYSTEM

Chevrolet opened its Engineering Center within GM's 25-building Technical Center in December 1956. Begun in 1949, the $125 million, 990-acre campus was located in suburban Warren, about 10 miles north of the General Motors building. One of the first projects engineers completed in their new digs was one started downtown in engineering's former home, the old, drafty bank building. Intent on improving intake/exhaust flow on the 265, engineering increased cylinder bore, yielding a 283-cubic-inch displacement engine. For 1957, Corvette offered two four-barrel carburetors with the engine, to produce 245 horsepower. A still hotter version cranked out 270 horsepower. The wildest tune developed 283 horsepower, the first GM engine to make one-horsepower-per-cubic-inch-of-displacement. It did it with Ramjet Fuel Injection, Chevrolet's production successor to Rochester's experimental system that Burrell ran on Fitch's 1956 Sebring B-class winner. While publicly announced in October 1956, cars with the "Fuelie" system didn't appear in large numbers until spring 1957 (prior to the May 1 four-speed introduction). Of the 6,338 Corvettes produced for 1957, Chevrolet made 1,040 with the Rochester Ramjet injection. They delivered just 664 cars with the four-speed gearbox. *Road & Track* recorded 0–60 miles per hour times of 5.7 seconds in a test car with a 4.11:1 rear axle.

Alfred Sloan's intention had been to restyle car bodies every other year, but this was costly and had become challenging since each division was adding new models. GM's product lead time slowed to three years. Chassis and powertrain engineers had mechanical improvements ready for the entire truck and passenger car line-up. Substantial engineering improvements and a new body were in the works for the Corvette. Ed Cole knew Chrysler and Ford had new bodies on much of their 1957 lineup; however, engineering delays held up GM's introductions.

"We were in the studio," former stylist Robert Cumberford explained, "working on the '57 Corvette. It just got behind. The regular car line had too many new things and they couldn't handle it: a new engine, gearbox, chassis, suspension, body and interior. The new pick-up truck had a hood with Corvette-style hood speed-bumps. That took body engineers away who would have made the four-headlight, three-grille 1957 Corvette. This is the car that everyone knows as the 1958." Between timing and dismal production and sales of 1954, a quick nip and tuck was all that were possible for the 1957 Corvette model year.

When faced with saving weight, money was no object. Zora Duntov, who had plenty of seat time in Porsche's 550 Spyders at Le Mans, knew their Spyder seats were not only light but comfortable. He acquired two and fitted them into the SR-2.

"Corvette was not a plum assignment anyway," Cumberford explained. "There was nothing really desirable about it at all. I got the Corvette to do the year they sold 700 cars. Chevrolet dealers didn't like them. How rich a plum can that be?"

Cumberford was assigned to Chuck Jordan's Studio 5, doing drawings for Earl for the intended 1957 Corvette. The young designer came up with ideas for a car for which he'd gotten no directions. Dave Holls, former GM director of corporate design, and automotive journalist Michael Lamm collaborated on a history of car design, *A Century of Automotive Style,* published in 1996. Holls worked for Earl from 1952 through 1958 and knew his procedures. This one was typical.

"Earl developed ways for getting the most from his designers," Holls wrote. "He rarely dictated and never gave clear, precise instruction. He purposely kept his suggestions vague . . . , and by changing

Many enthusiasts have suspected Jaguar's D-type racer inspired the SR-2 fin. Its creator, Bob Cumberford, recalled that it grew from a desire to improve vehicle stability, which is also why Jaguar used the fin.

Its production origins are apparent behind the oversize 8,000 rpm tachometer where the speedometer is visible. The machine-turned dash was a styling addition. Designer Bob Cumberford was responsible for stretching the nose 10 inches farther and adding the headrest and fin to the SR-2.

direction often and unexpectedly, Earl gave his designers the greatest possible latitude to use their imaginations." Studio etiquette dictated that designers took direction from their studio managers.

"This was common practice," Cumberford explained 40 years later. "I sat in this studio by myself drawing a Corvette the way I thought it ought to be and I would draw a Corvette the way the drawings were going on the wall. I'd been around long enough to know what Harley Earl and his design committee didn't like. Harley Earl had this high, squeaky voice. And he stuttered. Well, he really talked that way to fill time so that nobody else could talk. It was his way to keep everybody else silent. You could see he was appalled [by drawings on the walls]. This project was not to go in the direction that the wall showed." Cumberford emptied his drawer onto his table, and Earl asked him why these weren't on the wall as well. Cumberford said that while he liked his own ideas, he followed the studio direction. The next morning, Security told Cumberford to report to Chevrolet studio manager Clare MacKichan.

"You and a kid from drafting are doing the Corvette around the corner," MacKichan told him.

Every studio in the building had a name or a number. The room Cumberford and the "kid" would use was Harley Earl's temporary office before his own had been completed in styling's administration building. It was a windowless 20 x 40-foot space. Tony Lapine was the "kid from drafting," and Cumberford had a photostat made of an X and put it up on the door, christening the room Studio X.

"We had no direction from anybody. Zora would come in, and he and Tony would tell stories," Cumberford said. Lapine raced in Europe, as had Duntov, and Cumberford had designed race cars in California before taking his job at GM. The three of them shared this interest. So some tasks, especially racing related, just walked in the door.

Despite tight budgets and stressed stylists and engineers, many enthusiasts regard the 1957 models (and those from 1956) as the loveliest of the early Corvettes. Harley Earl had already anointed Bill Mitchell as his successor. Mitchell regularly spent time removing Earl's excesses from each of the cars Earl had already completed.

Floridian Webster Benner Jr. joined GM Styling in 1955, transferring in late 1956 to Chevrolet engineering. However, he hated Michigan winters, and by mid-1957 he was back in Florida. He still had friends in styling and engineering, and they helped him initiate his own ideas, including fitting ribbed aluminum into the coves and mounting 1954 Buick Skylark wire wheels all around.

Jerry Earl, Harley's sports car enthusiast son, purchased a Ferrari to compete in SCCA events in 1956. Earl didn't want his son driving something foreign. He had Chevrolet designers and engineers build his son a race car. Cumberford did the styling.

"That car was done in four or five weeks," Cumberford remembered. "They brought in a car in early May, took the body off, did molds, and sent it off. The windshield panel was the same as the Sebring car. There was no headrest on it at the beginning and the fin came later too. Other than extending the front out 10 inches to make a better aerodynamic line over the hood, there were very few changes. It was just a stock car. It had a radio."

Duntov took the car to the styling mechanical assembly shops where he supervised SR-type modifications including Sebring-type Cerametallic brakes and a few other components. At the June Sprints at Elkhart Lake, Wisconsin, Jerry Earl entered the car, the first SR-2, but national-championship contender Dick Thompson drove it. To the SCCA, however, Earl's stylized bodywork made the racer a "modified" car. At the end of its race against much leaner machines, Thompson said it needed a lot of weight removed from it. When the car came back to Detroit, the mechanical shops removed about 300 pounds from the SR-2 without doing anything obvious.

Later Earl suggested molding a headrest into the SR's rear deck, similar to what Duntov did for the Daytona cars. But by this time, Cumberford was back doing drawings for Earl. "Then he got a wild hair about doing the SS," Cumberford said with a broad smile.

"The original idea was to provoke management. Harley Earl wanted to provoke management." The speaker here was Anatole C. Lapine, the "kid from drafting," who went on to work at Opel in Russelsheim, Germany, and later to Porsche in Stuttgart where, as design chief there, he did the 928 among other things.

"One day we found a dirty white D-type Jaguar waiting for us. 'Let's use the D-type,' Harley Earl said. 'Change the body and drop a Chevy into it. And let's go to Sebring and beat everybody!' He

Ex-Chevrolet engineer/stylist Benner, replaced the factory stock steering wheel with the wood-rimmed wheel. During the more than 20 years he owned the car, he seemingly changed its exterior color about every seven years. It was white from the factory, but by late 1967 it was blue (and he installed air conditioning). In the early 1970s, he had it painted red.

Benner drag raced this car through the first several years he owned it. He had ordered the fuel-injected 283 but couldn't get it to run well. He swapped the engine for the 270 horsepower, 283-cubic-inch version with these two four-barrel carburetors. He never went back to the fuel injection.

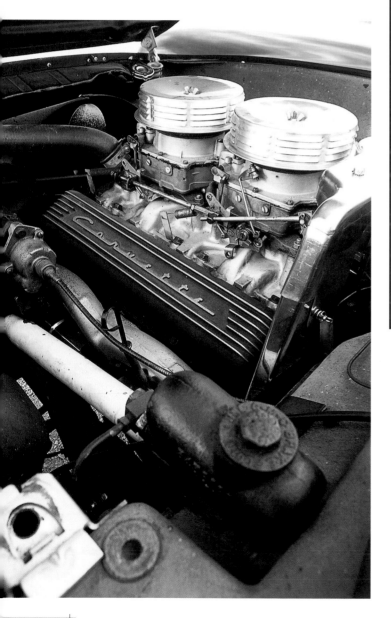

had a supporter in this plan, his heir-apparent, Bill Mitchell. That was the plan when Ed Cole and Harry Barr walked into the room. (Harry Barr was Chevrolet division's chief engineer by this time.)"

Lapine continued: "Harley and Bill outlined what they had in mind. Cole and Barr just stood there and smiled. Then Zora Duntov came over with Jim Premo (who had first visited Bob Morrison's fiberglass operation in Ohio and now was Barr's assistant chief engineer).

"We already knew," Lapine said, "that you couldn't change the body of a D-Jaguar by putting tin-snips to structure. It didn't matter that MistEarl didn't know this. Or that Ed Cole and Harry Barr *did*. Harley accomplished what he set out to do." Dissatisfied with the half-effort of the SR-2, Earl wanted a

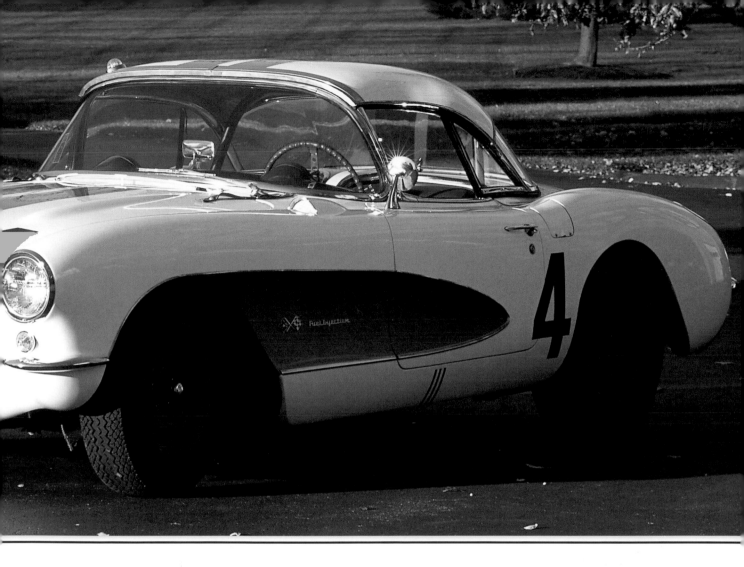

full-on styling exercise to go racing. "And soon, very soon, Stan Mott, Bob Cumberford, an engineer called Del Probst and I, as the kind of draftsman of the day, started on a car that became the SS Corvette. Zora purchased a Mercedes 300SL. They took the body off and underneath was its tubular space frame." Here Bob Cumberford resumed the tale.

"Once Zora had the body off the 300SL chassis, he put the chassis up on steel stands," Cumberford said. "Then he put a Chevrolet engine, transmission, and differential beside it. He made a tube frame out of wooden dowels, copying the Mercedes around Chevrolet running gear.

"It was really not possible to get a Corvette engine to fit the space of the Jaguar engine in the D-type. You'd have to redo a lot of stuff and Zora didn't want to do that. He wanted his own car. Of course, so did Harley Earl, so the SS came out of that."

Internally, the car was referred to as the XP-64, the letters standing for Experimental Pursuit, an abbreviation Earl had adopted from the military during World War II. It represented jet fighter planes still in development stage. Ed Cole funded one car. Duntov, through creative accounting methods, got enough spare pieces fabricated to assemble a second car, a vehicle dubbed "the mule." They built

This was Corvette's first Sebring class winner, driven by Dr. Dick Thompson and Swiss racer Gaston Andre. At the end of 12 hours, they had finished 12th overall, 1st in GT class. This car and its victory codified Duntov's idea to make high performance parts available through dealers. Many racers benefited from the competitive advantages of RPO 684, a complete suspension package that also included brake ventilation.

this test car, partially skinned in rough fiberglass, to evaluate innovations in the XP-64. The mule's engine developed much less horsepower than the aluminum-head 283-cubic inch displacement V-8 with special fuel injection that Harry Barr's engineers were preparing. What's more, while styling formed the actual race car body from magnesium sheets, the mule was thick fiberglass weighing 150 pounds more. The weight showed up new flaws in cooling and in the brakes.

Duntov and his engineers had developed a remarkable braking system. Delco-Moraine was working on disc brakes, but Duntov distrusted anything not race proven. His own front-wheel, two-leading-shoe, center-plane brakes came off a 1956 Chrysler. He put those inside 12-inch-diameter, 2.5-inch-wide cast-iron face/finned aluminum drums and used them at front and rear. He devised a kind of antilock braking system using two separate Kelsey-Hayes vacuum servos; pedal pressure modulated the front brakes. He connected the second servo using a pressurized air system so it reacted to the amount of pedal pressure and front brake force. It adjusted rear braking to that pressure. Duntov wanted 70 percent front/30 percent rear brake bias. He added an in-line mercury switch actuated by the car's angle during hard braking. Closing the switch sealed off the air-pipe, effectively holding the rear brakes at the last pressure that was applied. Without this clever system, as drivers increased front braking pressure, it almost ensured rear lockup, jeopardizing directional stability. Drivers could reorient the switch during a race as weather or track conditions required. In competition, Duntov learned that the rear brake lines were too small. This caused a delay in system

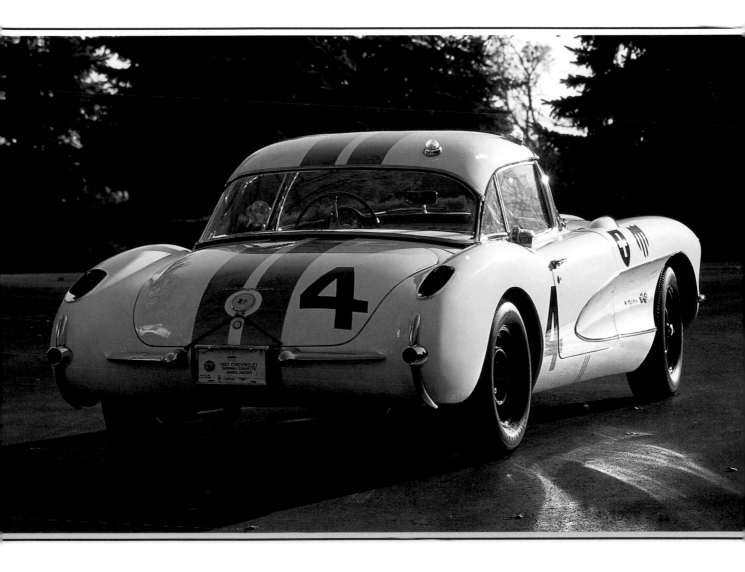

response that delivered spectacular brake lockups at the worst possible moment. Duntov eventually used larger diameter tubing.

In Friday practice at Sebring, both Juan Manuel Fangio, the Argentine grand prix world champion, and English racer Stirling Moss drove the mule, turning exceptionally fast times. Chevrolet had contracted with Fangio to drive the race, but the actual car arrived late, missing Fangio's cutoff date. This released him to drive a Maserati with whom Moss also had a contract. So John Fitch, who was managing Sebring production Corvette efforts, stepped in. He reached Italian grand prix and endurance champion Piero Taruffi, who flew overnight from Rome to join him.

They qualified the mule on the front row. Race morning revealed the magnesium-bodied car in its Harley Earl–specified blue finish. It was completed to spectacular Motorama show standards. As Karl Ludvigsen reported in *Corvette: America's Star-Spangled Sports Car*, it suffered inconsistent brake balance problems and hellish cockpit heat. The magnesium panels trapped the heat that the fiberglass

Chevrolet's new general manager, Ed Cole, as quoted in the media, was overjoyed with the Sebring finish. "That was the turn of the tide. That was when the car… began to confirm our original premise: there was a demand for a product that recaptured the sport and fun of motoring."

(above) Sebring in 1956 taught Ed Cole that outright victory came not to production cars modified for the track. Outright winners were outright race cars that did not evolve from existing models but led the evolution to the next product. Ironically, it was stylist Harley Earl who was the catalyst for this progressive step.

(opposite) Harley Earl had learned to throw challenges at management in order to get his dreams turned into reality. This Corvette SS started in Earl's imagination as a D-type Jaguar with enough bodywork modifications to install a Corvette engine. He let everyone know he wanted to race it at Sebring. When Ed Cole and chief engineer Harry Barr heard, they had a better idea, and this car was the result.

While it clearly brings to mind the striking lines of Jaguar's racing D-types, its dimensions came from a Mercedes-Benz 300SL that Harley Earl imported into his styling studios. Chevrolet chief stylist Clare MacKichan devised its shape. MacKichan was the man who supervised Sparky Bohnstedt's design for the first 1953 Motorama Corvette.

insulated from the drivers. Tin snips slashed the sleek body. But there was no remedy for brake bias problems without the Duntov system perfected on the mule.

Crowds swarmed the blue SS. Fitch started the race. As he had done the year before nursing a failing clutch, he quickly found a rhythm that kept the brakes from locking while cutting lap times to within a second of Fangio's qualifying effort. Yet problems and failures continued.

Taruffi noticed the car's handling deteriorating badly. The rear tires bounced into the body or hopped frantically after each bump in the airport's concrete surface. Overheated himself, he pulled in and engineers found the car was undriveable after only 23 laps.

"The failure of the SS, the only factory appearance of Chevrolet in racing," Bob Cumberford

With some time to work, Harry Barr's engine wizards developed aluminum cylinder heads and a heavily baffled magnesium oil pan for the standard fuel-injected 283-cubic-inch V-8. Engineering created a special intake manifold ducted through a scoop on the hood. Wind-tunnel testing suggested the normal manifold and intake was slightly better. On a dynamometer, the engine developed 307 horsepower at 6,400 rpm.

With weight clearly a consideration in this new Corvette prototype, the philosophy that brought the Porsche 550 Spyder's simple bucket seats to the SR-2 dictated development of new seats for this car. The passenger side is slightly smaller than the driver's; it appears tiny due to wide-angle lens perspective.

explained, "came when a rear bushing failed after eight laps. Mounted incorrectly, it split. It broke because Harley Earl would not let them run the race car on the track because it would damage the paint."

Despite the result at Sebring, Ed Cole still saw a future in racing the SS and continuing Corvette promotion. Duntov had given him a ride in the mule. Cole promptly approved manufacture of three more cars to race at Le Mans. He let Duntov begin work on a desmodromic valve gear (without springs) for the top end of the engine. This could permit 400 horsepower at 9,000 rpm. Cole authorized constructing a 1958 and making improved SR-2 models available to private entries. Now Ed Cole's Chevrolet division was going racing, publicly.

At the top of General Motors, another perspective had coalesced. From the beginning of the American automobile industry, through acquisitions, mergers, and failures, car makers had slipped past governmental scrutiny. GM had the largest market share of automobile sales and the most at risk if Washington legislators turned their attention to the Big Three.

When a Mercedez-Benz entry crashed horrifically during the 24-hour race at Le Mans, France, in June 1955, the tragedy moved accountability onto every company president's agenda. Mercedes withdrew from racing that day; unfavorable publicity shadowed the company for years. No U.S. automaker would risk the kind of public outcry and government examination such a tragedy might inspire.

A ban on racing by the Automobile Association of America ended Chevrolet's official involvement in racing, but customers continued to race Corvettes, and GM engineers continued to develop ways to make the Corvette more competitive. 2002 General Motors Corporation. Used with permission of GM Media Archives.

Similar to Jaguar's D-type with its stabilizing wing behind the driver's head, the Corvette SS fitted a headrest that Clare MacKichan tapered to a point to manage wind resistance and hide the roll-over bar. It earned the nickname "flying football" from MacKichan's colleagues in styling.

This version with its lovely sheet magnesium body never got the improvements or modifications that Duntov and his colleagues put into the heavier fiberglass mule. On race day, this car disappointed everyone. The magnesium body held the engine heat, roasting drivers John Fitch and Piero Taruffi.

Initially, Harley Earl's styling department sought approval to build four of these cars, known as XP-64 in their internal code system. The first was to be the development mule, followed by three additional Sebring entries. Time and money ran out. Still, Duntov wrote the budgets for a single car that were large enough to hide a second "mule" in them, and he did the engineering development on that fiberglass-bodied second car.

GM Chairman Harlow Curtice suggested to the Automobile Manufacturers Association (AMA) during its February 1957 board meeting that member companies "take no part in automobile racing or other competitive events involving tests of speed and that they refrain from suggesting speed in passenger car advertising or publicity." Every member ratified Curtice's proposal. It was the auto industry's equivalent of Prohibition. Factory participation never stopped; it just learned to hide better. (In fact, Chevrolet delivered 51 Corvettes in 1957 and 144 in 1958 manufactured with Regular Production Option RPO 684. This provided heavy-duty front and rear springs and shock absorbers, metallic brake linings, and heavily finned brake drums as well as fresh air ducting to rear brakes and air scoops to cool the front brakes. These last two were quickly nicknamed "elephant ears and trunks." (With their hard brake pedal pressure, they were not exactly the ideal for boulevard cruisers or grocery getters.)

"Testing and development [of the Corvette SS] would have made a big difference," Robert Cumberford concluded resignedly. "Had the car done well, Chevrolet might not have joined that AMA ban and gone racing under the table or out the back door.

"There were other designs already in the works for what became the 1958 Corvette," Cumberford continued the story. "There was one strongly influenced by the 1956 Motorama Oldsmobile Golden Rocket with the Torpedo top, probably the true source of the 1963 split window. We wanted to do the car on a 94 1/2-inch wheelbase, a car with an aluminum body and frame, aluminum V-8 in front, a full transaxle at the back. It would have given us a nice cockpit. This is what we wanted to do for the 1958 car."

Internally, the car was referred to as the XP-64, the letters standing for Experimental Pursuit, an abbreviation Earl had adopted from the military during World War II. It represented jet fighter planes still in development stage.

For 1959, Chevrolet offered a variety of colors for its Corvette. None of those included purple. Racer Jim Jeffords adopted a popular song whose lyrics spoke of a "one-eyed, one-horned flying purple people eater." As other historians have noted, Jeffords was a fearless Corvette eater, beating more than a dozen other Corvette racers to the national championship in both 1958 and 1959.

The transaxle was a less radical proposal than other parts of the car. Chevrolet engineering was developing a rear-mounted transmission and differential with the starter incorporated in the casing, designated Project "Q." It incorporated a full independent suspension that would have gone into production for the 1960 model year Chevrolet sedans. No one could have justified it solely for a sports car that sold barely 6,300 units in 1957, but Corvette could easily adopt it from a passenger car line selling hundreds of thousands. Lapine also worked out a retractable aluminum hardtop. Reynolds Aluminum was interested in doing the aluminum tooling in 1955.

"Tony and I were convinced that the '58 Corvette *should be* shorter, smaller, and narrower," Cumberford said. "The new aluminum 3.5-liter V-8 was much smaller. Harley Earl gave us carte blanche. No specifications. But we had to deal with Zora. He knew what was going on with hardware. It was fall of 1955, while Tony and I were in that studio. We wondered if there would even be a 1958 Corvette, the XP-94. The 1956 car wasn't out yet.

"So after hours we came up with this concept of the four-passenger Corvette. Tony, Stan Mott, and I called ourselves Automotive Research Consultants. We wrote a letter asking what readers thought about a four-passenger sports car. We sent it to John Fitch, [*Road & Track's*] John Bond, people in the SCCA, maybe 15 people. We got 15 wonderful responses, a lot of well-reasoned comments. And everybody was in favor of it. People said it evoked the Bentleys, that sports cars for racing used to be required to have four seats.

"Part of the motivation of the four-passenger car was the morality of the day. Guys didn't go out on dates by themselves with a girl. If you had a Corvette, you couldn't date. There always had to be a chaperon, or another couple, one to keep an eye on the other. Double dating was fine. A guy alone with a girl was not," Cumberford continued.

"So we got Barney Clark, who wrote the Corvette ads and who was enthusiastic about the idea, to write a description of the car as we conceived it. Big engine, so it would go as fast as European stuff. It was a chunky, high-deck, square piece of road machinery. We wrote a cover letter and took the car to Earl. He was furious. Absolutely furious.

" 'You fellahs,' he stammered, 'you got a lot of enthusiasm. My boys are just plain garden-variety boys. But you . . . We're not going to do anything with this. But as a reward for initiative, I'm going to let you design the 1961 Buick Special. . . .' "

GOING THE WRONG WAY

The Cumberford/Lapine Corvette meant the 1958 introduction had progressed to full-size clay models, but it was scrapped. Instead, the production studio did a quick face-lift on the 1956 to have it ready for production by fall 1957. Overall length grew from 168 to 177.2 inches. The car swelled 2.3 inches in width to 72.8. For sports car enthusiasts, the Corvette was going the wrong way.

It was, however, a better automobile with bumpers secured to the frame providing true accident

Jeffords was sponsored by Chicago's Chevrolet performance dealer, Nickey, spelled with a backwards "k" to increase its visibility. This was mostly the view other racers had of the Nickey-Jeffords car. It was a regular production option racer, ordered and delivered with Zora Duntov–sanctioned factory racing parts.

RPO 579D delivered to the buyer this fuel-injected 283-cubic-inch V-8 rated at 290 horsepower. What Nickey's mechanics and racing team wizards did to the car after delivery helped Jim Jeffords pilot both a 1958 and 1959 model to SCCA B-production national championships.

To anyone who followed SCCA professional racing in the late 1950s, this car and its driver will spark their memory. Jim Jeffords, an advertising executive from Milwaukee, Wisconsin, won SCCA B-production two years in a row in an RPO 684 convertible.

SCCA's production-class rules required cars to race with both seats and full carpeting as the car was delivered. It meant production class racers carried extra weight, but with 290 horsepower on tap from the factory, a few extra pounds were not critical.

protection. Acrylic lacquer replaced the nitrocellulose paints. Every instrument on the dash except the clock was relocated in front of the driver's eyes with a large 160-mile-per-hour speedometer surrounding the 6,000-rpm tachometer.

Improvements under the hood made up for added girth. Output reached 290 horsepower with the RPO 579D's Rochester fuel injection. Introduction followed General Motors' official adoption of the AMA racing ban by half a year. GM could not/would not promote racing or speed. Of course, if a customer wanted to order certain things, it only required reading the order form, and Chevrolet would never argue with its customers. One customer, Jim Jeffords, a Milwaukee advertising executive, followed the instructions at Chicago's Nickey Chevrolet. He found everything necessary except the car's exterior color. Inspired by a popular song, Jeffords painted the car a bright purple and named it *The Purple People Eater*. He won the SCCA B-production championship and under the full force of the auto industry's prohibition, Chevrolet's own carefully created RPOs heralded the birth of the muscle car in America.

CHAPTER FIVE

RUNNING IN PLACE MEANT PROGRESS AND FRUSTRATION

hat long seven-year stretch, beginning in 1956 and ending in late 1962, meant different things to different people. To customers watching the Corvette in dealer showrooms, the car moved forward in appearance slightly, following fashion as it shed fins and gathered double headlights, but it got much better mechanically, gaining muscle and agility. For Ed Cole's engineers and Harley Earl's stylists, it was a time of walking, running, and sometimes sprinting on a treadmill. Lots of work got done, but few people outside the studios ever saw it or knew of it until years later. The corporation, with its change of guard, made steady moves toward reversing progress. It was, all in all, a tough time.

Harley Earl probably would have styled Bill Mitchell into existence if the younger man didn't already exist. There would have been a Mitchell in side-elevation and then modeled into life-size clay and finally produced as another one-off, a Mitchell like a Y-Job and a LeSabre. When Earl got his Mitchell, he kept it longer than any of his personal cars.

William L. Mitchell inherited Earl's job as vice president of styling at General Motors on December 1, 1958, when he was 46. He had worked for Earl for 22 years, starting as one of his stylists. Mitchell's father had sold Buicks, and even before Earl ever touched one of those, Mitchell loved automobiles. He worked as an illustrator for the publishing and road-racing Collier family and filled his office with his own drawings of classics. The Colliers owned these kinds of cars, and they invited Mitchell into their close-knit circle of enthusiasts, where he made rapid stylized sketches of them racing. Earl saw these and hired him in 1935.

Mitchell watched his mentor work. He knew Earl had had to prove himself and the value of styling to skeptical division general *(previous pages) Normally cars painted Inca Silver appeared with white coves, though frequently second or third owners have eliminated the contrasting colors to unify the appearance, as Leonard Nagel has done with his 1959 convertible. All the colors received new names if not new formulation for the new model year.*

Dual headlights arrived with chrome frames for the 1958 model, although designer Bob Cumberford had conceived them for the 1957 production year. For 1959, Chevrolet painted the headlight frames to match the body color. It was another example of eliminating frills as time went on to clean up the body design.

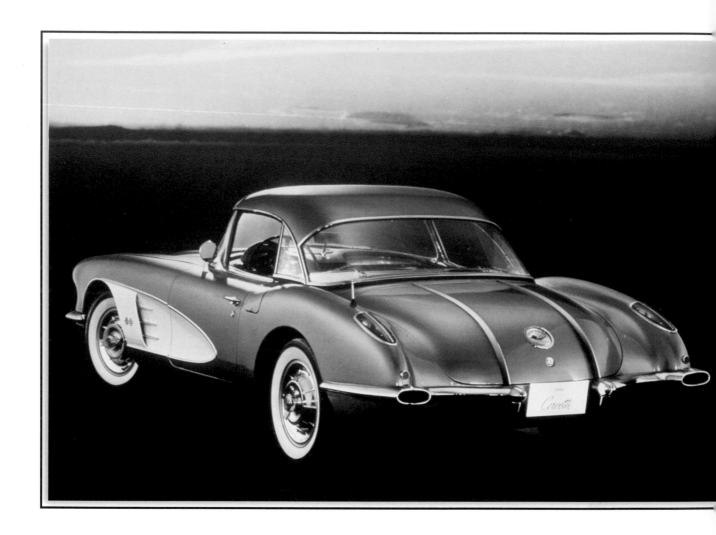

managers. As inheritor himself, now he had to fight his own battles against other successors who seized the opportunity of Earl's departure to regain some control. Some in GM's current management, oriented to finances, felt compelled to rein in some of styling's flamboyance and fiscal excesses, not an entirely improper idea. But Mitchell had allies, powerful division executives with "gasoline in their veins." Men such as Ed Cole understood that styling sold cars for GM, more than Ford's or Chrysler's design efforts did for them.

Mitchell tackled one perception almost immediately. He distrusted the word *styling*. He likened it to being fashionable, whereby something was "in" one day and "out" the next. He knew that industrial designers, contemporaries such as Henry Dreyfuss, Norman Belle Geddes, and Walter Dorwin Teague, argued that good design lasted forever. Soon after his promotion, Mitchell changed his department's name from *styling* to *design*.

Mitchell adopted Earl's technique of giving designers no direction with their assignment. Earl would demand a highlight line be raised or lowered as little as 1/32nd of an inch. He would trumpet displeasure across a studio if that change was not done. Mitchell's temper rivaled Earl's and he used it similarly, as punctuation, but Mitchell added a kind of volatile fickleness. He routinely flipped design concepts 180 degrees from one encounter to the next. For the 1959 Corvette, Bill Mitchell removed some of the design excesses that had marked Harley Earl's final years at GM. He took off the 1958 chrome trim strips along the trunk lid and rows of washboard-like simulated louvers on the engine hood from that model.

Chevrolet engineering carried over its 290-horsepower V-8 engine and sophisticated four-speed transmission. While the heater was still optional, hardtops and even extra-cost handling packages offered stiffer springs and heavily finned brake drums with roadworthy metallic brake linings (RPO 686). Chevrolet set the Corvette base price at $3,875. The countryclub set, ordering a boulevard cruise–ready Corvette with 245 horsepower-283, Powerglide, power top, radio, heater, sunshades, and

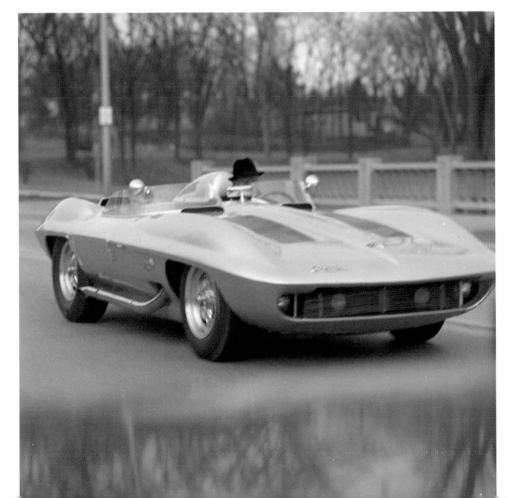

Bill Mitchell took over the Art and Colour Section in 1959 and made it the design center it is today. He created the Sting Ray racer, on which the Sting Ray production car was based. He used to drive his racer prototype in the streets of Detroit.

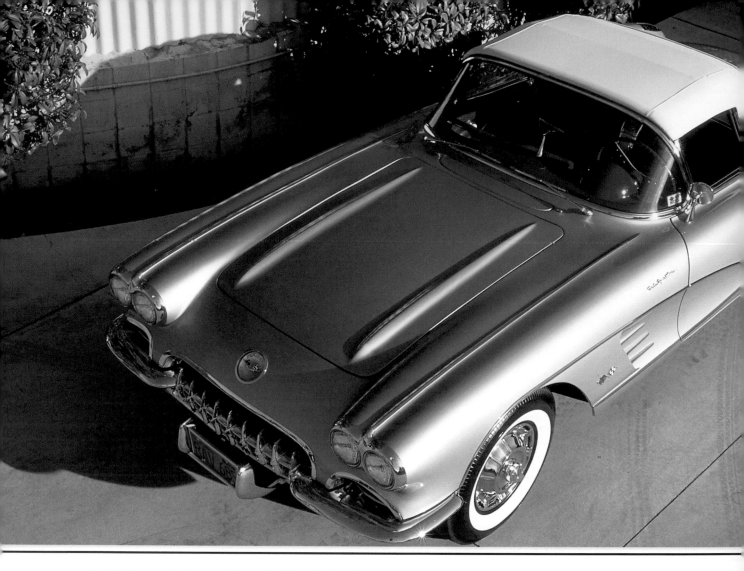

(above) The 1959 Corvette lost the decorative hood louvers of the 1958 model. Also missing were the twin chrome strips that set off the trunk contours. It was emblematic of new design chief Bill Mitchell and his growing recognition that less is sometimes more.

(bottom left) Chevrolet offered two fuel-injected versions of its 283-cubic-inch engine: the RPO 579 that provided 250 horsepower, and the wilder RPO 579D, which claimed 290-horsepower output. Curiously, Chevrolet charged the same price, $484.20, for each version, but not surprisingly, the higher performance version sold five times as many as the lesser model.

(bottom center) Inca Silver exteriors were offered with either red or black interiors, with either a black or white soft top. Chevrolet manufactured 9,670 convertibles in 1959, just 957 of which were this color. The $3,875 base price included the 230-horsepower 283-cubic-inch engine with 3-speed manual transmission.

(bottom right) Not quite half the 1959 cars produced were fitted with the four-speed manual, some 4,175 of the total. Much less popular was the Powerglide Automatic that was installed in just 1,878 of the cars manufactured. The Wonderbar AM radio was Corvette's most popular option, installed in 7,001 of the cars produced.

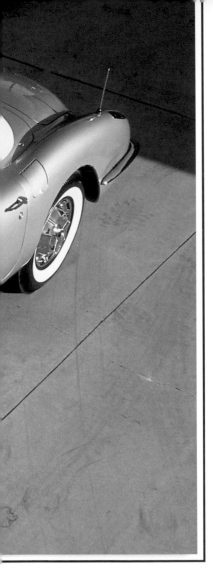

other minor options, paid $5,031, about what they spent for four years of their child's college tuition. Production for 1957 reached 6,339, nearly double that of 1956, and it increased to 9,168 for 1958 and 9,670 for 1959.

"BE BRAVE"

Back in 1956, GM hired another young designer, Peter Brock, out of the Los Angeles Art Center College. After his first few assignments, Mitchell transferred Brock to work with senior stylist Bob Veryzer in Bob McLean's advance design research studio. Brock joined Chuck Pohlmann, studio engineer Byron Voight, and chief modeler John Bird. Mitchell had gone to the Turin, Italy, auto show and returned to Detroit excited by several coupes he'd seen there. He announced that he wanted to do a new Corvette for production as a 1960 model. He described what he wanted and created a contest within the studios to see whose design came closest. According to Bob Veryzer's son, Robert, his father established his own theme in a two-word sign he posted in the studio: "Be Brave." Brock was daring, and Mitchell selected his concept for a car known internally as XP-84, the Q-car, to use Chevrolet's new sedan independent rear suspension and other innovations.

"I'd designed the car in coupe form, according to Mitchell's direction," Brock said. "At that point Mitchell said, 'I think we also want to do a roadster.'" Chuck Pohlmann, the other young designer in McLean's studio, and Brock became friends because they shared similar design philosophies. Pohlmann did a roadster version while Brock continued with details on his

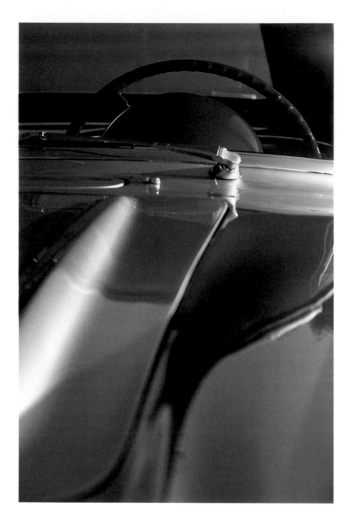

Late afternoon sunlight sculpts the hood and instrument binnacle on this excellent restoration. The twin "power bulges" first appeared on the 1956 hoods, and Chevrolet's designers openly admitted to copying those from the hood of the 1954 Mercedes-Benz 300SL.

coupe. "The two cars were nearly identical," Brock recalled, "except for the crisp horizontal line that formed the car's distinctive shape. Chuck's version, directed by Mitchell, fell away to the back. Mine forced a slight kick-up at the rear.

"Once we had the theme there were a number of versions," Brock continued. "We had one with a fully removable roof panel, like the Porsche Targa. In another, the car didn't have A pillars, just a single pillar in the center. Windscreen side glass wrapped completely around."

According to Robert Veryzer, Bob's son, who wrote about the origin of the Sting Ray in *Collectible Automobile* in June 2001, studio engineer Byron Voight and Zora Duntov together established the wheelbase and wheel track and penciled in engine placement, seat location, and other crucial dimensions while Brock and Pohlmann drew variations for Veryzer and Mitchell. Once Mitchell picked the design he liked, everything came into focus.

Chief modeler John Bird created a quarter-scale clay, then a full-sized model in coupe form. After Mitchell made his changes on it, Bird formed a roadster version of Chuck's variation. They set Brock's full-sized coupe alongside it so Mitchell, Brock, Pohlmann, McLean, and studio chief Bob Veryzer could compare details. At that point, Mitchell decided they would build only the roadster prototype because it would be easier and cheaper to do. "So they took the full-sized clay model roadster," Brock said, "and moved it out of the studio, so it wouldn't be discovered. We referred to that as the XP-96, but that car eventually became the Sting Ray race car."

"That car was built in secret," Brock continued. "With the AMA racing ban in force, there wasn't supposed to be any more sports or competition stuff at all." They set up the "hammer room," Mitchell's secret studio, "behind a tool room where design's fabrication specialists kept the hammers and tools they used to form the models. You'd go into this room and then walk around the back, through another door and the secret studio was back there. GM's high brass walking around the building wouldn't find it because, in theory, it didn't even exist."

Brock originally did the XP-84 coupe with a large single piece of glass for the rear window. The split window went in later. Mitchell imposed the hard line down the roof dividing the rear window because he admired the Bugatti-type 57SC Atlantic. He wanted the flavor of that elegant French car on the Sting Ray.

"Larry Shinoda and Chuck finished the production roadster. Larry did most of the form detailing on it, the things that Mitchell wanted on the car like the twin windscreens, hood louvers, side

The Corvette had its best year yet with the 1962 model, producing 14,531 of the convertibles. More than half of these, 8,074, went out with optional hardtops for an additional $236.75. This Roman Red was one of seven exterior colors offered.

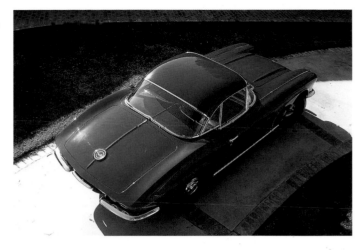

This was the last of a lot of things for the Corvette. A major styling/design series ended with the 1962 models, and along with appearances went an engineering and mechanical heritage. Everything new was coming for 1963, but very few people outside GM knew it.

vents, and such. Really, I think all three of us, Chuck, Larry, and I, provided about equal shares in developing the final appearance of that car, but the original lines were mine. The production Sting Ray became a much larger car. But that original car was really a graceful, pretty little automobile."

Engineer Byron Voight and modeler John Bird built the Brock/Pohlmann/Shinoda XP-84 on the same 94.5-inch wheelbase that Bob Cumberford and Tony Lapine had developed for the proposed 1958 replacement. This new car used the Q-project transaxle to provide more cockpit room without a large transmission sitting between the driver and passenger. It adopted the same advanced frame and also the independent rear suspension that Cumberford and Lapine had devised.

"There were always several engineering solutions," Brock recalled, "ideas to get room in a car when it was still in the research or styling end of things. These engineering ideas, systems, could solve styling and interior problems. The real problem was cost."

Harley Earl himself came up with one engineering upgrade for the XP-84, fitting the 283-cubic-inch displacement V-8 with dry-sump lubrication. The shallow oil pan allowed Brock to drop cowl height by nearly 2 inches, allowing the entire car to sit lower. The Q-car proposal stood only 46 inches tall.

Duntov promoted aluminum not only for certain engine components such as cylinder heads but also for entire blocks, manifolds, and transmission and differential cases. Aluminum would reduce weight, thereby improving handling and fuel economy of the entire Chevrolet line. Using aluminum, a Duntov Corvette would weigh less than 2,500 pounds. While he advocated aluminum for engine and drivetrain components, however, he pushed Chevrolet to build the Corvette's body out of steel.

"There was a lot of talk," Peter Brock recalled, "that after a certain production number, it would be feasible to do it in steel. It probably would have been cheaper too. Steel would have changed the car completely, made it stiffer, lighter, and stronger."

Had Chevrolet built the car in steel, they could have formed aluminum panels on the same dies to build a lightweight GT version. They stuck with plastic for several reasons. Stamping dies for steel cost much more. Also, this retained contact with plastic companies, ensuring the earliest possibility of working with new composite materials.

"But also," Brock continued, "they could change little details like the side scoops and hood blister and all the little panels really quickly in glass, cheaper than in steel. And since the Corvette was going to have longer production runs . . ."

In December 1957, the Engineering Policy Group saw the Q-Corvette. Under Mitchell's watchful eye,

(opposite) As Mike Antonick reported in his Corvette Black Book, *for 1962, Chevrolet formed the side cove lip using fiberglass body panels, not simply accented by bright trim as before. This meant it was impossible for the factory to paint the coves different colors from the rest of the body. Ironically, this gave some customers something they'd wanted for years.*

All new and plenty exciting, Chevrolet's 250-horsepower 327-cubic-inch V-8 was the base engine. Carbureted versions cranking out 300 and 340-horsepower and a 360-horsepower fuel-injected version were also available. The most popular choice was the 340 horsepower carbureted engine, a $107.60 option. This fuelie cost $484.20, and Chevrolet produced only 1,918 of them.

Larry Shinoda now added working hatches, and he relocated fuel caps to the left rear fender. Mitchell wanted the front fender scoops reversed, placing them at the rear of the doors. In this location, these primarily blew air onto the rear tires. Mitchell felt this accentuated the "Coke-bottle" taper he wanted for the car. Shinoda followed directions and finished a coupe and convertible, ready for presentation at the board of directors' show, the executive show-and-tell that codified or doomed production plans.

The full-size clay models and their accompanying engineering proposals for the 1958 car took the Corvette far beyond what the production 1958 model would be. Design and engineering made it equal to the most advanced, sophisticated sports—and racing—cars built anywhere in the world. Their one roadblock: one critical personnel change among the executives.

Harlow Curtice, GM chairman, retired in 1958. The GM accountant who rose to head Buick division had learned from Alfred Sloan what Harley Earl's styling could do to car sales, and he went to the top. He drove GM through the decade that saw Chevrolet division alone spend $90 million for advertising. Curtice may not have been born with "gasoline in his veins," Mitchell's measure of a man, but years of steady transfusions made him tolerant of design and engineering costs. Curtice's replacement was Frederic Donner.

Curtice wondered about car sales, respectful of Sloan and Donaldson Brown's concept of return on investment. Donner took that concept and twisted it into a Baroque art form whereby stockbrokers became even more important to GM than shareholders. Curtice had seen that interesting automobiles, produced with a pleasing appearance, sold. Donner knew that reducing costs, curbing the lavish expenditures of design and engineering, would increase dividends. Profits made GM attractive to Wall Street, not Earl's chrome and Duntov's independent rear suspensions. Experiments like the Sting Ray represented nonessentials with fiduciary downsides.

Sitting in Mitchell's Hammer Room was the car that Duntov, with prescient political savvy, knew was much too much of a reach. He retreated from his own goal and wrote to Chevrolet's chief engineer, Harry Barr. Duntov acknowledged the Q-Corvette's numerous technical advances were so expensive that current management might never allow such a car to be built. Forewarned by his perception of current corporate thinking, he suggested Chevrolet stick with the Corvette's faithful separate chassis-body assembly used from the beginning.

(above) Roman Red cars were available with black, fawn, or red interiors. This was one of just 65 cars produced with the larger 24-gallon gas tank and one of an indeterminate number built with no radio. While it never raced as far as the current owner knows, it was definitely built for speed and endurance.

Model year 1960 marked the end of the chrome teeth in the Corvette grille. This Ermine White exterior was the most popular color for that year, with 3,717 cars produced. Base price dropped $93, from $3,875 in 1959 to $3,782 for 1960.

Model year 1960 was the first year Chevrolet produced more than 10,000 Corvettes, peaking at 10,261.

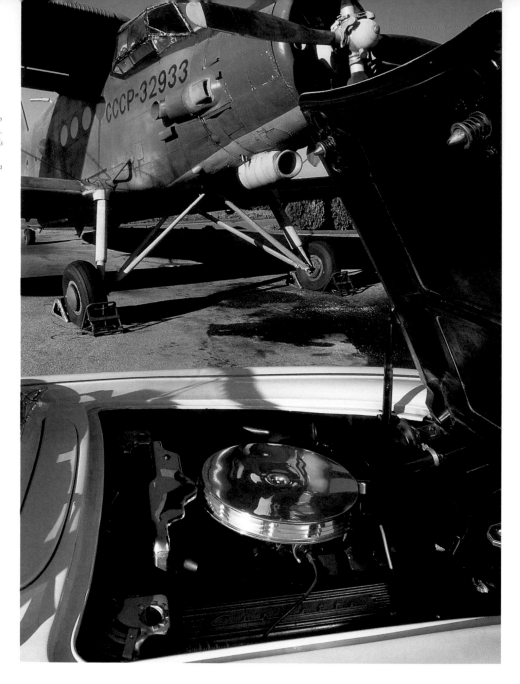

Engine options for 1960 ranged from a 230-horsepower carbureted version to a 290-horsepower fuel-injected version. The most popular power plant was this 270-horsepower carbureted model that Chevrolet installed in 2,364 cars, for a modest $182.95.

Ed Cole carried over the existing body from the 1958–59 model year for 1960, and Duntov set to work with the other engine development engineers to produce aluminum cylinder heads for the fuel-injected 283s. But production consistency difficulties made this a never-available option. Chassis engineers tamed the handling by deleting the optional heavy-duty springs while increasing the diameter of the front antisway bar and adding a rear one. The $336.60 RPO 687 was really a "PRO" (production *racing* option). It quickened the steering and fitted sintered-metallic brake linings inside new brake drums cast with large cooling fins. Base price of the car was $3,872. The top engine option was RPO 579D,

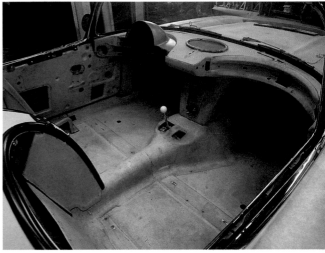

(upper left) A restoration work in progress, this significant racer was partially reassembled for a review session of its history. The car is currently being prepared for numerous vintage races and Corvette 50-year celebrations beginning in late 2002 and continuing throughout 2003.

(above) Racer John Fitch, who had headed the successful 1956 and 1957 Sebring efforts for Chevrolet, and co-driver Bob Grossman spent 24 hours in this cockpit. Production class rules required both seats and the carpet as well as the roll-bar and hardtop roof in place. Fighting off an overheating engine, they pitted according to the rules, but at each stop they packed the engine compartment with ice.

Legendary car builder/racer Briggs Cunningham entered three 1960 hardtops in the 24 Hours of Le Mans, specially prepared by Alfred Momo in New York (and with great assistance from Chevrolet's Frank Burrell and Zora Duntov). A sister car to this reached 151 miles per hour on the four-mile long Mulsanne straight, while this car finished 8th overall, 1st in its production class.

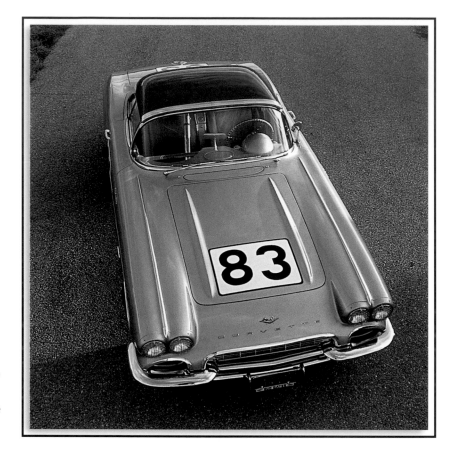

Indianapolis Chevrolet dealer Bud Gates had ordered the car with all the racing options, but only when reading the 1961 Sebring 12-hour race rules did he discover that the car needed a hardtop. At the last minute he sent a mechanic out into the new car lot at night to "borrow one." The mechanic took the first one he found, red.

Gates and co-driver Harry Heuer ran a sensible race, driving conservatively to a 22nd overall finish, good enough for 2nd in class. After the race, Bud drove the car back home to Indiana, selling it on his high-performance used-car lot 18 months later.

the 1958–59 290-horsepower 283 V-8 with the Duntov cam, solid valve lifters, 11.0:1 compression ratio, and fuel injection.

For Briggs Cunningham, the 1960 model had been a long-time coming. He entered two cars for the Sebring 12 Hours on March 26 and had New York Long Islander Alfred Momo prep his racers. Neither of them finished; car #2, with Dick Thompson and Fred Windridge co-driving, retired after an accident on the 41st lap, and the other, #1, which Cunningham shared with John Fitch, went out after a rollover accident at the Webster turn during lap 27. Four more Corvettes ran the race. Lloyd "Lucky" Casner's contribution-funded Camoradi team (the name meant Casner Motor Racing Division) entered two more Corvettes, #3 and #4, and Dallas, Texas, dealer Delmo Johnson raced with David Morgan in #5. Chuck Hall and Bill Fritts achieved the best Corvette finish, starting 6th and finishing 17th overall, first in class.

Accidents were risks of racing, and Cunningham repaired his rolled #1 car from Sebring. He entered the Sebring Corvettes and a third one (as well as a prototype E-type Jaguar) in the 24 Hours of Le Mans. Alfred Momo distrusted Duntov's prototype aluminum heads that were on the engines, so with Duntov's help, Momo got new cast-iron versions of the cylinder heads, with the larger valves and improved porting that would appear in 1961 as the production 315-horsepower engine. But Le Mans is never an easy race and Cunningham's effort was filled with drama. Bill Kimberly ran Corvette #1 off course in a thunderstorm. The car rolled and burned, but Kimberly escaped unhurt. Dick Thompson's car #2 suffered severe body damage in traffic early in the race, then lost an hour digging out of the sand during the night. It finally expired in a trail of black smoke while passing the pits on lap 207, five hours from the finish. Cunningham's Jaguar failed hours earlier that morning.

By noon, only John Fitch and Bob Grossman's #3, the Sebring rollover, was still racing. Then it started seriously overheating. Rules prohibited adding oil or water less than 24 laps, about 215 miles, from its last pit stop. They also required that all cars must complete at least four laps in the final hour. Momo told Grossman to run 15-minute laps and come in after each one. Team mechanic and GM employee Frank Burrell and Willy Frick (co-creator of the Fordillac who first introduced Cunningham to Ed Cole and Burrell) both packed the top of the engine compartment full of dry ice from Cunningham's trailer behind the pits. The fans in the main stands loved this, applauding vigorously at each ice down. When the race ended at 4 P.M., the Corvette passed the finish line in 8th place overall. It had completed 280 laps, 2,363.5 miles, averaging 97.9 miles per hour even with ice stops, and it

(continued on page 154)

(top) Gates had the car delivered to race preparer Ron Kaplan, in Chicago to complete modifications to the 315-horsepower fuel-injected 283.

(above) Ron Kaplan fitted the roll bar and the rear window tunnel for the quick-fill 37-gallon gas tank. When time came to head to Sebring, Gates' transporter broke down, so the car got thoroughly broken in while driving it to central Florida.

1960 CERV I

Zora Duntov named it the Chevrolet Experimental Racing Vehicle. Despite GM chairman Harlow Curtice's support of the 1957 Automobile Manufacturers Association ban on racing, Duntov and his colleagues built it to meet the specifications for the 1960 Indianapolis 500. Wise engineers seeking to keep their jobs soon renamed it the Chevrolet Experimental Research Vehicle.

Press releases described it as "a research tool for Chevrolet's continuous investigations into automotive ride and handling phenomena under the most realistic conditions." It had no fenders or taillights and seated one. The "realistic" conditions certainly were not rush hour traffic on Woodward or Michigan Avenues or 12 Mile Road. It was given not a name but an acronym: CERV (Chevrolet Experimental Racing Vehicle). In view of GM chairman Frederic Donner's adamant support of the AMA 1957 racing ban, the CERV was inexplicable. It looked like a flat-out single-seat race car built to 1960 Indianapolis regulations.

After the problems Zora Duntov had experienced with the Corvette SS in early 1957, he began looking at new solutions to vehicle balance, braking effectiveness, cornering stability, power transfer to the ground, and driver comfort. He first relocated the engine behind the driver so its heat would not roast the cockpit, but the AMA ban against racing prohibited Duntov from battle testing his concepts. It wasn't until early 1959 when Duntov took the risk of starting a project to test his ideas. By now, Duntov had the nucleus of a team, with Harold Krieger and Walt Zetye who had come to work for Chevrolet back in 1946. In 1958, Zetye joined Duntov and took responsibility for the chassis development up until the mid-1970s.

The three engineers created the CERV on a 96-inch wheelbase (the Indy minimum), with front and rear track at 56 inches, the actual body width only 52 inches, and the overall length was 172 inches. It was nicknamed the "Hillclimber" because Duntov's first idea was to run it at Pike's Peak. Duntov developed an all-aluminum block 283-cubic-inch engine to power the car. This engine used a high-silicon content alloy that required no cylinder liners. They cast the heads and most of the hang-on parts—water pump housing, flywheel, clutch pressure place, and starter motor case—in aluminum. A magnesium fuel-injection intake manifold provided sufficient airflow to produce 353 horsepower. They fit what was basically a stock four-speed close ratio transmission behind the engine, ahead of the final drive. This configuration required extra car length, but there was no money available for a final drive between the gearbox and flywheel. Duntov's design kept the weight between the axles, resulting in more neutral handling, one of the goals of his experiment.

For brakes, Duntov and Zetye fitted regular production-option Al-Fin large-diameter drums, the rears mounted inboard, alongside the differential.

The rudimentary antilock rear brake system from the SS reappeared, more refined, in the first CERV. Duntov improved on the rear independent suspension from the prototype Q-Corvettes to use for the CERV, while he essentially carried its front suspension over from the SS racer.

This first appeared to the public at the U.S. Grand Prix at Riverside Raceway in California in November 1960. Duntov let Stirling Moss take a few "demonstration laps" before the world's motoring press. The wheelbase of 96 inches was the Indy minimum, with overall length stretching to 172 inches. In early 1964, near the end of its development life, in the configuration shown here fitted with a 377-cubic-inch engine and Hilborn fuel injection, it lapped GM's Milford, Michigan, test track at 206 miles per hour.

The body was barely 52 inches wide and weighed just 80 pounds. Total vehicle weight without oil or gas was only 1,450 pounds. Throughout its brief life, it served as a test bed for both Firestone and Goodyear wide-tread tires for racing and street uses. Both makers admitted it was a real challenge meeting the car's potential for straight-line acceleration and its hard-cornering capabilities.

They mounted all of this on a chrome-molybdenum alloy steel tube frame, surrounded by a two-layer paper-thin fiberglass body that Tony Lapine and Larry Shinoda created in the Hammer Room. Without liquids, the completed CERV weighed only 1,450 pounds.

Other projects interrupted Duntov, Zetye, and Krieger through the spring and summer of 1960 (including Cunningham's Le Mans Corvette effort). Duntov couldn't run his first trials up Pike's Peak until September. He felt fast but bystanders who had no accurate records of others' test times exaggerated their recollections. They convinced Duntov and his colleagues they were off the pace.

Disheartened, they returned to Warren with the CERV. Firestone withdrew its support and everyone got back to work. Of course, after the event, when winning times were published, Duntov learned his CERV would have set records.

The real value of the CERV then appeared. Its formidable power-to-weight ratio—less than 5.25 pounds per horsepower—provided both Firestone and Goodyear with an excellent platform on which to test and develop the wider tires they wanted to introduce. Walter Mackenzie, former racing manager for Chevrolet who was then director of product information, renamed the CERV, Chevrolet Engineering Research Vehicle. This kept the management calm while Duntov resumed work.

In 1960, NASCAR founder Bill France challenged racers to lap Daytona speedway at 180 miles per hour, offering a $10,000 reward. Duntov had already topped 170 miles per hour at GM's Proving Grounds. He had topped 170 again at Riverside and yet again in testing at Sebring. He thought 180 miles per hour was achievable.

Back in Warren, he and his crew tried a supercharger and then twin-turbochargers. Working when time permitted through 1962, they developed the engine's reliability. Dynamometer tests measured 500 horsepower with an 8.5:1 compression ratio. Then work began with the 377-cubic-inch engines destined for other competition projects, filling most of 1963. But Duntov used one of the 377s, with Hilborn fuel injection, an extremely efficient cross-ram induction intake, and a slightly cleaner front, body nose cone. He reached his magic 180 miles per hour around GM's Milford Proving Ground 4.5-mile oval, and he kept going, finally averaging 206 miles per hour.

(right) Chevrolet division manager Ed Cole and Zora Duntov both had good experiences testing prototype Corvettes at Pike's Peak, and their goal for the CERV was similar. In early days it was even called "the Hillclimber." Its seat back is very vertical to give the driver excellent visibility, unlike more reclining Grand Prix and Indy car seating positions meant to keep drivers out of the wind.

The first engine displaced 283 cubic inches, cast from high-silicon aluminum alloy that allowed Chevrolet to run the engine without cylinder liners. Duntov also fitted the very limited aluminum cylinder heads that had been proposed as regular production options but never made it. Equipped with his high-lift cam and other intake and exhaust modifications, Duntov recorded 353 horsepower at 6,200 rpm. Later, fellow engineer Denny Davis tried a supercharger and also turbochargers on the engine, ultimately achieving nearly 500 horsepower from the aluminum 283.

For 1961, the Corvette received a new grille.

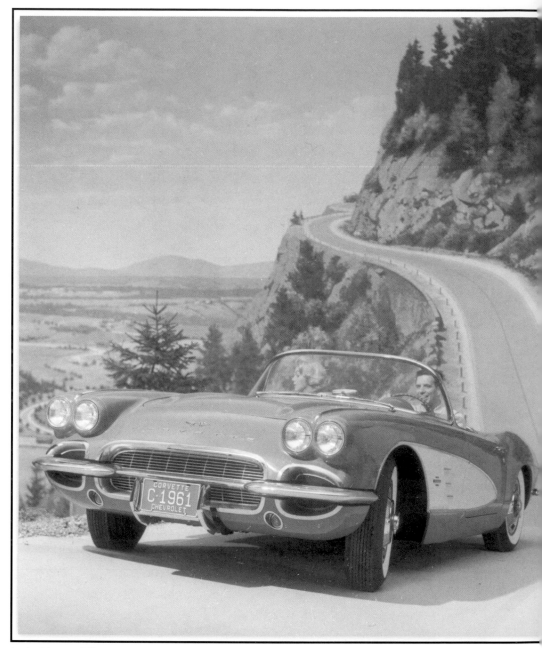

(continued from page 149)

won its class. One of Casner's Camoradi USA-entry Corvettes, driven by Lou Lilley and Fred Gamble, finished 21st overall, about 500 miles back.

In 1960, Chevrolet produced 10,261 Corvettes, cracking the break-even point for the first time in its eight-year life. After Ford had enlarged its Thunderbird to seat four, Ed Cole hoped the Corvette would absorb the two-seater enthusiasts who felt betrayed. There were very few.

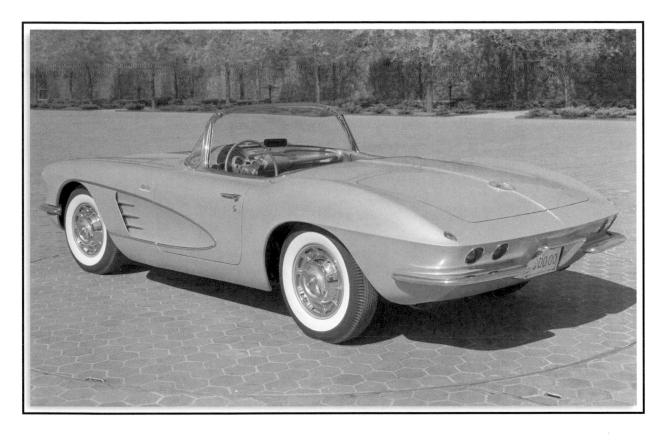

A PERSONAL RACE CAR

In 1961, the taillights were changed too. The four-lights design remains a styling cue today.

Bill Mitchell was a racing enthusiast by osmosis, never having competed himself. He was enthralled by these purpose-built vehicles, however. His involvement with Sam, Miles, and Barron Collier Jr., gave him a passion for motorsports. Mitchell urged along the completion of Jerry Earl's SR-2 in 1956, and later he acquired, for $1, the 1957 SS mule chassis on which Duntov had done his brake development work for Sebring. The AMA racing ban covered corporate involvement; however, Mitchell saw no problem in his being a private race car owner. He asked designers Larry Shinoda and Ed Wayne to convert the hidden Q-Corvette XP-96 roadster theme into his own personal race car.

Mitchell and Shinoda ran it with a modified 283, similar to the 1957 SS engine, developing 280 horsepower. The first Sting Ray body was 1/8-inch thick fiberglass, nearly production heft, reinforced with aluminum. Dick Thompson premiered the bright red racer at Marlboro Raceway in Maryland in mid-April 1959. Despite a repeat of Sebring's 1957 race with unreliable brakes, too much unrestrained power, and no limited-slip differential, Thompson still managed to finish fourth in the first appearance.

Aerodynamics was an "engineering solution," in those days, like Harley Earl's dry sump. "The Sting Ray was terrible aerodynamically," Peter Brock remembered. "When Thompson first drove the car, the front wheels came off the ground at 140 miles per hour. The lift on the hood was like an airplane wing."

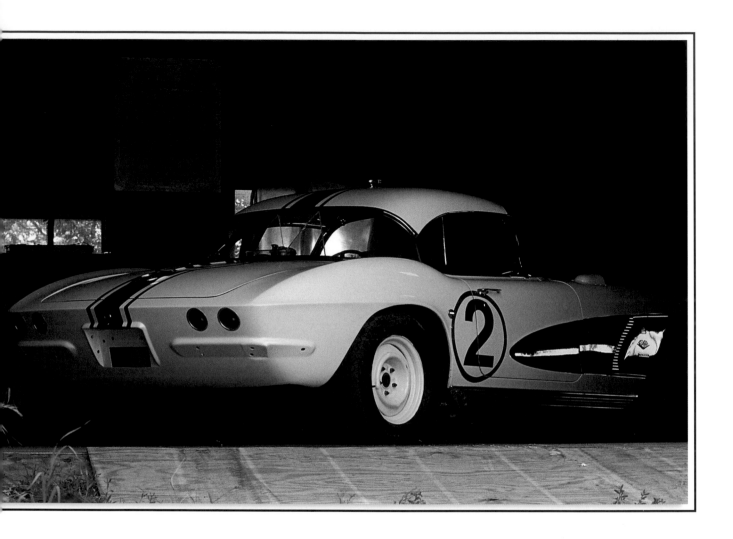

Gulf Oil Corporation's chairman Grady Davis was a racing enthusiast. He recognized the value of promoting his company's products. For Sebring in 1962, he entered this car to be driven by experienced racers Duncan Black and M. J. R. Wylie.

Mitchell's team manager was Dean Bedford, a GM engineer who also supervised the engineering development of the road car. He partially solved the front lift problem by shimming up the rear springs, creating a nose-down "hot rod rake." This eliminated some, but not all, of the problem. Then the thick body panels cracked from stress. After Road America, Bedford formed a new nose and tail section of three-layer fiberglass silk reinforced with balsa wood. These thinner panels gave the nose and tail such flexibility that it deformed but popped back when hit. Thompson said they literally waved at high speed; however, it saved 75 pounds over the original body. Throughout the season, one problem after another vexed Mitchell, Bedford, sometimes-mechanic Shinoda, and driver Thompson. Thompson even rolled the car on a downhill stretch racing at Meadowdale International Raceway in suburban Chicago. Mitchell's deep pockets were not bottomless. He handled each problem according to the budget he had available, and somehow the Sting Ray showed up at the next event. Tony

Lapine even slipped in to co-drive a 500-miler at Road America. Through the season, because the car's slippery shape allowed higher speeds than production Corvettes could achieve and came close to production car weight (2,360 pounds without driver), it used up brakes relentlessly. In the winter of 1959 and 1960, Bedford completely overhauled the braking system, throwing out the Kelsey-Hayes system and installing a single Hydrovac booster that Bendix had modified to allow better pedal modulation. But Mitchell once again ruled out disc brakes, the obvious solution, because of costs.

During the 1960 season, the car reappeared in silver with the simpler braking system and a paper-thin fiberglass skin that pulled body weight down to 2,000 pounds. With so many other problems to control, Mitchell, Bedford, and Thompson agreed to a modest tune, 280 horsepower at the flywheel, for reliability. With a 3.70:1 rear end, Thompson could see 155 miles per hour on tracks like Bridgehampton on Long Island, New York, and Meadowdale in northwest suburban Chicago. Thompson put it to good use, thrilling spectators and chasing—but rarely beating—Augie Pabst in his Chevrolet-engined Scarab. Still, long before the last race of the season, Thompson won the C-modified class championship through his consistent, careful driving.

Mitchell retired the car after the 1960 season. It had cost him a fortune, yet it established the Sting Ray as *the* racing Corvette. He returned it to design for a complete renovation, where it got new paint and, finally, a Corvette badge. It went on the GM show tour, exhibited first at the Chicago automobile show in mid-February 1961. After a year on display platforms, Mitchell took it back to use as his fair-weather commuter car, eventually installing Dunlop disk brakes and a 427-cubic-inch displacement engine.

THE STING RAY

Months passed. Calendar year 1960 became 1961. Harry Barr's engineers were at work on an enlarged 283, and externally the Corvette changed enough for customers to fall once again into Alfred Sloan's trap of satisfaction one year and dissatisfaction the next.

"Gene, go down to the basement, you're going to be working with one of the guys on the sports car." That was the late Gene Garfinkle's introduction to what would become the Sting Ray production design project. He was another product of the

Black and Wylie qualified the car second fastest, but it was last to leave the grid when the green flag dropped. Wylie admitted he'd flooded the engine trying to get moving. It just wouldn't start. No matter; 12 hours later they finished 1st in class, 18th overall.

Chevrolet factory support of outside professional racers was extensive in these days. Factory engineers would show up at major events "on vacation" from their drawing boards or fabrication shops at the new tech center in Warren. With the design engineers in the pits, problems got solved at racing speeds.

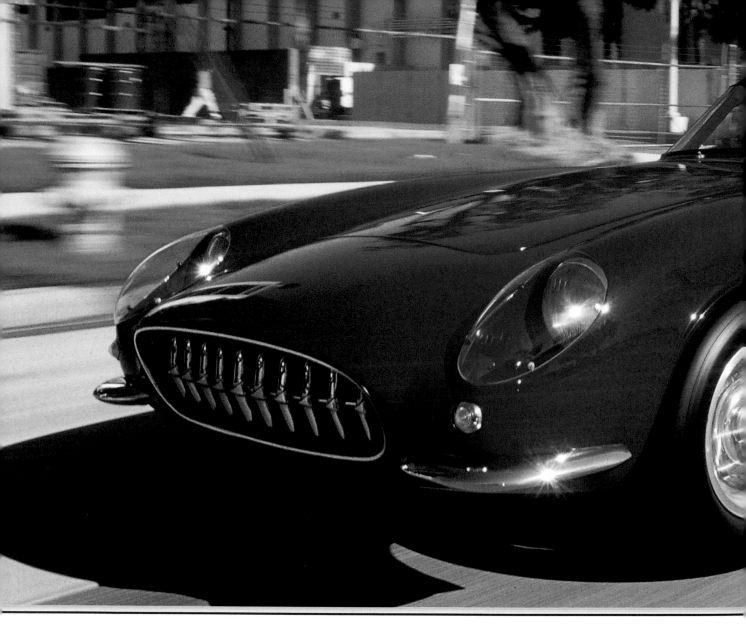

Art Center, plucked from California before graduation. He was working in the Buick production studio when one of Mitchell's people came in and sent him to the Corvette.

"Ed Wayne and I ended up doing all the drawings," he went on. "We had Chuck Pohlmann's Sting Ray roadster there to work with as a reference. We were just doing the lofting [elevation] drawings. The production car is actually on a shorter wheelbase and its body sections were a little steeper.

"The coupe had its split rear window. Mitchell certainly loved the Bugatti but, remember, there was also the Scaglione-designed Bertone Alfa Romeo design study B.A.T. cars. The B.A.T. 5, the 7, and 8 had split back windows too. We even did a folding hardtop for the car. But in order to go through the complication of folding it up to fit into the trunk where all the suspension was, the cost was just way out of line for what they wanted to do.

Laughlin had three mechanically complete chassis delivered to Scaglietti in Modena, Italy, in late 1959. Scaglietti proposed to modify an existing aluminum coupe body to fit the Corvette chassis, a challenge with Corvette's four-inch wider wheel track. Still, when it was finished, the aluminum car weighed 400 pounds less than the complete Corvette in fiberglass.

"They brought in the Sting Ray racing car, and we had the original drawings up on the wall. Mitchell was in there three or four times a day with Ken Pickering and Harry Ellsworth, his personal secretaries.

"'Nah, I don't want to do that,' Mitchell would say 'Can't you do that? Can't you move that over there?'

"That's how they worked. And you'd be down there for five weeks and then sent somewhere else. You'd never know what happened to the car you'd worked on. Never see it again. Until one day you'd be walking somewhere else in the building and see a full-size model of it being wheeled down a hall."

Mitchell followed Earl's precedent of producing show cars and design study vehicles meant to introduce the public to ideas that he and his design staff were looking at for future production, but he was restless. He loved power and speed as much as he loved distinctive style. Unlike many Earl Motorama studies, Mitchell's dreams ran.

While his Sting Ray raced, Mitchell had prepared the XP-700, a road-going showpiece, built in 1958. He had taken Cumberford's ideas such as the extended nose and grille from Jerry Earl's SR-2 and pushed them further. The nose of the XP-700 was three-dimensional. The rear end hinted strongly at shapes for the 1961 production car. Its removable hard top was a transparent plastic bubble, parted in the middle by a metal strip with air vents down the back and a rearview mirror perched outside on top.

Scaglietti's three coupes had nearly identical lines. He fitted each car with Borrani wire wheels. To make clear the car's lineage, he installed the "chrome teeth" grille into each car, though over time at least one of the owners removed the Corvette grille.

(opposite) Unlike some less successful European attempts at rebodying Corvettes, these Scaglietti cars stop nearly every observer in their tracks. The lines of the car seem most Italian in their sensuousness.

When the 1961 car reached the dealers, enthusiasts saw a frontend slightly changed from the 1960 car, but the rear end was a successful transfer from Mitchell's XP-700, becoming the next hint, the suggestion of what would be the Corvette in 1963.

Mechanical changes were subtle. Engineering replaced the heavy copper-core radiators with aluminum versions that were half the weight yet provided 10 percent greater capacity, improving weight balance and cooling. These had first appeared midyear in 1960 but were available only for 270-horsepower and fuel-injected cars. Two-thirds of the 1961 buyers ordered the close-ratio four-speed transmission, while about one-fifth still wanted the three-speed manual; slightly more than 10 percent chose the two-speed Powerglide automatic.

In all, Chevrolet produced 10,939 of the 1961 models. The top performance engine was now the 315-horsepower 283-cubic-inch displacement V-8 with Rochester fuel injection. Base price was $3,934, and more than half the buyers ordered the optional removable hardtop, RPO 419, at $236.75.

Private racers campaigned Corvettes around the United States, competing first, and rather successfully, with a five-car Sebring effort. Delmo Johnson, a Chevy dealer in Dallas, entered three of these, and the other two came from Don Yenko in Cannonsburg, Pennsylvania. At the end of the 12-hour event, Johnson and co-driver Dale Morgan finished 11th overall, the best finish to date for a stock model.

Corvette mechanicals had evolved to the point in 1961 where the performance was reliable, its racing pedigree was established, and the car had earned respect. It had reached the stage in its life where outsiders wondered if a Corvette by any other name might smell so sweet, work so well, look so good, or race so successfully.

Fort Worth, Texas, entrepreneur Gary B. Laughlin drilled oil, processed petroleum, and owned Chevy dealerships. For pleasure, he raced a Ferrari 750 Monza in SCCA events, where he met and formed an idea with two other Texan racing buddies, Carroll Shelby and Jim Hall. Hall and Shelby wanted a true GT-version of the Corvette, lighter and possibly lovelier. Laughlin, tired of his huge Ferrari repair bills, offered to finance the project, and Shelby offered to engineer it. Together they'd race them. They hoped to make enough cars to qualify for SCCA's B-production class and planned to sell some to their competitors. Memos flew early in 1959 from Fort Worth to Warren, to Modena,

(previous) Every hand-built car body is slightly different, a benefit to owners of rare luxury sports cars because it guarantees individuality and exclusivity.

Building the Scaglietti coupes required shutting down the St. Louis production line to manufacture complete chassis without bodies. It was the shutdown time that killed the project; its costs were too great for either Laughlin or Chevrolet to tolerate.

Italy. Sergio Scaglietti, car-body fabricator for Enzo Ferrari, agreed to revise an existing fastback aluminum coupe to fit the Corvette chassis for Laughlin. Three 1959 mechanically complete, bare chassis arrived at Scaglietti.

Laughlin's oil operations took him to Europe regularly, and he always visited Modena. The car got closer to what he wanted, though Scaglietti had trouble stretching his body to fit Corvette's four-inch wider track. With a Spartan interior, the new aluminum coupes weighed 400 pounds less than the fiberglass production cars.

They completed their first one, painted silver, in early 1961, on a chassis with a 1960 engine, the 290-horsepower 283-cubic-inch displacement V-8 with Rochester fuel injection, the close-ratio four-speed transmission, and Positraction. Scaglietti refitted the Corvette teeth into the front air intake. His spare interior contained two thin competition seats facing a crackle-finish instrument panel. The only identification was a hood medallion and two fender badges with the symbol of Scaglietti & C., Modena. The second prototype was done more luxuriously with an automatic transmission. This car was intended for Hall, who had begun experimenting with racing automatic transmissions. It and the third car, another four-speed transmission version, bore Corvette crossed flags on the nose and egg-crate grilles.

Some 20 years later, Zora Duntov remem-

Scaglietti provided leather-covered racing seats in the otherwise simple interior.

bered the project only from memos he saw at its beginning and end. He recalled questions about the time the regular production line had to shut down to produce cars without bodies. These interruptions were too costly when weighed against the increasing demand for production cars. Shelby recalled Laughlin saying the project was dead. Whether it was GM's faithful adherence to the AMA ban or corporate concern over controlling the Corvette (lest someone else build something that might successfully compete against it), neither one could say. Laughlin, after driving his car briefly, soured on the idea; it was a handful of ill-mannered handling and horsepower. He sold his first car for about $9,200 to a business acquaintance in Chicago. Hall barely used his car and had sold his by 1964. Carroll Shelby sold his soon after delivery, but he had not soured on the idea of running an American V-8 in a smaller European car body. He took that idea and went shopping elsewhere.

This was the last styling year for exhausts vented through the rear bumpers and taillights faired into the fender curves. The rear-end design would change completely for 1961.

While Laughlin worked with Scaglietti, Wisconsin industrial designer Gordon Kelly began a redesign project with Carrozzeria Vignale on his 1960 Corvette. Kelly worked with Brooks Stevens Associates designing Studebaker Hawks. He produced a one-eighth-scale clay model of a Corvette body and showed it to Bill Mitchell. Mitchell offered Gordon a car if he'd find a builder who would display it at the Paris Auto Show in October 1961. Vignale agreed. Kelly's lines, stubbier but more aggressive than Scaglietti's coupes, were striking behind an oversized oval egg-crate grille. The Kelly/Vignale-bodied car

(above) The 3.8-liter, in-line six-cylinder engine had become nearly a perfect power plant after years of racing and production development in the preceding XK series. With dual overhead camshafts and three side-draft carburetors, the engine produced 265 horsepower.

(left) The sleekly shaped body of Jaguar's new XKE was the product of Malcolm Sayer, who described himself as an aerodynamicist. Sayer drew his designs full-size on long paper rolls, calculating the effects of various shapes as he created them.

appeared in auto shows for a year before Kelly finally got to drive the car and test its fuel-injected 283, the RPO 687 brakes and suspension option, four-speed transmission, and Positraction differential.

CHANGES AT THE TOP

Chevrolet management changed at the top again in 1961. Semon E. "Bunkie" Knudsen was promoted from Pontiac division to head GM's biggest seller. (His father, William, had done something similar 30 years earlier.) Bunkie liked racing and understood what the AMA hoped to deny: "speed" promoted sales. He ushered out a great amount of parts, support, advice, and even money through a back door at Pontiac and into the hands of stock car and drag racers. Knudsen's actions and Pontiac's successes led to Ford's public repudiation of the AMA ban in 1962.

Knudsen arrived at Chevrolet just in time to enjoy the success of Ed Cole's hard work with Duntov, Mitchell, and their staffs. The 1962 Corvette introduced another legendary powerplant. Harry Barr's engineers started with the 283-cubic-inch displacement V-8 and increased the bore to 4.00 inches and the stroke to 3.25, to reach 327–cubic-inch displacement. The meekest engine produced 250 horsepower, while the solid lifter, Duntov-cam, fuel-injected engine developed 360 horsepower. The most powerful optional engine still cost $484.20, the same price since 1958. A car ready to prepare for racing ran $5,243, while a civilized back-road tourer with every comfort option sold for $5,014 in 1962.

The body retained the heavy steel-and-aluminum reinforcement first used in mid-1957 around the cowl and doors. This still provided stiffness and body integrity. Even with all the improvements, the body weighed nearly the same as in 1953 because engineering had identified and deleted unnecessary fiberglass layers in some panels.

A NEW CHALLENGE

Corvette designers and engineers labored on. They tackled the few lingering criticisms, their work improving the perceptions that sports car enthusiasts held about Corvettes. Inside GM, they knew great things were in store. Yet Chevrolet's only remaining competitor—Jaguar—did not rest either. The English firm accepted that the V-8 was necessary for most American buyers; however, a dual-overhead camshaft on top of a proven in-line six-cylinder engine would turn heads on their side of the Atlantic Ocean. Packaging it in a stunning body form would help even more.

Jaguar introduced its new 1962 XK-E in the spring of 1961 at the New York Auto Show, 18 months before Bunkie Knudsen could show the new Sting Ray. Jaguar's slender cars, both coupe and roadster, threw down a new challenge to Corvette. As Briggs Cunningham had predicted, the United States had become the world's largest market for sports cars. Jaguar sold most of its cars on this side of the Atlantic. Its new body on its new chassis, with independent rear suspension and four-wheel disc brakes, would sell for $4,915.

For Knudsen, Mitchell, Barr, and dozens of engineers and designers, the Jaguar XK-E meant a little more running in place, hurrying to get the last of the work perfect before everybody in the world could see what they'd been working on for seven years.

The fastback design offered similar cargo potential to the Sting Ray coupe. Unlike the Corvette's rear deck lid, the Jaguar's opened. Oddly, the big rear door opened from the side. Introduced in 1961 at $5,595, it reached nearly $6,000 by the time the Sting Ray appeared.

CHAPTER SIX

THE BIRTH OF A MODERN CLASSIC

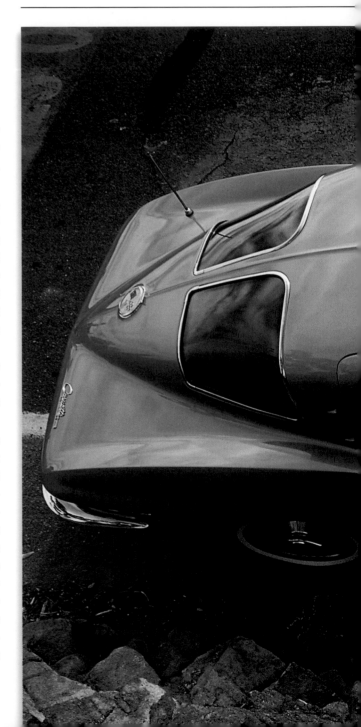

he 1963 Sting Ray etched Bill Mitchell's influence and power into GM's corporate granite. Its rear-end design was startling. Peter Brock's coupe, finished by Mitchell's lieutenant, Larry Shinoda, paid homage to the classic sporting "Boat-tail" roadsters from the 1930s. By now, Mitchell's power nearly rivaled that of Harley Earl. When Zora Duntov complained that the stylish center spine hindered rearward vision, Mitchell retorted, "If you take that off, you might as well forget the whole thing." Corvette was making money, and because Earl's department had created it, the car belonged to design, not to engineering. Mitchell had the highest authority, and he made it clear that engineering's input was accepted when it did not interfere. This stopped Duntov. If there was no spine, there might be no independent rear suspension, no disc brakes.

Yet the engineering inputs had made the new car as impressive mechanically as it was visually. The car benefited from the Q-Corvette project, from Mitchell's Sting Ray race car, and from Zora's pet project, the CERV I.

Engineering settled on a 98-inch wheelbase for the production Sting Ray, called the XP-720 internally. This was 4 inches shorter than the previous car's old XK-120 dimension of 102 inches, and it improved maneuverability and handling. Using a new ladder-type frame with five crossmembers to replace the original car's X-frame, engineers dropped the center of gravity nearly 2.3 inches because this new frame let them place passengers inside the frame rails rather than on top of them as before. Engineering ran its designs through computer analysis to predetermine the necessary steel wall thicknesses and structural placement, then intentionally built their test frames too rigidly to determine what was proper not only for routine buyers but also for serious racers. The convertible frame was 10 percent and the coupe 90 percent stiffer than the 1962 car.

(previous pages) This was the view that caused the greatest attention and controversy. Observers either hated the center spine that divided the rear window or they loved it. Zora Duntov hated it, claiming it seriously obstructed rear vision. But by 1963, Design Chief Bill Mitchell had so much corporate influence that he easily defeated the powerful engineer.

Success has many parents, and more than a few Chevrolet designers claim the origin of this Sting Ray's appearance. Even its inspiration is unclear because Bill Mitchell knew European classics; everyone from France's Bugatti to Italy's Alfa Romeo had done cars with raised center spines and divided rear windows.

Engineering knew it had only so much to spend to improve the car. The frame took some, but Duntov especially wanted to use the new rear axle with fully independent rear suspension (IRS). They could devise one from the Q-sedans and Q-Corvette prototype. Engineering had done the development work years before, writing off the costs against other budgets, but GM Chairman Donner killed the production passenger car, so there was no big series project to pay for it. Whenever Duntov stated his need for an IRS, the newly important bean counters challenged him on its cost. He already knew the car business was a numbers game. He prevailed by constantly telling his inquisitors the new car with IRS would sell 30,000 units, despite clear logic suggesting most drivers would never recognize the difference.

The system that Duntov, Harold Krieger, Walter Zetye, and the Corvette engineering staff devised also adopted technology from the CERV I. It incorporated twin half shafts that emerged from a frame-mounted differential, connected (and suspended) by a transversely mounted nine-leaf spring bolted to the back of the differential housing. This system, common on race cars, used the driveshafts as part of the suspension system, saving money over more intricate European systems and a great amount of weight over the 1962 solid tube rear axle. They used a transverse spring, the only application for such a system in a U.S. automobile since the 1937 Cord front suspension. It was necessary because there was no room beneath the body for rear coil springs that also would have increased overall and unsprung weight.

Chevrolet offered its 327-cubic-inch V-8 in four power levels, from a base 250-horsepower version to a potent 360-horsepower fuel-injected version. The most popular engine was this 340-horsepower L76, which powered 8,033 Corvettes in 1963.

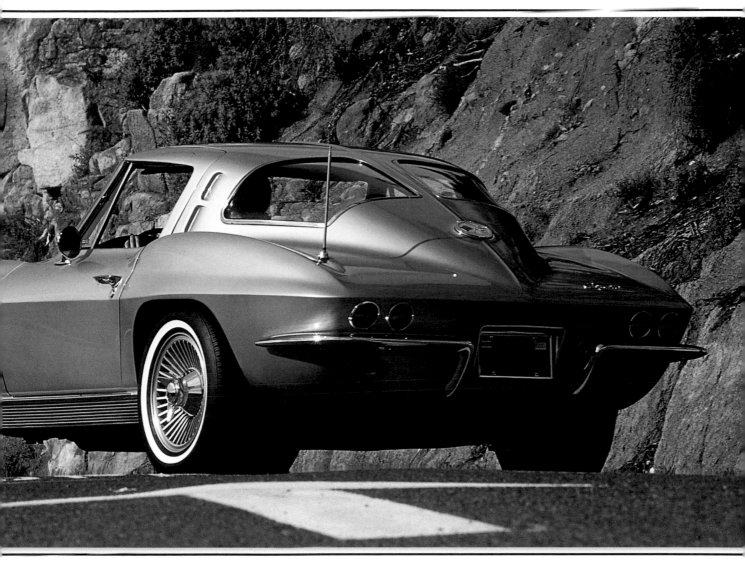

Krieger, Zetye, and Duntov carried over the front suspension with subtle changes using mostly passenger car production parts that had appeared in new configurations on the CERV I. A faster steering ratio, 2.9 turns lock-to-lock instead of 3.4, capped their labors to improve road feel, steering response, and ride comfort. The Sting Ray also introduced hydraulically assisted steering, available on all but the two most powerful engine options.

Engineering's development dollars were nearly gone, so they carried over the 11-inch diameter cast-iron drum brakes all around. Buyers could order optional sintered-metallic linings and finned aluminum brake drums that provided greater fade resistance and better cooling. Corvette offered power-assisted brakes as well.

Once all this new technology was gathered together, engineering built development mules. Zetye, Duntov, and Krieger used these as daily transport, living with their work and making constant

Regardless of its authorship, the 1963 split-window coupe is one of automobile history's most striking shapes. Yet this sensuous body hides significant engineering advances, including disc brakes and a ride-improving, road-hugging independent rear suspension.

The distinctive 1963 Corvette looked unlike any car then on the market.

adjustments. Bill Mitchell wanted his own mule, but he knew that was not possible without giving away the design. So he devised another show car that he could drive.

Mitchell again called on Larry Shinoda, who had done all the production drawings of the Sting Ray and probably knew its lines better than anyone. Mitchell gave him a new project number, XP-755, and described a design study theme that had come to him on a fishing trip to the Caribbean. Where his first Corvette was the Sting Ray, his new car would honor the shark with a paint scheme to match. Shinoda adopted the strongest features of Mitchell's Sting

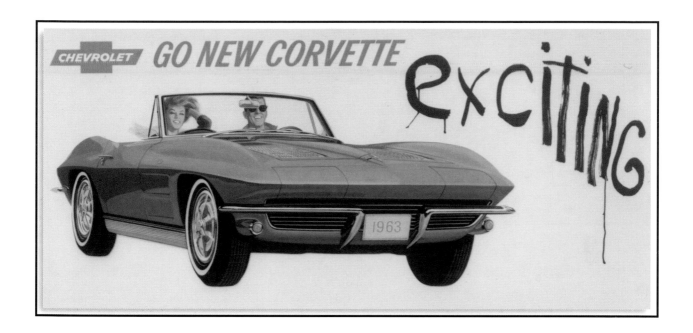

Ray racer and of the upcoming production car, exaggerating some of them. He included the double-bubble glass top from Mitchell's first show car, the XP-700.

Alfred Sloan's first specification for Harley Earl's Art and Colour Section gave stylists a mechanical assembly area. The new Warren Tech Center had a better facility where Earl's and later Bill Mitchell's auto creations became mobile. Leonard McLay had kept Earl's supercharged Buick LeSabre running. Over time he tamed a great number of temperamental engines. He and his crew supercharged a 327 for Mitchell's new car. (Over its 10-year life, the Shark's engine compartment "tested" power steering pumps, power brake boosters, and a 427-cubic-inch displacement Mark IV engine.) Mitchell first showed it at the New York Auto Show in April 1962.

A DUAL-PURPOSE SPORTS CAR

Only Mitchell's car sported a supercharged engine; production models used the 327-cubic-inch displacement engine just as customers had seen it in 1962, mated to three- and four-speed manual transmissions as well as the Powerglide automatic. Corvette engineers offset the engine 1 inch to the right in the frame to increase driver foot well space, though naturally this trimmed passenger foot room.

Designers created a new instrument panel and gauge cluster that gave the tachometer and speedometer equal importance. The steering column offered 3 inches of length adjustment (albeit a job only accomplished in the engine compartment with a wrench). Behind the seats in the coupe, designers and engineers created a large luggage storage area, although both engineering and design exhausted their budgets before completing a working trunk lid. The only access to the luggage was from inside, lifted over the seats.

(opposite) Bill Mitchell enjoyed teasing the public as much as Harley Earl did, and this New York and Chicago auto show model continued the tradition. While it was basically a 1963 Sting Ray convertible, it picked the exterior exhaust headers and side pipes from the 1961 SP-755 Shark show car.

It was, of course, the Sting Ray body that seized viewers' attention. Frederic Donner's board approved the full-size clay coupe body in April 1960 and the interior, done in a studio separate from those doing the body, in November. Mitchell, mad about his coupe, reluctantly created a convertible in the fall only after being told to do so. Once the board committed to building the new car in fiberglass, engineering and design collaborated to make the new body stronger, tighter, and quieter. They doubled the reinforcing steel within the fiberglass panels from 1962's body, yet they thinned the panels enough to get the body weight below the previous model. Design ran 3/8th-scale models of both coupe and convertible bodies through the California Institute of Technology wind tunnels before showing them to Donner. This helped them devise the rotating housing to tame the wind resistance that quad headlights generated. The wrap-over, limousine-style doors not only launched a new design trend but greatly improved entry and exit. Shinoda drew in working vents on the hood and behind the doors. The design and development sums were gone, however; there was nothing left to make that air ventilation plumbing work.

Ever since the effects of Curtice's AMA racing and performance ban rippled throughout GM, Zora Duntov cautiously commented that private customers would race Corvettes whether GM approved or not. As plans advanced for Sting Ray production, he continued to suggest it was in Chevrolet's best interest to carry on parts development to benefit racers. His sense was correct, especially when Ford's Total Performance program in 1962 effectively returned them to racing. Duntov had made sure Corvette racers were ready.

Zora and his cohorts created RPO Z06. This Special Performance Equipment package included a vacuum brake booster, a dual master cylinder, sintered-metallic brake linings within power-assisted Al-Fin drums cooled by front air scoops and vented backing plates, a 20-percent larger diameter front

Cast-aluminum wheels—RPO P48—were supposed to be available to all customers for $322.80. Casting quality control problems that caused air leaks delayed introduction until the 1964 model year. The through-body headers were never offered to the public.

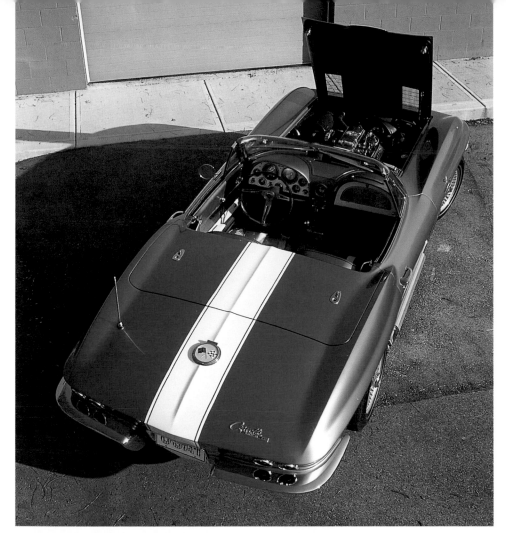

Once this car finished its show life, retired Styling Chief Harley Earl used it for a while. Eventually, Chevrolet Styling produced a second show car body like it. They built it for Chairman Frederic Donner to placate him after Design and Engineering's efforts to circumvent the racing ban. Mitchell painted Donner's car Candy-Apple Red.

(bottom center) The auto show car used a real wood-rimmed steering wheel, not the optional plastic wood version that 130 Sting Ray buyers ordered with RPO N34 for a mere $16.20. The two-toned seats repeated the white racing stripe motif of the car's body.

(bottom right) Mitchell's design department engineers started with the 360-horsepower L84 fuel-injected 327 and modified it to develop closer to 375 horsepower. The car they produced for Harlow Curtice used the 340-horsepower carbureted L76 engine.

By 1963, the Corvette had earned a reputation as the ultimate dream car for many U.S. enthusiasts.

antiroll bar, larger diameter shocks, and springs nearly twice as stiff as standard. Initially, the package fit a 36.5-gallon gas tank instead of the new 20-gallon container. This package, which also included the 360-horsepower 327-cubic-inch displacement engine, M-21 close-ratio four-speed transmission, Positraction, and cast-aluminum knock-off wheels, cost the buyer an extra $1,818.45 over the base coupe price of $4,257. Initially, buyers could order the package only for coupes (because the over-size tank could not fit in the convertible). It was a pricey race-ready package; deleting the heater and defroster saved $100, but the total tipped in at $5,975.45. Later in the model year, Chevrolet discovered problems with air leaking through the porous aluminum castings. The knock-off wheels and the extra-large gas tank were deleted from the Z06 package (although the tank was available on any coupe separately), and its price was revised down to $1,293.95. At that point, Chevrolet offered it for the convertible as well. Chevrolet produced 199 of these Z06s.

Production began at St. Louis just as Bill Mitchell introduced his Shark in New York. Crews working inside the plant but outside the regular production line manufactured about 25 pilot 1963 models, getting kinks out of a system involving entirely new body pieces. They completed these cars by late June and quickly parceled them out, some going to enthusiast magazines so they could publish their stories the same time dealers unveiled the new car. (Chevrolet priced the new convertible at $4,037, one dollar less than the 1962 model had been.)

"The 1963 Corvette," *Road & Track's* publisher John Bond wrote, "has come a long way in 10 years—from a stylist's plaything to a full-blown, out-and-out dual-purpose sports car."

In *Car & Driver's* April 1963 report, technical editor Jan Norbye wrote that "the key to the personality of the [1963] Corvette lies neither in the power available nor in the revised styling, but in the chassis. Up to now the Corvette has been struggling to rise above a large number of stock components, notably in the suspension where their presence created all kinds of problems that required extensive modifications for any competition use beyond normal road rallies. The new all-independent suspension has completely transformed the Corvette. . . ."

Jim Wright, *Motor Trend's* technical editor, led off his May 1963 reexamination with a three-quarter rear view of the car sliding through dirt and a headline in letters one inch tall: "For the first time in its 10-year history, the Corvette String Ray is . . ." and then the text jumped to the next page, where it continued, ". . . in such demand that the factory has had to put on a second shift." He reminded readers of his past observations.

"The factory has never made any big profits on the Corvette but . . . Chevy brass was more than satisfied as long as it carried its performance image and prestige over to the bread-and-butter lines. We also ventured an opinion that as long as the factory kept building the car on this basis, it would be a great automobile, but if they ever put in on a straight dollar-profit basis, the Corvette would probably be ruined."

Chevrolet issued a press release late in the fall announcing double shifts at St. Louis. Their production goal for the 1963 model was 16,000 units. When the counting was done, they had sold 10,594 coupes and 10,919 convertibles, a total of 21,513 cars, It hadn't quite achieved the numbers Duntov predicted would flock to the independent rear suspension, but it far exceeded Chevrolet's own estimations, and it beat 1962 by nearly 50 percent.

A topside view of the split-window design that makes the 1963 coupe so distinctive.

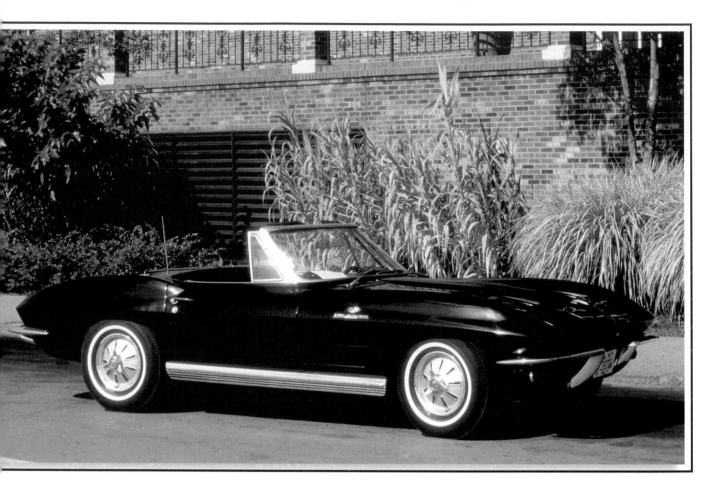

Four versions of the 327-cubic-inch small-block V-8 engine were available in 1964, including a 300-horsepower version.

CORVETTE WINS

In racing, Duntov's Z06 coupes proved formidable in their first outing, the *Los Angeles Times* Three-Hour Invitational Race at Riverside, California, in October 1962. Bob Bondurant, Dave MacDonald, and Jerry Grant drove the three cars, a silver, a white, and a blue coupe, out from the St. Louis factory to break them in while another car was trucked out earlier. Duntov supervised their preparation for the A-production race. From the start, this event quickly became a contest between MacDonald in his Z06 and one of Carroll Shelby's new cars. After Chevrolet declined to sell him cars without bodies, Shelby took his idea to Ford. Upon hearing of Chevrolet's reaction, Ford gave Shelby all the engines and help he could use. Shelby stuffed Ford's 260 V-8s and then 289s into the English AC Ace and renamed the car after a predatory snake. Bill Krause raced the Cobra hard. Both MacDonald's Z06 and Krause's Cobra broke after the first hour, and two more Corvettes retired by the end of the second; but the fourth Corvette, entered by Mickey Thompson and driven by Doug Hooper, won the race. Thompson was pleased, but Duntov knew Shelby. Whatever failed on the Cobra was something Shelby would find and fix. Duntov had no budget for that. Next time the Cobra could win, and soon it would dominate.

Shelby's Cobra had won the A-production championship by June, yet Duntov remained philosophical. While he was disappointed, he knew that under current GM management the Cobra was insignificant. It won where it didn't matter to Donner, and Shelby didn't race in the contest Donner cared most about, the one for the pocketbooks of thousands of customers who never raced cars.

MUSCLE CAR IMITATORS

After the first year of production, Bill Mitchell sacrificed his split rear window. In preparing the body for 1963 production, body engineers had to make the spine much wider than Mitchell intended. For 1964, the car dropped the nonfunctional hood grilles but left their indentations. Styling made the left roof vent functional (but not the right). To improve handling without sacrificing ride quality, engineering replaced the front coil springs with a progressive rate version and revised shock valving to address problems on the 1963 cars. Engines got stronger with the addition of Holley 4150 carburetors, and peak power of the solid-lifter engine rose from 340 horsepower to 365 horsepower. Engineering provided a new intake manifold for the fuel-injected version, increasing output to 375 horsepower. During 1963 production, Chevrolet also replaced the Borg-Warner gearboxes with four speeds produced at GM's Muncie, Indiana, transmission plant. In the coupe, a small fan circulated air in the rear, addressing the greenhouse effect of sweltering heat under the large back windows. In all the

In 1965, the final year for fuel-injected Corvettes, Chevrolet offered a big-block 396-cubic-inch V-8 in a Corvette for the first time.

As early as 1956, Chevrolet offered optional racing car parts hidden in the order form if the buyer was diligent and perceptive. With the 1963 model year, the option was complete. Called the Z06, the $1,818.45 package included everything from improved cooling, suspension, and brakes to stronger engine and drivetrain components.

bodies, more insulation and revised body and transmission mounts quieted the complaints about too much interior mechanical and road noise. Duntov the European fought to create a true European sports car, but Duntov the pragmatist recognized that the real nature of the American grand-touring customer kept crying for attention.

Another group within GM, hungry for Corvette's performance image, found a new direction. Muscle cars, born in the 1950s at Chrysler as big cars with powerful Hemi-head engines, spawned imitators who were quick studies. Pontiac division general manager Elliot M. "Pete" Estes, its former chief engineer, launched the Tempest LeMans and GTO options in 1963 and 1964. These were compact cars stuffed with 389-cubic-inch displacement "tri-power" engines fueled by three two-barrel carburetors. These small cars were cheap to build and therefore inexpensive to purchase. Because they were not thoroughly re-engineered, their ability to handle the extra power was always in doubt, but they cost thousands less than a fully optioned Corvette. Yet they went just as quickly at the stoplight-to-stoplight drag races, the so-called American grand prix, that took place on every Saturday night on any main street. Worse for Corvette, they offered the still politically correct benefit of room for two couples on a double date. These big engines began pulling the Corvette away from Duntov's goals for the car. Yet Chevrolet's general manager, Bunkie Knudsen, fresh from Pontiac himself, felt the sports car could not be entirely left out of this new definition of sporting cars. Big engines were inevitable.

For 1964, total production reached another record, 22,229 cars, broken down into 8,304 coupes and nearly twice as many convertibles, 13,925. Chevrolet held the 1963 prices, keeping the coupe at $4,252 and the convertible at $4,037. The racers' package, now assembled from a variety of RPOs, not one alone, would set the buyer back a total of $6,526.40, a price that included the 375-horsepower "fuelie," four-speed, aluminum wheels, sintered brakes, Positraction, the F40 special front and rear suspension, and a few other necessities. (By comparison, a 389-cubic-inch displacement dual-quad, fully performance-optioned Pontiac GTO coupe cost less than $3,800.) Breaking up the Z06 option also led to some very interesting one-off cars, those created by customers with very specific needs, includ-

No radio, no heater, no clock, no air conditioning but a 36-gallon fuel tank nestled in behind the seats marked this race car as all business. Four-speed transmissions were manufactured by Borg-Warner until midyear when Muncie took over. All Z06 cars got early Muncie four-speeds.

ing such cars as a 300-horsepower, air-conditioned, automatic coupe fitted with the large fuel tank, ordered by a salesman who worked the American southwest during the summer months.

GOING TO DISC BRAKES

Design did more with an eraser than with pencils for 1965, eliminating hood and roof vents while opening the former "speedlines" behind the front tires to make real working vents. Years of battling over their cost and arguing their benefit paid off when engineering was able to provide four-wheel disc brakes at no extra cost (although for reasons few people understand, some 316 individuals ordered cars with drum brakes for which they received a $64.50 credit). Engineering had achieved near disc-brake performance from its sintered-metallic Al-Fin drum brakes, yet critics and journalists alike complained that the Corvette simply was not yet a sports car without discs.

Chevrolet engineering insisted brake performance had to be measurably better than its drums, particularly by providing superior "braking feel." GM's board refused to approve the expense of developing a power boost solely for the Corvette, and this became a requirement of the systems brought in from outside. Chevrolet engineers worked with Delco-Moraine to devise a new approach. In their system, pads barely touched the disc at all times. This provided instant pedal response and alleviated an early problem: When the rotors got wet, they were less effective than drums. Designing the caliper so the pads floated against the rotor swept it clean of moisture and road grit. Engineering selected ventilated, 1.25-inch-thick rotors for production, a full quarter-inch thicker than those used on the Grand Sport racers that evolved from the Z06 cars. Engineering adopted another racing idea and used the

There was only one engine available for the Z06—the L84 327-cubic-inch engine with Rochester fuel injection. With factory exhaust manifolds, required to run the cars in SCCA's production classes, Chevrolet rated the engine at 360 horsepower.

(opposite) Chevrolet produced 199 Z06 models, yet careful study of Mike Antonick's Corvette Black Book *suggests that fewer than this number were intended to race. Chevrolet delivered only 124 cars without radios and just 63 with the 36-gallon fuel tank. Admittedly, only those planning outings at Sebring and Daytona benefited from the big tanks; for shorter club races the extra capacity would be wasted.*

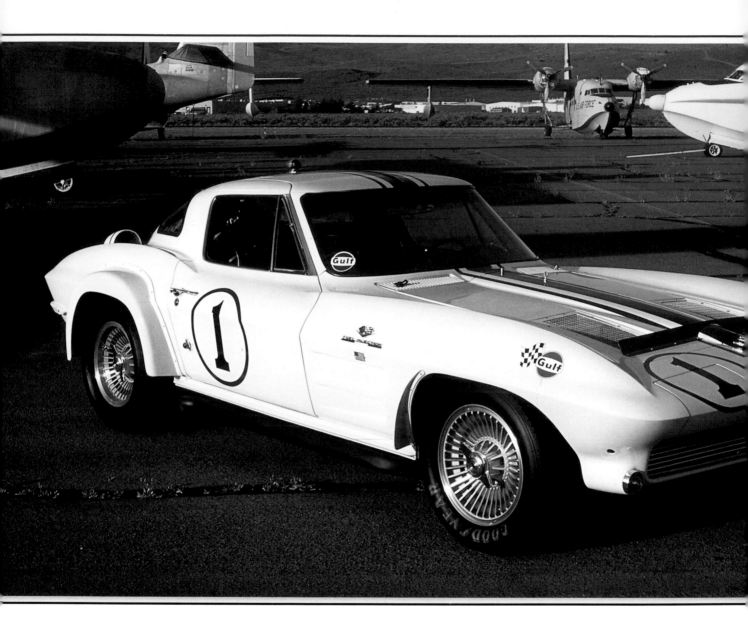

By the time Gulf Oil's Grady Davis picked up his Z06 to campaign at Sebring and Daytona, Zora Duntov had already begun working on Sting Ray prototype racers called Grand Sports. As a result, Grand Sport bits and pieces such as larger rear brakes, air cooling ducts, and front hood wind deflectors were available to Z06 competitors.

dual master cylinder similar to what it did with the Z06 package in 1963, fitting it as standard equipment on all disc–brake equipped cars, ahead of expected federal safety standards. It was a mid–1965 engine introduction that made these new brakes more valuable, however.

BANNING THE RACING BAN

GM's pursuit of performance resumed publicly within months of Ford Motor Company's announcement in mid-June 1962 that it would no longer adhere to the AMA racing ban. Once the first manufacturer broke ranks officially, no engineering department would be last, no matter what their board chairman felt. New engines and running gear appeared quickly, confirming that engineers had never

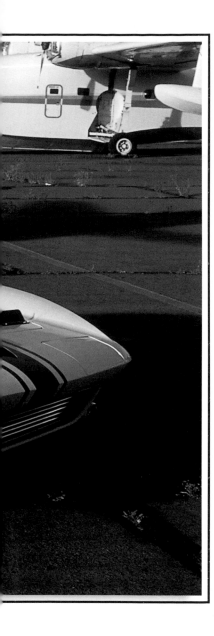

stopped tinkering. Chevrolet first revealed its 427-cubic-inch displacement V-8 big, block "mystery" motor, at the Daytona 500-mile stock car race in January 1963.

Chevrolet's 427 came from less than successful roots. Back in 1958, Chevrolet introduced its W-engine, the 348-cubic-inch displacement V-8. Engineers quickly found ways to increase its capacity to 409, but this block was large and heavy. It had many of the characteristics that Zora Duntov and others felt were exactly wrong for the Corvette.

When Jim Premo succeeded Harry Barr as Chevrolet's chief engineer, he found vigorous supporters in Bunkie Knudsen and Zora Duntov. Everyone knew Corvettes would get the larger engines; however, Duntov's high-performance engine group had been working, with Knudsen's blessings, on its own solution to that inevitability.

Richard Keinath had developed heads for a completely new engine dubbed the Mark II, heads that led to an odd configuration of intake and exhaust valves. These allowed much better breathing, but the seemingly random angles of the valve

There were two most significant developments for 1965. First was the new big block 396-cubic-inch engine. The other was that Chevrolet installed disc brakes on all four wheels, rather than just up front. Another subtle distinction improved airflow and engine cooling when engineering and design made the three louvers functional behind the front wheels.

To combat roasting heat inside the Sting Ray's storage area, Chevrolet installed a three-speed fan that pulled air in through the functional louvers behind the driver's door. The outside vents on the passenger side were not functional.

(above left) All 1,897 of the Tuxedo Black Sting Rays had a choice of black, red, silver, or white interiors. Of nearly 22,000 1964 coupes and convertibles produced, 19,034 had the optional $188.30 four-speed transmission.

(above right) Chevrolet offered the carbureted 327 in three power levels starting with the 250-horsepower base (which about 3,500 buyers selected). Nearly half—10,471—of Corvette customers ordered this $53.80 300-horsepower, L75 version, while 7,171 ordered the 365-horsepower L76 configuration. Chevrolet sold 1,345 copies of the fuel-injected 375-horsepower L84 engine.

Even without the split rear window, the Corvette remained one of the most stylish cars available.

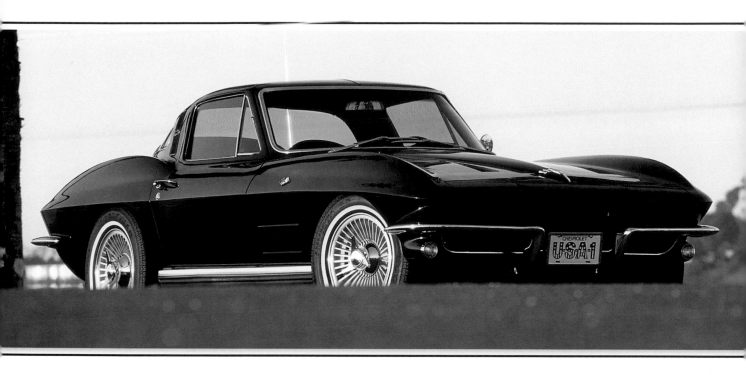

stems quickly earned the nickname "porcupine heads." Engineering had developed the Mark II engine for stock car racing and had one completed and running by the end of 1962. Chevrolet first ran it at the Daytona 500 in 1963 and established a mystique as the "mystery engine."

California racer Mickey Thompson got a Mark II late that year and stuffed it into a Corvette that Bill Krause drove to third place overall in the February 1963 Daytona three-hour sports car races prior to the 24-hour international event. Donner heard about it, and while outside racing wasn't factory participation, his attention killed any chance of regular factory production of these engines beyond the few already assembled.

That is, they were ruled out until end-of-year sales figures spoke to Donner. When the numbers from all divisions made it clear that big engines were selling better than small ones, the manufacture of a street version of the Mark II was authorized. Because the federal government and the auto insurance industry paid more attention to car makers, especially after GM's troubles with its overly cost-controlled Corvair handling, GM management had held down the product planners' and engineers' tendencies to produce larger and more powerful engines. A board policy limited intermediate-size cars, Chevrolet's Chevelle, Pontiac's Tempest, and the like, those most suited to muscle car performance, to engine displacements below 400-cubic-inch displacement. With that in mind, the engine developers produced the Mark IV with 4.09-inch bore and 3.76-inch stroke for total capacity of 396-cubic-inch displacement.

For 1965, Chevrolet introduced this powerhouse engine, the L78, with 425 horsepower on tap. The rating was conservative, as a number of enthusiasts discovered when they simply had their engines blueprinted. Available as an option for only $292.70, some 2,157 Corvette buyers exercised the option. The price included a visual cue, a new hood that swelled in the center in a "power bulge"

While Bill Mitchell won the 1963 skirmish against Zora Duntov, magazine criticism aided Duntov in his battle against the rear split window. The most notable difference between 1963 and 1964 was the solid back glass. Aluminum alloy knock-off wheels reached regular production.

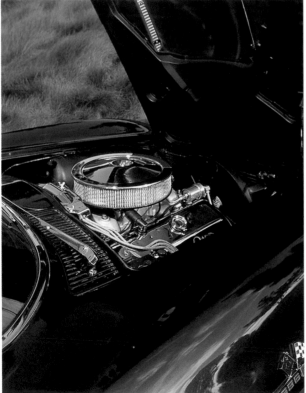

to accommodate the engine's bulk. Option N14 was even more visible. This new $134.50 package put exhaust pipes along the side of the car as they had been on countless Bill Mitchell show cars. Only 759 buyers had the nerve to announce so clearly to local police what they intended.

For 1966, the muscle power wars turned serious. By the end of 1965, Chevrolet division had a new chief executive, "Pete" Estes, fresh from Pontiac division where he and fellow collaborator John DeLorean had intensified—if not invented—muscle cars. Estes followed a similar route as Ed Cole. Both had been division chief engineers prior to their promotions. Both liked products.

Engineering stretched the Mark IV closer to its full potential by increasing bore to 4.25 inches, raising displacement to 427 cubic inches. Chevrolet offered it in two versions, an L36 with 390 horsepower using a single four-barrel carburetor, high-performance camshaft, hydraulic lifters, and 10.25:1 compression ratio to help accomplish this output. They quoted the mechanical valve lifter–equipped, higher-output L72 for 1966 production at 425 horsepower. Soon everyone knew that was an extremely conservative rating. The engine transformed the Corvette. Runs from 0–60 miles per hour took a scant 4.8 seconds, and the car hit 100 miles per hour only 11.2 seconds after leaving the line.

Beginning in 1966, option codes became mantras for performance junkies. Young men, many just eligible for the draft with a 1A classification, preferred to know L72 (427-cubic-inch displacement, 425 horsepower), M-22 (four-speed, close-ratio, heavy duty), C48 (heater/defroster delete), G81

(continued on page 202)

(top left) Disc brakes, now standard all around, were included in the base coupe and convertible prices. Yet not everyone was convinced of the improvement they represented. Some 316 Corvette buyers exercised RPO J61 refitting drum brakes instead and saved some $64.50.

(left) Chevrolet began producing the Mark IV "porcupine head" 396-cubic-inch engines in January 1965, and the first cars reached showrooms in April. The L78, available for $292.70, developed 425 horsepower at 6400 rpm and a massive 415 foot pound of torque at 4000 rpm. Chevrolet produced 2,157 L78-powered Corvettes the first year.

(right) The side-mounted exhaust system—RPO N14—improved engine breathing somewhat for the $134.50 price that buyers paid. Just 759 customers opted for the system. Positraction was much more popular, with 19,965 of the 23,562 buyers selecting that $43.05 option.

1962 CERV II

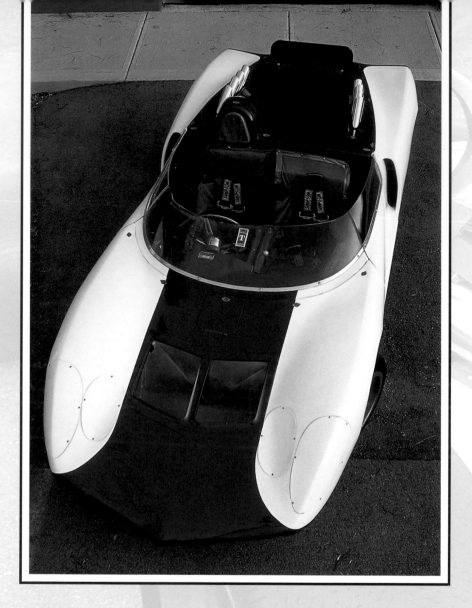

Duntov's champion, Bunkie Knudsen, had approved the CERV II in early 1962 as a follow-up project to the CERV I on the basis that it would perpetuate the valuable engineering lineage that Duntov and his colleagues had begun with the Corvette SS and CERV I. In fact, as Karl Ludvigsen explained in *Corvette: America's Star-Spangled Sports Car*, "Duntov hoped to reawaken the Corvette SS concept of a separate and parallel line of experimental/racing Corvettes."

This new vehicle was to use an alloy tube frame with a 92-inch wheelbase. The 1,800-pound sports racer would be powered by a new 244 cubic-inch engine to meet 1962 FIA regulations for 1963 prototype race cars' 4.0-liter maximum engine displacement. There was the possibility of using Mark II 427-cubic-inch engines in this car, and with 550 horsepower on hand, other opportunities arose.

All-wheel drive was one such opportunity. Knudsen and Duntov believed in using racing and competition as a means to improve and promote regular production vehicles. They understood that racing forced fast engineering solutions to problems, short cutting normal development times from months to days between one race and the next.

(above left) Duntov experimented with both magnesium and aluminum castings for the prototype 240-cubic-inch (4-liter) engine block. He also had a three-valve head to make better use of the Hilborn fuel-injection system first introduced on CERV I. With everything attached, the engine weighed just 382 pounds, yet it produced nearly 400 horsepower at 7,000 rpm. Duntov gave the car all–wheel drive and created a unique three-speed semi-automatic transmission.

(above right) One odd feature of the transmission system was that drivers started it in gear and moved off without first shifting. Changing from low to reverse requires shutting off the engine, because Duntov's experiment used neither input torque-converters nor hydraulic couplings. Internal multi-disc clutches and brake bands transmitted power.

(below) Crackling exhaust sounds bark from the four equal-length pipes on each side of Zora Duntov's prototype 4-liter/240 cubic-inch aluminum V-8 behind the driver's and passenger's seats of CERV II. Its mid-engine layout and short wheelbase put 58 percent of the vehicle weight on the rear tires.

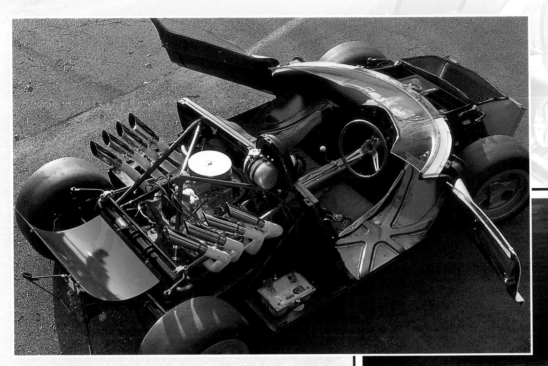

Its thin-wall aircraft steel tubing truss frame weighed just 70 pounds. Draped with a paper-thin body of fiberglass adding only another 192 pounds, the entire package, minus oil, cooling water, and fuel, tipped the scales at just 1,378 pounds. Fully loaded with driver, it still came in just under 1,800 pounds.

Duntov worked on the all-wheel-drive CERV with Frank Winchell, Chevrolet's head of Research and Development. As Bill Mitchell had his locked styling studios, so Winchell had secret engineering labs. He was responsible for the Corvair rear-engine development. He didn't care much for racing but he loved solving problems. While they considered a four-speed manual transmission, the solution he and Duntov created for an all-wheel-drive CERV II was dual torque-converters: one front and one rear. They incorporated quick gear change capability to accommodate different track speeds. Winchell did away with the usual hydraulic coupling, using internal multi-disc clutches and brake bands to start the engine and get the car moving through its three manually selected forward gears. The paper-thin aircraft sheet-steel unit-construction tubular chassis used the engine as a stressed member. The basic structure was surrounded by a tubular substructure to carry the other loads.

Word of the CERV II slipped out and got to Donner, who suspected that Knudsen might aim to go racing again. The corporation slapped Knudsen's wrists and closed down CERV II, which already had completed wind tunnel testing as both a coupe and roadster. Chevrolet racing in internationally sanctioned events against the likes of Ferrari would not happen. At least not in the prototype category, not in anything so radically, noticeably different as a tiny, mid-engine, sports racer.

This immediately set Duntov and Knudsen to wondering about a plan B, something not quite so obvious to Donner, something that would appear much more like a regular production product. Perhaps they would involve Mitchell and even call it one of those deep sea creature names the design chief favored.

Front and rear differentials ran at slightly different final drive ratios to ensure proper power delivery. Under hard acceleration, the less heavily weighted front tires spun faster than the rears. The multi-disc clutch and automatic transmissions later proved indomitable when Texan Jim Hall adapted them to his sports racing Chaparrals. His earliest racers even resembled the CERV II.

(continued from page 196)

(Positraction), N14 (side exhaust) or N11 (off-road exhaust system), F41 (special front/rear suspension), or J56 (special heavy-duty brakes) than to think about Southeast Asia. Always there in the shadows, on the six o'clock news, in NBC-TV's "Vietnam Weekly Review" and CBS' "Vietnam Perspective," and in *Life* magazine, was the war. The baby-boomer generation, children born after World War II into the greatest period of prosperity since the mid-1920s, had trouble accepting that their time was becoming the worst of times. It was far more enjoyable to read in *Car Craft, Hot Rod,* and *Road & Track* at year-end that Chevrolet's Corvette had another banner year, selling 9,958 coupes and 17,762 convertibles, a total of 27,720 cars.

For Corvette, 1967 turned out to be the best Sting Ray yet, because delays in production engineering held up a replacement once again. Mild design updates had to do, but under the hood, the changes were far more substantial.

New code numbers entered Corvette order books: L71, the 427-cubic-inch displacement V-8 with a trio of progressively linked two-barrel carburetors, produced 435 horsepower. Some 3,754 buyers paid $437.10 and went this route. Savvy buyers got an option on the optional engine by checking L89, which fitted aluminum cylinder heads on the L71, although only 16 of these were delivered at an additional $368.65 over the engine cost. One code became legendary: L88. This was 427-cubic-inch displacement with 12.5:1 compression. Chevrolet engineering knew what it had. Hoping to keep speed-hungry trust fund–endowed youngsters from buying something far beyond their abilities, it discouraged unknowing

(lower left) It could be promoted as a weight-saving improvement. The RPO L89 aluminum cylinder heads fitted onto the L71 427 cast-iron block, cutting 75 pounds off the front end, taking engine weight down to within 40 pounds of a fully equipped 327. A Car and Driver road test saw 13.6-second quarter-mile times, at 105 miles per hour. The lighter weight improved handling as well.

(lower right) Nothing inside this coupe betrays the stunning potential of Chevrolet's most potent package to date. Just 16 buyers ordered the aluminum heads, an unproven $368.65 option on an engine already developing 435 horsepower. Even the wild L88 option costing $947.90 was more popular, with 20 produced.

buyers by quoting 430 horsepower, five less than the lesser L-71, yet doubling its price to $947.90. Topped by a single Holley sucking 850 cubic-feet of air per minute and capable of running on 103-octane fuel, the true output of this engine was closer to 560 horsepower. Buyers could get the car only with the transistorized ignition, Positraction, F41 suspension, and J50 power brakes. Ordering the engine automatically deleted the heater and radio "to cut down on weight and discourage the car's use on the street," according to a release at introduction. Only 20 individuals paid for it, many of them seeing it for what it was: a flat-out racing engine with a regular production option code.

The first of the engines appeared in late 1966, slipping out the back door to select competitors. Chevrolet's director of promotions, Vince Piggins, was more accurately the division's director of racing. Characterized as someone with deep pockets but also with "high pockets," Piggins was generous with information and advice but less willing to use his resources to provide freebies. To help customers capable of paying their way, he created an ordering system, the Central Office Purchase Order (COPO), to take advantage of what he knew Duntov and others were doing in their back rooms. Piggins released a 1966 coupe body with the L88 and other "production options" to Roger Penske, a friend known to Duntov and Chevrolet from his Grand Sport efforts. Penske and Sunoco Oil had entered the car in the 24 Hours of Daytona in February 1966.

Dick Guldstrand picked up the car at St. Louis in mid-January and drove it to Penske's Newton Square garage in Pennsylvania to supervise additional preparations, though there was not enough

(lower left) No matter how many years it has been since its introduction, the Sting Ray coupe's boat-tail body still strikes automobile-design enthusiasts as a thing of beauty.

(lower right) While badges and louvers either disappeared or became totally functional, one new design flourish appeared. Chevrolet's 427 cubic-inch big-block engines now fit under a non-functional scoop set off with contrasting color paint.

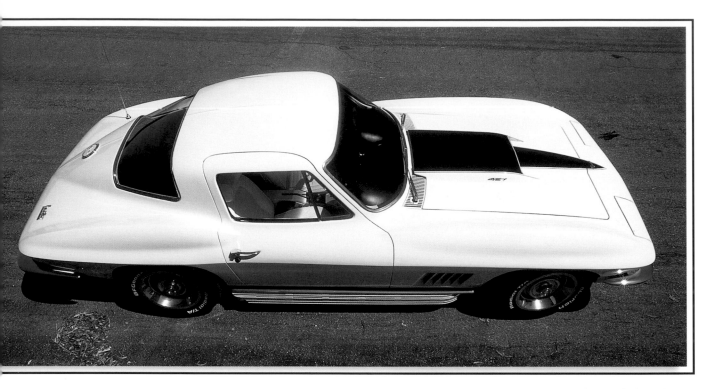

time to paint the red coupe Sunoco's blue. Guldstrand teamed Ben Moore and George Wintersteen to drive the race.

During the night, Wintersteen crashed in the car, heavily damaging the front end and losing the headlights. Guldstrand improvised and Penske's pit crew "racer taped" two flashlights onto the fenders. Guldstrand spent most of the night following the taillights of one of the Ferrari team cars. Incredibly, he broke the GT class distance record and the first production L88 finished the 24 hours in 12th place overall, first in class.

A month later in Sebring, Penske's car, now blue, finished 9th overall, tying Corvette's best ever at the airport circuit and once again winning its class.

By June, Piggins had commandeered a 1967 "pilot" preproduction car, and he helped California dealer Peyton Cramer obtain the first 1967 L88 coupe to take to Le Mans. Cramer, who owned Dana Chevrolet, knew racing; he had been Carroll Shelby's general manager at Shelby American. While L88 weighed 300 pounds more than the closest competitor in GT (opposite top) The hood scoop and its contrasting color made a strong visual impression for the 1967 models. Beneath this hood, the 427 cubic-inch RPO L71 engine fed by three two-barrel Holley carburetors developed 435 horsepower.

(left) Hot Rod magazine writer Eric Dahlquist tested an L71 tri-power 427 and recorded quarter-mile times of 13.8 seconds at 108 miles per hour for a convertible with four-speed manual transmission. While air conditioning and the automatic transmission might have cost an extra second or two, it still was an impressive performance.

(opposite bottom) While 3,754 buyers ordered the L71 engine, some 2,324 purchased the automatic transmission and 3,788 customers selected air conditioning, there is no way of knowing if anyone other than this owner combined the three. This combination offered highway cruising comfort and romping, stomping performance in the same car.

(left) Chevrolet's factory air conditioning was efficient, and the Ermine White exterior and white interior added to the impression of frosty coolness on even the warmest day. In many ways, this automobile hints at what Corvette's designers and product planners saw for the future: combining performance and luxury.

Racers say that the Mulsanne Straight is the only place at Le Mans to actually relax. Imagine the sensation for co-drivers Dick Gulstrand and Bob Bondurant as they relaxed with the large speedometer bouncing 11.5 miles per hour beyond the peg.

Despite its weight—at 3,265 pounds it was at least 300 pounds heavier than the nearest competitor in the GT class—it still reached 171.5 miles per hour on the long Mulsanne Straight. This was some 22 miles per hour faster than the Ferrari that ultimately won the class.

class, Dick Guldstrand, now Cramer's high-performance manager, and Bob Bondurant, by this time Dana's regular driver in its SCCA and Can-Am entries still clocked 171.5 miles per hour on the Mulsanne Straight, 22 miles per hour faster than the nearest GT Ferrari. Sadly, the blistering pace took its toll and the L88 expired after 11 hours, leaving the slower Ferrari to win GT.

While Chevrolets had raced on NASCAR ovals, road courses, drag strips, and across the salt flats at Bonneville in Utah, by the time the Sting Ray appeared, the division had adopted an unofficial and unspoken snobbery. It held that Corvettes belonged on road courses, while Impalas, Chevelles, or Camaros could drag race or go fender-to-fender around the ovals. Corvettes already had a reputation among drag racers for being expensive to buy and race and fragile to operate because they broke down regularly. But racers such as Bo Laws and Dick Moroso had another view. They said, "That car 'hooks' like nobody's business." Despite its drawbacks, and because of the efforts of outside aftermarket parts

Rumors exist that an L88 prototype went to Roger Penske to run alongside his Grand Sport roadster at Daytona in February 1966. Until that can be confirmed, this coupe is known to be the first L88 outside of the factory development versions. Dana Chevrolet entered it in the 1967 Le Mans 24-hour.

(right) Twenty-four hours is a long hard run for a company officially not promoting racing and therefore not getting anywhere near enough test time. The engine failed, a connecting rod punching through the side of the block, after 11 1/2 hours of racing.

One of Bill Mitchell's strongest influences was the proliferation of blues in the color palette for the Corvette. Chevrolet offered three separate variations. The most popular were Marina Blue (3,840 produced), Lynndale Blue (1,381), and Elkhart Blue (1,096.) There were even several colors available for the big-block hood scoop.

Charlie Snyder from Astoria, New York, ordered an L71-equipped convertible with the hardtop to run in AHRA local and regional races. Snyder took the car directly to Motion Performance after picking it up from Baldwin Chevrolet in February 1967. Very quickly Charlie began winning races, and he made a name for himself and the car, routinely running 11.5 seconds at 124 miles per hour.

suppliers and speed shops that cooperated with local dealers, a few drag racers made their place in history racing Sting Rays.

On Long Island, New York, Baldwin Chevrolet and Joel Rosen's Motion Performance had a working relationship with Vince Piggins, who helped get them parts and engines just as he did with other dealers. Rosen, barely older than his customers, created 427-engined "Stage III" muscle Chevrolets. When he heard from Piggins that the L88 would be available in a box in midsummer 1967, he ordered two through Baldwin's parts manager John Mahler. Rosen and Mahler knew at least one likely customer.

Charlie Snyder was born and raised in nearby Astoria, and the 20-year-old loved racing. In early February 1967, he took delivery of a Marlboro Maroon hardtop convertible with the 425-horse-power 427-cubic-inch displacement engine. To protect himself from outrageous insurance rates in car theft–prone Queens, he titled the car in his mother's name, Grace Snyder. He drove the car straight to Rosen for tuning and modification. Over the next several months, "Astoria Chas," as he became known, drove to the track, raced, and won, regularly turning 11.5-second times at 124 miles per hour. He also ran after midnights on the connecting highways in Queens where crowds lined the roadway three deep to see racing under the streetlights Friday and Saturday nights. Rosen's increased power

An incoming mortar round killed young Charlie Snyder within a month of his arriving in Vietnam in mid-1968. His mother and sister put the car in his mother's garage until a year later when Motion Performance owner Joel Rosen and Baldwin parts manager John Mahler asked if they could continue to race the car in Charlie's name.

The side pipes looked stylish but drivers and passengers soon learned to step well away from the car when getting in or out. The RPO N14 Side Mount Exhaust System sold for $131.65, and of 22,940 cars produced in 1967, 4,209 buyers liked the look.

A few modifications to the car made it a full-scale Baldwin-Motion Phase III. With John Mahler at the wheel, the Ko-Motion, as Charlie had named it, rocketed into the record books in 1969 with an 11.04 second/129 miles-per-hour run made "in memory of Astoria Chas." A day later, Mahler ran a 10.74, and together with Rosen, they returned it to Charlie's family and rolled it into his sister Sharon's garage where it remained for 30 more years.

and torque eventually twisted the chassis. Snyder ordered a replacement and the car sat for a month in a service bay at Baldwin. Rosen's two L88s were on the same truckload with Snyder's chassis, and he wasted no time securing one of the two (the other went to a neighborhood Camaro). To handle the new power, Baldwin's mechanics gusset-welded the chassis. Over the next few weeks, Snyder raced regularly and won repeatedly in the car he named "Ko-Motion."

Snyder got drafted in the winter of 1967. In the spring of 1968, on leave after basic training, he returned to Queens, repainted the graphics on his car, and raced several more times. Then the army sent him to Vietnam. One month after arriving, he died of injuries from an exploding mortar round. Back home, his Corvette sat in Grace's garage throughout the 1968 summer season while his family grieved the loss of their only son.

John Mahler and Joel Rosen thought about the car often. After a year passed, they approached Grace Snyder. They wanted to race it, they said. They would pay all its expenses, running it "in memory of

After a spring and summer of hard running, Charlie had to replace the chassis, which had twisted from the torque. Later, his factory original 427-cubic-inch 435 horsepower L71 engine expired. Snyder learned through Joel Rosen that L88 engines with aluminum heads would be available in crates. Snyder took one of the first two Rosen got, likely to be the first L88s in private hands.

Astoria Chas." They reminded her it had been Charlie's dream to set an AHRA record. After some hesitation, she agreed. Mahler and Rosen prepped the car through the winter and resumed racing in the spring of 1969 with Bill Foster, a local pro, often driving for them. The car made headlines, turning 11.04 seconds at 129 miles per hour and winning the A/Corvette World Record in Charlie Snyder's name. After taking the title, Mahler and Rosen performed one final modification, changing heads and fitting an 850-cfm Holley carburetor. With this set up, Mahler pulled a 10.74 at National Speedway in Queens one Saturday night, registering the accomplishment in Charlie's name. The next afternoon, with its time whitewashed in shoe polish on the window and its trophies stuffed in the foot wells, Rosen and Mahler trailered the car to Charlie's sister Sharon's home. They pushed it into her garage and covered it. It remained there for 30 years, one of a handful of Corvette drag racing legends.

CHAPTER SEVEN

GREAT PROJECTS ARE OFTEN THE VICTIMS OF CORPORATE AND INTERNATIONAL POLITICS

n March 1962, Ford announced its return to racing as part of its "Total Performance" program. It blamed GM for side-stepping the AMA ban for years, though Ford's own NASCAR wins put Ford in no position to cast stones. GM Chairman Frederic Donner was embarrassed. He reiterated General Motors' intentions to honor GM's 1957 commitment.

Bunkie Knudsen had become Zora Duntov's corporate godfather. Knudsen, the new division general manager, liked seeing his cars in the spotlight. He knew that in October 1962, a Corvette Z06 had beaten Carroll Shelby's new Cobra at Riverside Raceway in California. But Duntov's description of Shelby's car made its potential clear to Knudsen. He encouraged Duntov to be discrete, above all, but to think as ambitiously as Ford and Shelby.

Duntov understood that the FIA's recent rule changes that made Grand Touring cars eligible in the World Championship for manufacturers was a subtly worded invitation to U.S. manufacturers. Yet he also recognized that entering his mid-engine CERV II four-wheel-drive coupe in Le Mans in 1964 was not discrete. He knew what it took to win the French race outright having won his class there in a Porsche 550 Spyder.

Duntov considered a "lightweight" 1,800-pound Corvette. He would need 600 horsepower to propel the car with its aerodynamic disadvantages. He and chassis engineer Walt Zetye fabricated an aluminum frame from two large-diameter parallel tubes joined at the back end by three transverse tubes and at the front by a massive 6-inch-diameter crossmember. Using aluminum saved 94 pounds over steel, and Zetye and Duntov transferred onto this car the IRS Zetye devised for the CERV that would later appear on the production Sting Ray. They cast an aluminum differential case and fitted a Dana-limited slip to replace the GM Positraction. They shortened the *(previous pages) In early 1965, Notre Dame University engineering student Tony De Lorenzo had volunteered to help classmates find interesting cars for a campus auto show. Tony called his father, who worked at GM at the time, and asked him if there was anything interesting in design or engineering that they could send. Dad visited Duntov and Mitchell. The unpainted #002 Grand Sport roadster got a coat of "Mitchell blue" and was sent to the show.*

Chevrolet dealer Dick Doane first raced chassis #003, using a nearly stock 327-cubic-inch 360 horsepower cast iron engine. At the Road America 500 in September 1963, Doane blew up the engine after 92 laps. The car returned to Chevrolet to prepare it for Nassau Speed Weeks. For Nassau, the car got a quick fill gas cap and wider fenders to house 11-inch Halibrand wheels and Goodyear tires for John Mecom's racing effort.

The Z06s raced as production cars, so Duntov's idea was to produce Grand Sports that, properly developed, would compete against the world's finest prototypes. Chairman Frederic Donner upheld the 1957 AMA racing ban and cancelled the project just as it became visible.

body slightly, from 175.3 inches to 172.8, and lightened it considerably by using paper-thin fiberglass carefully laid over an aluminum substructure. Overall height grew 2 inches because the seats rested on top of, not inside of, the two major longitudinal frame members. Ground clearance, however, dropped from 7.4 to 4.3 inches. Because the race car weighed nearly 1,000 pounds less than the production car, Duntov decided to try four Girling disc brakes.

FIA racing regulations for 1963 placed no limits on engine displacement, another subtle invitation to the Americans. Engineering's 427 Mark II "mystery motor" could produce the power Duntov wanted, but it weighed too much. Boring out an all-aluminum 327-cubic-inch displacement block to within a couple of thousandths of its life might meet the same ends through different means. A 4.00-inch stroke as well as 4.00-inch bore would give him a lightweight 402-cubic-inch displacement engine. Zora and Yura Duntov, his brother, had devised the Ardun head, a hemispherical-combustion chamber, for flathead Ford V-8s in the 1940s. For the aluminum 402, they created twin-plug Hemi-heads, assembled the engine and tested it, and then discarded it as too far stressed. Back at the drawing board, they reconsidered stroke at 3.75 inches. This required less intrusive modifications to accommodate the spinning crankshaft. This engine measured 377-cubic-inch displacement. Duntov even produced three prototype dual-overhead cam versions, which produced an estimated 550 horsepower. This was less than his target of 600 horsepower, but it was more than any other option they had tried.

(below) Throughout the summer of 1963, Duntov developed his aluminum-block 377-cubic-inch V-8. He installed these with four 58mm side-draft Weber carburetors into each of Mecom's "private" Grand Sports, #003 (shown here), #004, and #005. (Number 001 and 002 remained with Chevrolet.) The engine developed 485 horsepower at 6,000 rpm, but its tall induction system required a higher hood. Then in March 1965, Duntov created a 427 that would literally lift the front tires off the ground in all four gears.

Duntov took this first car, known by now as the Grand Sport (GS), to Sebring in mid-December 1962. Equipped with a race-prepared 327-cubic-inch displacement engine, he used it for shakedown runs and tire testing with Firestone and Mickey Thompson. The GS outshined Thompson's purely production-based car, but the Girling brakes proved inadequate. Actually, the Grand Sport shined a little too brightly. As they replaced the Girling rotors with new 1-inch-thick factory-produced ventilated discs, word came down from the corporation. Chevrolet was not Ford; these efforts had become too visible behind Donner's back.

Chevrolet had already filed specification papers with the FIA in Paris two weeks before Donner's edict hit Duntov's operation, forcefully halting the program. To qualify for the "Grand Touring" Group III category, the FIA required 100 identical cars constructed before June 1, 1963 (with Le Mans running June 15 and 16). Duntov had intended to produce 125 "production" cars for sale to customers to meet the FIA homologation (legalization) requirement. Later, 1,000 street-legal production cars would follow for public sale. Engineering had spoken with outside vendors about manufacturing the customer-racing cars and the street cars as well. Knudsen, however, had authorized building only 25 cars total, and just 40 of those special 377-cubic-inch displacement Hemi engines. It was clear now that Donner would never allow manufacture of 25 lightweight Corvettes. In fact, the five prototypes that Duntov already had underway were to be "scrapped, sold or used as testing and evaluation vehicles." But they would not race.

In a heartbeat, the Grand Sport project was over.

Dick Doane, a Dundee, Illinois, car dealer and racer, and Grady O. Davis, vice president of Gulf Oil and an enthusiastic driver and car owner, were the beneficiaries of Donner's edict. Duntov sent out one of the completed cars to each of them, on loan, with instructions to keep their activities "low key" and not cause Chevrolet any embarrassment. Each car was white, and Duntov equipped them with production stock 360-horsepower 327-cubic-inch displacement fuel-injected engines.

Because Duntov had built only five, these cars did not qualify for production racing classes, but instead they had to go up against modified sports racers like Jim Hall's Chaparrals and Lance

Reventlow's Scarabs. This class elevation, however, allowed Doane and Davis to build real racing engines. The privately held Grand Sports went through teething troubles but eventually came to hold their own.

Grady Davis put Dr. Dick Thompson in his car. After a shaky start, Thompson and Davis had the car sorted so well that by early June it consistently finished in fifth or better overall. Through July and August, Davis' crew reworked and improved their "modified" Corvette, and when it reemerged in late August at the Watkins Glen Nationals, it was closer to Duntov's original vision. Somehow, when the SCCA totaled the points, Thompson finished fourth for the year in the C-modified category.

This frustrated Chevrolet engineers and Bunkie Knudsen, who recognized how close they were with the car. Carroll Shelby and his drivers steadily teased them. The byword around Chevrolet had been "discretely," but now through Chevrolet's back corridors, another word was whispered in a few ears: escalate.

Texas oil heir John Mecom Jr. had begun running a Cooper-engined sports racer, the Xerex Special. He had acquired the car, its builder, Roy

Unlike the production models, the air vents behind the front wheels were functional to help eliminate engine heat and underhood air pressure.

Gane, and its driver, Roger Penske, and throughout the 1963 seasons he added Augie Pabst and A. J. Foyt to his stable. The team was highly regarded, thoroughly professional, and extremely successful. Because Mecom was a newcomer, he owed allegiance to no one yet, making him the perfect team owner for Chevrolet's whispered plans.

Duntov arranged to ship Mecom several engines to install in a variety of sports racers. He called back Doane's and Davis' Grand Sports. He pulled a third car from the storage garages and set to work, preparing cars for Nassau Speed Week scheduled for early December 1963. He had Knudsen's unwritten but enthusiastic blessing.

New body modifications accommodated 11-inch-wide Halibrand wheels, necessary to fit the Mickey Thompson–inspired new wide Goodyear low-profile racing tires. Duntov's staff improved ventilation to engine and driver by liberally perforating the car nose, hood, sides, and rear. They dropped in the 377-cubic-inch displacement, all-aluminum block, aluminum-headed engines originally developed for the car with their four twin-throat Weber side-draft carburetors. Duntov's dynamometers saw 485 horsepower.

Duntov had the three Corvettes, chassis 003, 004, and 005, painted in Mecom Racing's Cadillac blue and shipped to Nassau, timed to arrive on November 30, the day before their first race. Coincidentally, several Chevrolet engineers arrived, all vacationing at the same time. Along with the Grand Sports, Mecom sent his three mid-engined Chevrolet-powered sports racers, a Lola GT, a Cooper-Monaco, and a Scarab. With this stable, piloted by some of racing's best drivers, Duntov believed that if the Corvette lightweights themselves did not win, at least a Chevrolet engine was likely to come home in first.

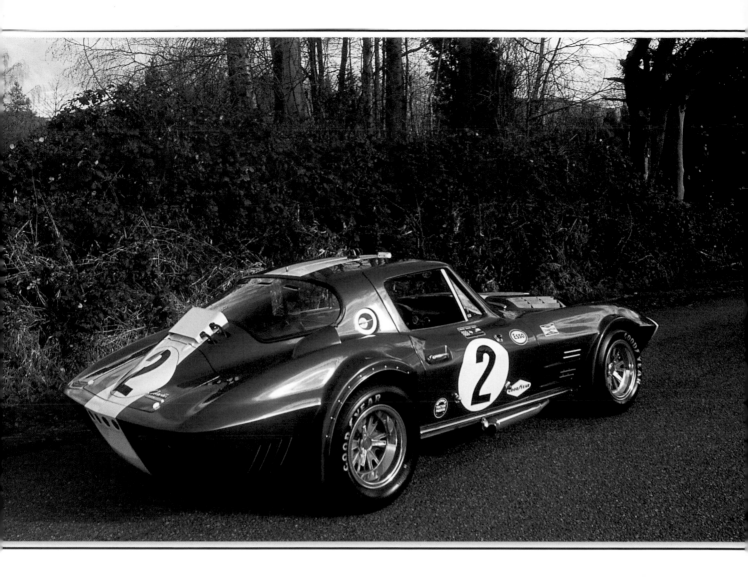

The Corvettes won the five-lap qualifying race, but Mecom's Lola took the 99-mile Tourist Trophy on December 1. The Grand Sports' final drives, not broken in before the races, couldn't handle the torque of the 485-horsepower engines or the pounding of the old airport course. Another Chevrolet engineer suddenly was overcome with the need for a Caribbean vacation. He flew down with carefully seasoned rear axles in his baggage.

The second weekend's 112-mile Governors Cup was a better show. A. J. Foyt won in Mecom's Chevy-engined Scarab, and the Grand Sports finished third (Roger Penske), fourth (Augie Pabst), and sixth (Dick Thompson), beating Shelby's best placed Cobra by two places. The next day's finale, the 252-Mile Nassau Trophy, ended with Dick Thompson in fourth, a Cobra in seventh, and new Mecom-inductee John Cannon in eighth. But this longer race pointed out once again the foul aerodynamics of the cars. Air pressure built up under the hoods and continually blew the fasteners. Each driver endured several pit stops to cut in new vent holes and apply racer tape to the panels.

The outside-mounted oil cooler sits under its own shroud behind the rear window. Vents everywhere funnel cool air to rear brakes and the differential.

When GM Chairman Frederic Donner shut down the Grand Sport program, he issued orders to destroy Chevrolet engineering's two remaining cars: #001 and #002. Yet friends of the project hid the cars until 1966 when Roger Penske learned they were available. He bought #001, recommending this car, #002, to his long-time friend George Wintersteen.

Somehow Nassau escaped Frederic Donner's sharp eyes, at least temporarily. The Grand Sport operation returned to Warren for further improvements and modifications before the 1964 season openers at Daytona and Sebring. Each race presented specific problems. Engineers fitted a new Rochester fuel-injection system to even out the engine power curve, and they installed a pneumatic air jacking system to speed pit stop tire changes, changes that would benefit the Mecom team at both venues.

Daytona was a track where maximum speed was beneficial, as it would be at Le Mans and a few other circuits in the world. Duntov knew the Sting Ray body was a brick punching a big hole through the air. A sports-racer body like Mecom's other cars, or like his originally planned CERV II, would have been ideal. But those would introduce all new development problems. Instead, he decided to cut down the big brick, knowing that he'd pick up speed.

Duntov removed the roofs from two coupes, chassis 001 and 002. Engineers replaced the tall windshields with low windscreens and incorporated roll bars into lower fiberglass fairings. But spies were loose in the back halls at GM engineering, and shortly before the Daytona Continental 2,000-kilometer race in mid-February, Bunkie Knudsen's bosses called him in for a chat. A press release stated that Chevrolet was not associated with John Mecom Racing, ever. Donner applied effective leverage over Knudsen, and the general manager registered the threat as another permanent blotch on his record. More clearly than ever he saw little future at General Motors.

Quickly, Chevrolet sold the three coupes, two to Mecom and the third, chassis 005, to Jim Hall. Duntov had the two roadsters wrapped under covers and buried in storage in Warren. The three coupes began an odyssey of owners, races, and modifications that has filled other entire books, most notably Lowell Paddock's and Dave Friedman's 1989 history, *Corvette Grand Sport*. The cars campaigned privately, valiantly, and with some success for another three seasons, beating the best that Ford of Dearborn, Venice, and England could throw at them.

In late winter 1966, Roger Penske retired from driving but remained active as a team owner. He acquired the two remaining roadsters from Chevrolet, selling one quickly to friend George Wintersteen. Prior to Sebring in 1966, Penske put a 427-cubic-inch displacement Mark IV engine into 002, and during practice his crew bolted on aluminum heads, a first for the Mark IV and an indication that creative thinking was not dead within Chevrolet, only in hiding. Both roadsters and the coupes soldiered gamely on through the 1966 season, thrilling fans and inspiring loyalists.

TO RACE OR NOT TO RACE

In late 1962, as Chevy gave birth to the Grand Sports, Peter Brock moved back to the West Coast, joining Shelby's organization, where he watched Chevrolet and GM's board futzing and fidgeting from the long view in Venice, California. Decades later, he wrote about racing in Shelby's most intriguing car, the Cobra Daytona coupe, which Brock designed: "This dilemma [to race or not to race] split the board of directors. In the GM boardroom the battle lines were redrawn: bean counters versus engineers and marketing experts."

Neither group, Brock observed, seemed capable of convincing the other that they were right. Both sides did agree that Shelby's Cobras were too strong and only a new Chevrolet racer could meet

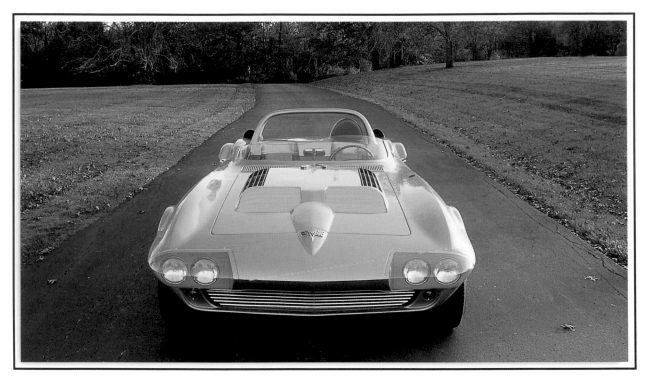

In their wildest versions, these "Lightweights," as Roger Penske and Dick Guldstrand called them, weighed in at just over 2,000 pounds and ran with "detuned" race engines developing 500 horsepower. This car would "go down the straights looking like a speedboat," as driver Wintersteen recalled.

Wintersteen had to cut a notch in the front cross member to shoehorn in the big L71-block 427-cubic-inch engine.

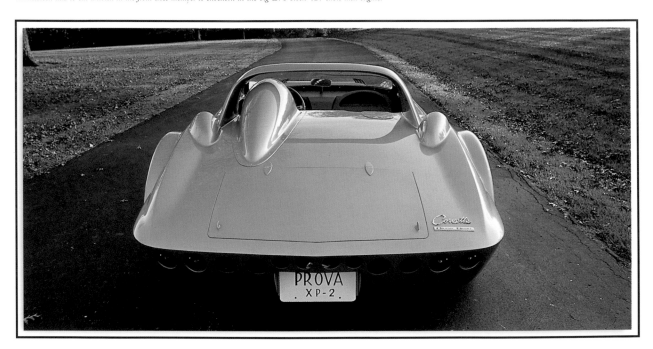

Ford's challenge. It was clear to everyone that any solution would be costly. Could they afford to meet the challenge? Well, yes, but was it worth it?

It created a conundrum. Could Chevrolet even sell Duntov's planned 125 racers at a reported $9,200 each? Further confusing things was the value of public visibility in Europe versus America. Ford, for example, had a vested interest in competing in Europe. The blue oval logo appeared on cars built in Germany and the United Kingdom. Chevrolet had no presence in Europe; in fact, at times GM had de-emphasized its ownership of Vauxhall in the United Kingdom and Opel in Germany. For Chevrolet to produce race cars that might win major races in Europe would necessitate an expensive advertising campaign just to explain to Europeans what it meant and why they should care. GM didn't plan to sell production Corvettes there, and the car wasn't well-regarded compared to other European sports cars.

Donner would not consider risking public embarrassment by circumventing the AMA ban with a racing effort in Europe. The fabulously expensive prospect of producing so few cars made Donner's accountant's blood boil. It had only been during his rule that Corvette had begun to pay for itself. He understood that little projects like this served to keep his engineers excited and loyal, and he turned a blind eye on things as long as they didn't cast the wrong light onto an observant public. Yet the Grand Sport simply could not be. The corporation, he believed, should not spend the money.

Then, in a master stroke of public relations good fortune, Donner turned a purely economic decision into a safety conscious issue. He was still smarting from the secret, seamy Ralph Nader investigations and from congressional subcommittee questions on Corvair safety. He had blurted out that GM had spent less than 1 percent of its net profit on safety-related research. It was an awful moment. The Grand Sport was the perfect project, then, for him to shut down. In the newspapers, it would read as purity of motive: Donner was upholding the June 6, 1957, AMA speed and racing ban even if no one else did so. In the eyes of the wary public, he had begun to redeem himself and General Motors. In the eyes of Wall Street stockbrokers, individuals who were far more important to Donner, he had exercised fiscal responsibility.

It was pure and simple, with a 200 miles per hour speedometer. The driver's seat adjusted while the passenger's was bolted in place. Because these cars raced in C-Modified class, they never had a chance to prove their potential, always outrun by pure sports racers with similar power but even less weight. Since there were only five Grand Sports, they became instant legends.

1968-1982

CHAPTER EIGHT

THROUGH THE MIDYEARS, CORVETTES SACRIFICE MUSCLE TO LUXURY

ven before the St. Louis production plant started its preassembly runs of the 1963 Sting Rays, Bill Mitchell told his designers to think about the next Corvette. The Sting Ray was to remain in production only through 1965, possibly carried over into 1966, and so it was not too early to begin.

He set Larry Shinoda on a flight of fancy, a wild excursion with an open-wheeled single-seater not unlike Duntov's CERV I. It drew technical inspiration from Frank Winchell, Chevrolet Engineering Center's R&D chief. Winchell had developed the production Corvairs and the Monza GT and SS prototypes in 1962 and 1963. Mitchell called his new car the X-15, a project named after the Air Force's black rocket plane. Shinoda worked with John Schinella and a small group of designers and modelers in another one of those invisible, locked studios. While few people ever saw the car, it became the reality check at the far end of the spectrum from down-to-earth production products all the way to pie-in-the-sky daydreams. From it, Mitchell refined and defined what he wanted in his next personal car and in the next Corvette.

Shinoda's design, known internally as the XP-830, actually filled in at the last minute as a future Corvette when earlier plans failed. Duntov's work on the CERV II had led to suggestions that the next generation Corvette, perhaps now delayed until the 1967 model year, could be a mid-engined two-seater, reflecting the racing technology that Duntov believed Corvette customers wanted and deserved. Winchell's group had promoted the idea of a true lightweight (2,650-pound) rear-engined car, using the 327-cubic-inch displacement V-8. Its 70 percent rear weight bias rendered the car's handling frightening. Duntov's idea was mid-engined, with *(previous pages) This represented the most complete redesign since the 1968 Corvette. Chevrolet produced 6,502 of these Indy 500 pace car replicas. At $13,653, it was the first Corvette to sell for more than $10,000.*

The sculpture artists in Bill Mitchell's design studios created another striking hood for the small block. While vents in this hood were not functional, they still introduced cold air at the windshield's lowest pressure point.

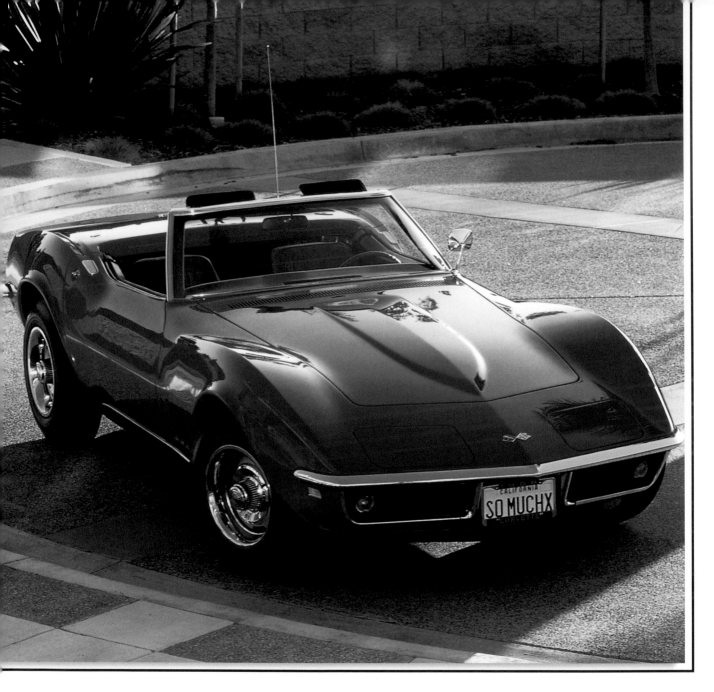

While the wheelbase remained the same, the exterior was dramatically redesigned. It was so successful that Chevrolet General Manager Pete Estes ordered the St Louis factory to work a third shift to meet the demand.

the Mark IV 427, but had more neutral handling. Yet because the Corvette had always been built out of parts produced for other Chevrolet models and no pieces existed to build such a car as Winchell, Duntov, and Mitchell imagined, it was impossible. The costs to develop such pieces, even to a wealthy corporation such as General Motors ruled by an accountant like Donner, were prohibitive when balanced against the volume of Corvette sales and the likelihood those expenses might never be repaid. Design exercises produced cars with shapes as striking as Lamborghini's mid-engine Miura. But while European exotic-car buyers might accept a price tag above $20,000, GM management was sure

Corvette buyers were not ready for that. It was purely economic considerations, plus Donner's publicized indignation at the exploits of the Grand Sport and CERV I, that doomed the ambitious mid-engine next generation.

It took time and effort to make a Corvair chassis handle Corvette engines. When engineering eliminated that possibility, they and Mitchell's designers found themselves fighting an unforgiving timetable. In something like a forced-march pace, the two sides worked to bring a new car into existence.

Shinoda's creation for Mitchell became known as Mako Shark II. He renamed the earlier 1961 Shark show car, the XP-755, as the Mako Shark I, to give consistency and longevity to styling exercises that would become the new car. Chevrolet premiered the Mako II at the New York International Auto Show in April 1965. By October, design was able to ship a running, functional model, powered by a Mark IV 427-cubic-inch displacement V-8, to the Paris Salon. Throughout the rest of 1965, the two prototypes, created for something like $3 million, toured North America and Europe. They created a near frenzy of publicity and speculation based on Chevrolet's past performance. Magazines pronounced themselves certain that viewers were seeing the next Corvette when they looked at Mitchell's Mako II.

Chevrolet discontinued the two-speed Powerglide automatic transmission and introduced the new three-speed Turbo-Hydra-Matic M40 transmission. On base engine models such as this, it was a $226.45 option, and of 28,566 cars produced, 5,063 left the factory with the new automatic.

While they evolved from Larry Shinoda's Shark and Mako Shark II show cars done for Design Chief Bill Mitchell, the new production models tamed the stylistic excesses that made the show cars exciting. The new street cars just took people's breath away.

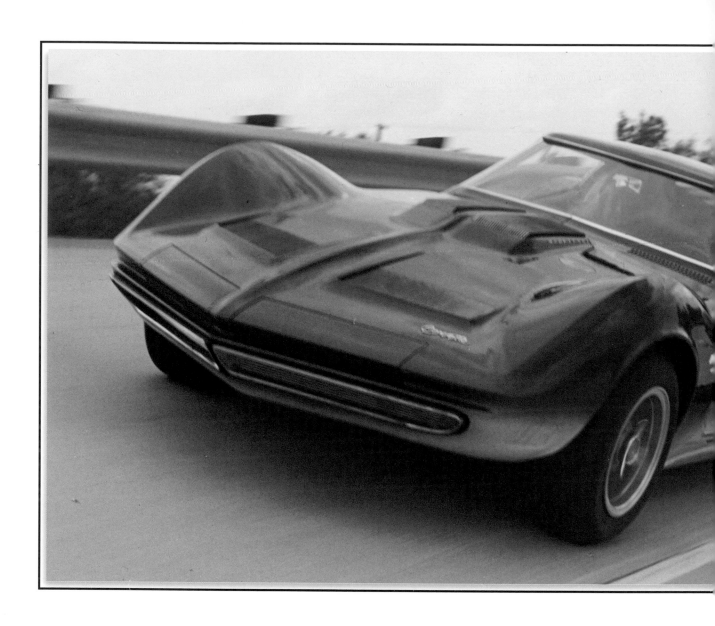

Meanwhile, in Washington, D.C., and Sacramento, California, lawmakers proposed rules and wrote regulations that would greatly affect the products of Detroit and its suburbs for nearly 20 years. As early as 1955, California began monitoring exhaust emissions. (This inspired Zora Duntov to perfect a cleaner burning fuel-injected engine. Its improved performance was a happy by-product.) For model year 1962, California required all cars sold new in the state to have positive crankcase ventilation (PCV) systems. By 1965, Congress had begun looking at legislation that would formulate acceptable levels of auto exhaust gas emissions. California mandated smog pumps on all 1966 models. These same regulations would go into effect nationwide with the 1968 model year. In 1966, the Traffic Safety Act began setting front, rear, and side-impact and visibility standards for cars sold in the United States. It also established procedures requiring manufacturers to recall vehicles on which mechanical and safety flaws appeared. California introduced its own auto emissions standards, stricter than the rest of the country, to become mandatory with 1969 models sold in that state.

At the same time, the Chevrolet studios worked to revise the Mako Shark II into something that could be produced. They built it on the Sting Ray chassis, carrying over virtually everything mechanical from the production cars. By November 1965, Hank Haga's Production Studio had produced full-sized clay models very close to what the finished car would look like. Haga's designers replaced the Mako II boat-tail rear window with a scoop-like treatment derived from Duntov's mid-engine prototype and two of Haga's favorites, Ferrari's angular 1964 250 GTO and Porsche's 904 GTS. But as soon as engineering tested these prototypes in their wind tunnel, Corvette's perpetual aerodynamics problems reappeared. The new shark nose proved even more air-worthy than the previous Sting Ray had been. A duck-tail lip at the rear helped hold that end down, but that lifted the nose up further. Duntov fitted a small chin spoiler across the front, well below the small grille and slender fenders. It helped some.

Design carried over the tall front fender bulges from the Mako Shark II. Once again Duntov found himself fighting against Mitchell. The design chief's preferences ran counter to engineering's practicality and driver visibility. Duntov sought support

The Mako Shark II had a fastback boat tail rear end reminiscent of the first generation Sting Ray, while the production car used a small backlight under a targa-type rear roof. 2002 General Motors Corporation. Used with permission of GM Media Archives.

To improve weight balance, engineering moved the battery from the already-tightly packed engine compartment to another compartment behind the two seats.

Most L88s also arrived with other options, including Muncie's "rock crusher" M22 four-speed close-ratio transmission, J56 heavy-duty brakes, and the F41 heavy-duty front and rear suspension. These were often necessary to get the phenomenal horsepower to the ground without waste.

from Pete Estes, Chevrolet's new general manager, who came to the division from Pontiac in 1965. Like Ed Cole, Estes, who replaced Knudsen, had been a division chief engineer before his promotion to Chevrolet. Estes disliked the sight lines over the wheel humps and sent the car back to the drawing boards. Work piled up in the engineering and design departments already overburdened with the brand new Camaro, Chevrolet's response to Ford's Mustang and Pontiac's GTO. It was Chevy's entry into the nationwide muscle car wars. Chevrolet knew it had to introduce this car in 1967. Product planners could count sales lost to Pontiac and Ford every hour. Everyone involved with the Corvette agreed to hold over the Sting Ray replacement until 1968.

Under supervision from Chevrolet chief stylist David Holls, Larry Shinoda now collaborated with production studio chief Hank Haga and his staff to reduce those excesses of Shinoda's Mako Shark II that had continued onto the prototype. Mitchell had Haga's staff resurrect a removable roof panel idea that had appeared in the small experimental studios off and on since the late 1950s. By the time Mitchell approved the Corvette final clays, Porsche had introduced its 1967 model 911 Targa with a completely removable roof center section and rear window. Chevrolet design wanted to do

The badge and the sticker command attention. Anything less than 103 octane put the engine at risk, and running pump regular was an invitation to an expensive rebuild. The car thrived on Sunoco 260 and other barely disguised racing fuels of the period.

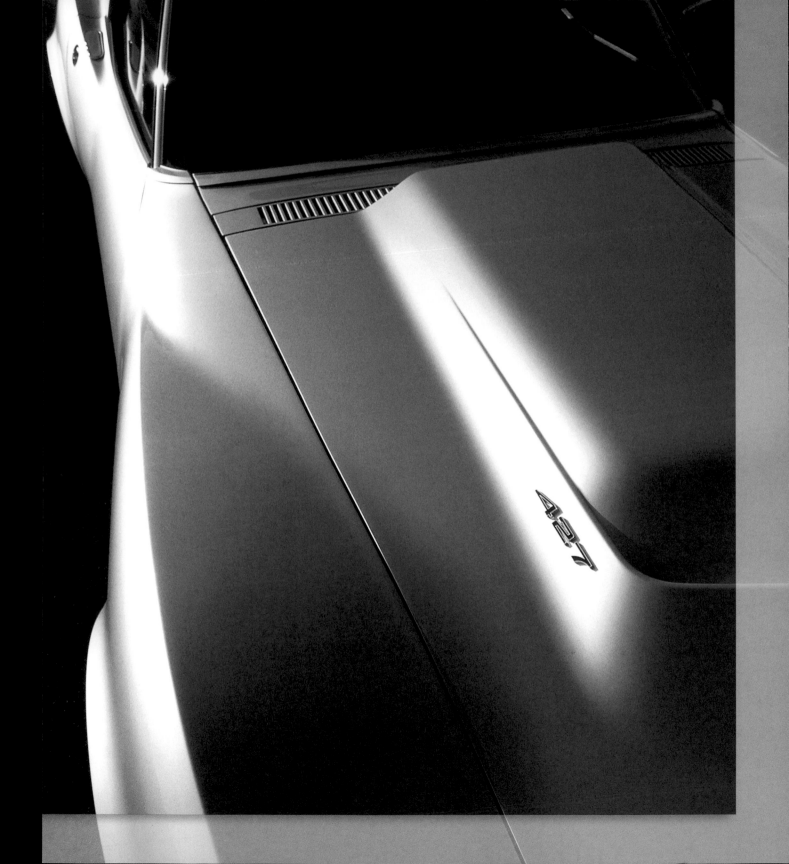

that but learned from Targa designer Butzi Porsche that the 911 was not stiff enough to support a completely open car. Its rollbar added the necessary stiffness to the steel-bodied Porsche. The Corvette's fiberglass body and steel frame were nowhere near stiff enough to accommodate an open roof. Incorporating a center beam that tied the windshield to the rear section, Chevrolet design adapted an innovation from outside industrial designer Gordon Buerhig, the T-roof.

Mitchell moved Shinoda's hidden headlights and windshield wipers from the Mako II to the production prototype, causing new problems and delays. The headlights, when closed, hung down into the airstream used for engine cooling. Yet the retractable headlights had become part of the iconography of Corvette. They would stay. Developing the vacuum plumbing to operate lights and wiper covers powerful enough to punch through snow or ice took time. Through late 1966 and early 1967, there were other problems to solve.

One of those concerns was engine cooling. Duntov had taken time off in the spring of 1967 to recover from a serious illness. Somehow engineering forgot to complete engine cooling tests. He returned to work three weeks before the press introduction for all the 1968 models, which he was to supervise. Public relations had specified that the press-preview Corvette be a heat-absorbing dark blue, powered by the Mark IV 427 big block. Duntov nearly panicked when he learned that engine cooling had been forgotten. In a typical racer's response to a problem, he lengthened the front chin spoiler and then sliced two large scoops into the bottom bodywork just ahead of the spoiler to channel more air in for engine cooling. The journalists never noticed and the combination worked well, going

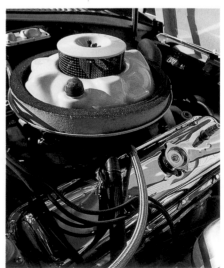

Racers never divulge horsepower figures to the public until years after the car has retired. But educated guesses ran to around 580 horsepower from the English-prepared L88. It was good enough for 8th overall at Daytona and 4th overall at Sebring. At Le Mans, drivers Dave Heinz and Bob Johnson routinely saw 212 miles per hour along Mulsanne, finishing 15th overall, 1st in the over-five-liter class.

through immediately as a last-minute design change. Still, through the 1968 model year, cooling was barely sufficient for big-block engines with air-conditioning. (What's more, air-conditioning was a popular accessory. Buyers learned that inside the pinched cockpit, the newly introduced flow-through Astro-Ventilation system was completely inadequate.)

This was the laundry list of challenges that styling and engineering faced to get the Corvette completed—it would no longer be called the Sting Ray—for 1967. When Donner delayed the launch another year, it benefited the other engineers faced with meeting U.S. emissions and safety standards.

Soon after introducing the 1968 model to the press, Chevrolet reorganized its division management, disbanding Corvette engineering. Duntov was shuffled into special assignments as a roving jack-of-all-trades. Others were not so lucky, relocated to Chevrolet passenger car responsibilities.

Then the magazine reviews of regular production Corvettes began to appear. Most notable was *Car & Driver,* known for its biting wit. Editor Steve Smith didn't even bother with humor, writing in the December 1967 issue about his plans to road test the 1968 Corvette he had just driven out to Watkins Glen. "But we won't," he wrote. "The car was unfit for a road test. No amount of envious gawking by the spectators could make up for the disappointment we felt at the car's shocking lack of quality control. With less than 2,000 miles on it, the Corvette was falling apart." With a few strokes of the typewriter keys, Smith succeeded in restoring Corvette engineering. Duntov and his group were reassembled, and Duntov was named chief engineer of the Corvette. The new group worked tirelessly, but it often seemed an uphill battle with few thanks offered to also-rans.

The St. Louis factory had produced just three L88s in time for the 1968 Daytona 24 Hours. Actor James Garner bought them and prepped them in California. Those and two others that were not created in St. Louis but from over-the-counter engines installed by the racers all lost to a 1967 L88 coupe entered by Sunray DX. In February, Sunray got its first factory L88 hardtop. Don Yenko prepared that car and freshened up the other two put-together cars for Sebring. At the end of the race on March

(opposite) Goodyear, anxious to try for the most prestigious of endurance races, began investigating ways to enter. Goodyear had sponsored Enzo Ferrari's Grand Prix and Sports Car racing efforts for years, and Ferrari's North American Racing Team, run by Luigi Chinetti, also raced on Goodyears. So Goodyear's international competition director Leo Mehl approached Ferrari's U.S. team.

(lower center) Called Le Mans Blue, Chevrolet named most of its colors after racing circuits for 1969. Others included Monza Red, Riverside Gold, Daytona Yellow, Monaco Orange, and Can-Am (named for the series) White. The "coke bottle" tapered shape of the car appears most clearly in the convertibles.

(lower right) The L71 engine, with its 427 cubic inches and 435 horsepower operated through three Holley two-barrel carburetors. This induction system provided remarkable fuel economy for cruising (the linkage operated only one of the carburetors) until acceleration was needed. Then the engine could easily melt the tires.

(left) RPO P02 with the deluxe wheel covers, also known as the turbine wheels. In details everywhere, Larry Shinoda's Mako Shark lines and shapes appear.

(right) The luggage rack was a dealer-installed option, but the chrome trim on the front fender vertical louvers was an option. For 1969, Chevrolet returned the name "Stingray" to the fenders, though now it was spelled as one word.

(lower left) This aluminum L88, appropriately painted Daytona Yellow, represents an anomaly. Just two were built, and while one of them drag raced extensively, neither participated in road course events where the lighter engine weight would have aided handling as well as performance.

23, Hap Sharp and Dave Morgan, after qualifying third, won GT class in Sunray's factory-built L88, finishing sixth overall. Two Camaros and a Mustang finished ahead of them.

By year-end, in the sweetest of ironies, *Car & Driver* readers voted the 1968 Corvette the "Best All-Around Car in the World," beating out the hyper-exotic, mid-engined $21,900 Lamborghini P400 Miura with its transversely mounted V-12 as the car they wanted most.

THE MANTA RAY

Bill Mitchell, ever in search of a more provocative commuter car, began to get antsy once his Mako Shark II-based production model appeared in showrooms. Advanced design studio artists reinvented Mitchell's car, creating something that looked as though modeling clay had been pulled, stretched, and extruded like taffy into a new sea creature. Mitchell called it the Manta Ray. By 1969, the elongated Mako Shark/Manta Ray was out on the show circuit, stopping viewers in their tracks, hinting at things to come in the future from Bill Mitchell's multimillion dollar playground.

Among racing efforts, one of the best known was that of Floridian Or Costanza, who got his yellow prototype L88 lightweight (one of just four built) in January 1969. Costanza's engine came with the new open chamber cylinder heads and an unusual dual disc clutch. While the public could buy the heads in June, Costanza's clutch was the only known example. Both Costanza and fellow competitor Doug Bergen of Ohio, who took delivery of a black roadster, got them through a Vince Piggins creation, the Buyer's Key Pass Program. This program allowed known racers to get special products far ahead of the general public. While Costanza didn't finish at Sebring, Bergen came in second in GT class behind Tony DeLorenzo, the son of GM's vice-president of public relations, in another L88 sponsored by fiberglass-maker Owens-Corning. In Europe, Henri Greder ran his Corvette constantly, finishing second in the Tour de France, qualifying fastest in the 1,000-kilometer race at Nurburgring and setting the fastest racing laps at Le Mans.

A two-month-long autoworkers strike created a backlog of public orders for the 1969 model, named the Stingray as one word, not two. New division gen-

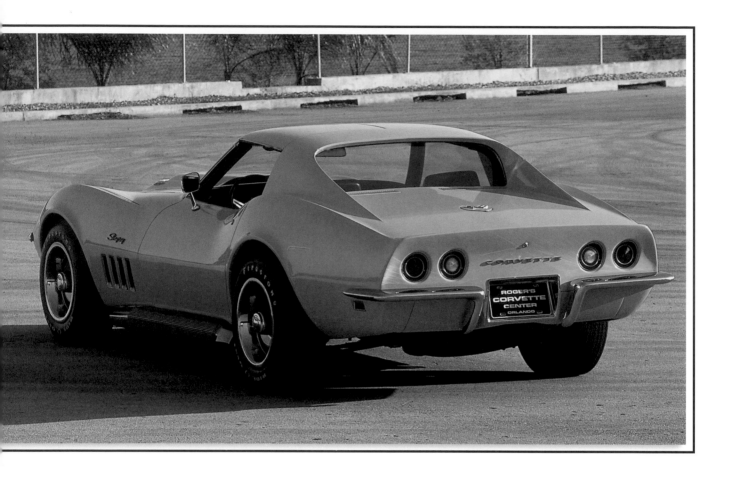

It is a deceptively subtle package at a time when manufacturers often emblazoned their "muscle cars" with wild, often outrageous graphics. This most potent of muscle cars, with more than 500 horsepower under the hood in stock trim, could easily be mistaken for Corvette's most popular 427-cubic-inch 390-horsepower package with the popular side-mounted exhausts.

eral manager John DeLorean, another Pontiac graduate promoted to Chevrolet in February 1969, set back the new model introduction to February 1970 (which partially explained the very high sales number for the 16-month 1969 model year). The corresponding eight-month 1970 season, however, recorded only 17,316 sales: 10,668 coupes versus 6,648 convertibles.

Chevrolet announced late in the 1969 model year an engine option that did not appear until 1970. This small-block, solid-lifter-equipped, LT1 350-cubic inch displacement engine came much closer to Zora Duntov's own hopes for the car. He had never favored the big-block Mark IV engines. Even the aluminum ZL1 was too heavy for his liking, unbalancing a car he had worked so hard to get into shape. Yet every optional engine advanced the high-performance motivation of the muscle car era. When Frederic Donner retired as GM's president and chairman, the board selected former Chevrolet chief Ed Cole, and overnight performance was welcomed. In fact, the concept had become such a battle cry that even the LT1, with its lighter weight but inferior output to the outrageous 427s, could find a slot on an option list. However, product planners, marketing personnel, and advertising executives were aware of public sentiment and a rise in insurance premiums. The LT1 probably produced 370 horsepower, but like the L88s of the previous years, its output was down-rated to keep the safety-conscious less mindful of Chevrolet's products.

At the other end of this spectrum, engine builders stretched out the Mark IV further, increasing stroke from 3.76 to 4.00 inches to 454-cubic-inch displacement. New designations appeared, the LS5 being a 454 with hydraulic valve-lifters that, at a loaf, rated 390 horsepower. An all-aluminum LS7 was listed but never offered; its price hinted at about $3,000 while rating a conservative 460 horsepower. Racers' minds reeled at what an unrestrained LS7 might actually produce. Surely it would exceed 600 horsepower.

To address the embarrassing quality-control problems, DeLorean sent every single Corvette through a water bath with an inspector riding inside looking for something like six dozen possible leaks. After that they ran the car over a two-mile "Belgian Road," exaggerated cobblestone and potholed surfaces, followed by a short stint on a vibration table that flexed and torqued every car repeatedly. DeLorean allowed no failures to leave the plant.

Once Ed Cole arrived in the chairman's suite, his perspective changed slightly. He remained unquestionably a friend of performance, but his concerns assumed broader views and encompassed a greater variety of legitimate voices. On the one hand, the financial climate outside his doors was fairly healthy, if inflationary. America was in a wartime economy, supporting the conflict in Vietnam. The gross national product was up 7 percent, inflation up 5.7 percent, and unemployment at a decade-low 3.5 percent. The average U.S. salary was slightly more than $7,500, enough, by popular rules of thumb, to purchase or finance any product sold in any GM line.

(lower left) It was an astonishingly expensive option. The all-aluminum block L88, RPO ZL1, added $4,718.35 to the base coupe price of $4,781. So few people understood its potential that only two were built for customers, though a white convertible floated around Chevrolet engineering as Zora Duntov's development mule. In all, Chevrolet produced 154 of the engines.

(lower right) With its hood up, the cowl induction system's plumbing comes into focus. The low-pressure area at the base of the windshield draws air into the rear of the hood, sucking it forward to the low-restriction air cleaner in the hood. The foam circle around the carburetor air intake seals the system.

Cole's other concerns lay outside the financial world and outside Detroit. The nation was growing less hospitable toward the automobile. Insurance, premium rates for an unmarried 20-year-old male driving his own high-performance car to work or school reached $1,000 a year in 1968 and nearly $2,000 in 1970. Massachusetts introduced the country's first no-fault automobile insurance. On Earth Day, April 22, 1970, a nationally televised teach-in painted a grim picture of the world's environmental pollution, indicting the automobile as the chief perpetrator.

Cole, who loved and had already saved the Corvette in the mid-1950s, set out again to ensure its continued existence. He began eliminating low sales-volume options. He ordered engineers to rework all GM engines to run on low-lead 91-octane fuel. He told engineering, marketing, advertising, and public relations to use Society of Automotive Engineers (SAE) net measurement standards for engine horsepower output, numbers substantially lower than the gross-horsepower ratings previously published.

The hunkered-down stance improved weight transfer during takeoff. Joel Rosen, who owned Motion Performance, built perhaps 12 of these Phase III monsters with the help of nearby Baldwin Chevrolet and parts manager John Mahler.

Neither Baldwin nor Motion did much with the interior. The single four-barrel 950 cfm Holley hiding below the Mr. Gasket air cleaner helped pump 500 horsepower out of the original L71 engine.

(top opposite) By 1973, the U.S. was in the grips of environmental and insurance concerns. The horsepower race that brought about L71, L88, and the 425-horsepower 454-cubic-inch LS6 engines was quickly strangled. In addition, safety became a major concern; the 1973 models got steel beams in doors to protect against side impact.

(lower opposite) No badges designated this special option. Chevrolet reported producing just eight of these ZR1 "Special Purpose LT1 Engine Packages" in 1971. It sold for $1,010, and in the era of new 454-cubic-inch options pumping out 425 horsepower for $1,221, paying almost as much for much less was a hard sell.

(below) No one can confirm or deny that this ZR stood for Zora's Racer. But the car, with its highly developed 350-cubic-inch engine, is much closer to Duntov's vision of what the car should be, with less weight up front imparting better balance and handling.

The result was a slight improvement in auto insurers' regard for GM. The LT1 dropped its already conservative numbers to a 330 gross horsepower/275 horsepower net rating while the LS5 454 dropped to 365 gross/285 horsepower net. The LS7 never appeared, but an aluminum-head 454 called the LS6, rated at 425 horsepower gross/325 horsepower net, appeared and provided 0–60 miles per hour times of 5.3 seconds. (The LT1 followed quickly behind at 6.0 seconds, and it offered far better ride and handling.) Throughout Duntov's career as Corvette's chief engineer, the compromise between ride and handling had vexed him. He was in charge of building a production car with a top speed of more than 140 miles per hour in a country where that was illegal everywhere except in one state. Yet to Duntov's mind, if any Corvette owner should need to drive at 140 miles per hour, for whatever reason, the car should do so in safety. The dichotomy of Corvette buyers, some who bought the car simply for its looks in front of the country club or nightclub, and others who wanted its 140 miles per hour capability, would frustrate him into his final days with Chevrolet.

Cole wanted to keep racers as Chevy customers. Corvette introduced the ZR1 and ZR2 packages similar to the earlier Z06 options. No radio, power steering, power windows, or air-conditioning was possible with either of these. The ZR2 used the LS6 454-cubic-inch displacement 425-horsepower engine, and only 12 hardy racers bought one. The ZR1 was an even rarer breed, based on the LT1; only eight buyers shared Duntov's vision of what the Stingray could be as a competitor in SCCA's B-Production classes. Yet again it was the L88 that proved to be the racer's final choice. Jerry Thompson and John Mahler won GT (at sixth overall) in Owens-Corning–sponsored cars at

Throughout model year 1973, production couldn't keep up with demand and dealers had to turn away 8,200 orders. So for 1974, Chevrolet General Manager F. James McDonald ordered the St. Louis plant to increase output from eight cars an hour to nine.

The transition of body shape was complete with the 1974 model. Front and rear crash absorbing bumpers made the car look as if it had a one piece body though, as always, it was composed of multiple panels of several materials.

Urethane, crash-resistant materials reached the rear end of the Corvette for 1974. The body-colored membrane covered an aluminum "bumper" fixed onto two telescoping shock absorber-like mounts.

Daytona. At Sebring, Tony DeLorenzo and Dick Lang won GT class with a new distance record, while finishing tenth overall. Production car sales crept back up for 1971, totaling 14,680 coupes and 7,121 convertibles—21,801 in all.

CLEAN AIR STANDARDS

The real impact of the new U.S. clean air standards was clear in the 1972 model year. Cole's cleanup had its effect as well; the LS6, which had sold only 188 copies in 1971, disappeared. (The legendary Muncie heavy-duty M22, close-ratio, four-speed gearbox, known as the "rock crusher" because of its durability and the gear whine, remained available through 1972 but only as part of the ZR1 package.) The only 454-cubic inch displacement engine left was rerated down to 270-horsepower SAE (of which 3,913 sold) and the solid-lifter LT1, listed at 255 horsepower, sold 1,741 copies while the ZR1 package saw its last year on the options lists with only 20 copies delivered.

In late 1971, Or Costanzo sold his yellow L88 to Toye and Dana English, father and son racers, who nicknamed it "Scrappy" because they were constantly scraping off materials to lighten the car. Just before Daytona in February

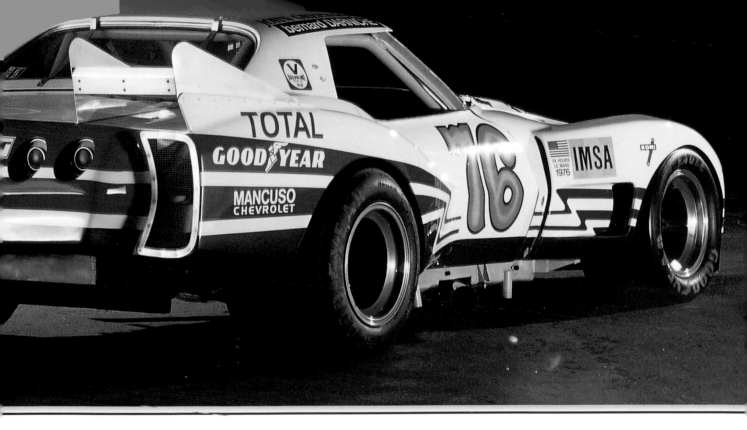

1972, Goodyear Tire approached them, asking them to run on special unmarked tires. Knowing they'd be competing against B. F. Goodrich–sponsored John Greenwood, who'd taken to painting his cars in an American flag stars-and-stripes scheme, the English team painted its car in rebel flag colors. When Dave Heinz and Bob Johnson (the Ohioan) won GT class, finishing eighth overall, Goodyear took out an ad in the *Wall Street Journal* announcing their first victory on racing radial tires. They went on to win GT class again (fourth overall) at Sebring, further thrilling Goodyear.

By early April, Goodyear realized it had a chance at the triple crown of endurance, Daytona, Sebring, and Le Mans. But invitations had already gone out (racers don't "enter" Le Mans; the organizers, L'Automobile Club de l'Ouest, the Automobile Club of the West, invites recognized competitors). Leo Mehl, Goodyear's racing director, had a long business and personal relationship with Enzo Ferrari and Ferrari's U.S. importer, Luigi Chinetti, who operated Ferrari's North American Racing Team (NART). Mehl had personally arranged tires at the last minute for their 275LM in 1963 that went on to take first overall. He knew Chinetti had six cars entered and he called in a favor.

"We want to run a Corvette in one of your spots on our new tires," he said. Chinetti balked. Mehl

These cars were Corvette in inspiration. Greenwood had Protofab build him extensively modified steel tube frames to mount the Corvette suspensions, engines, and drivetrains. He designed his own coil-over shock, twin A-arm rear suspensions to accommodate enormously wide 17 x 15-inch wheels and 28.0 x 17-15 Goodyear racing tires.

Florida's John Greenwood built two legends for endurance racing in 1976. One, the Spirit of Sebring, won that race outright. This car, the Spirit of Le Mans, qualified on the pole and ran well ahead of the pack until its engine failed.

Starting with the all-aluminum ZL1 L88 engine, Greenwood worked his magic, and rumors report he and Dick Smothers had better than 850 horsepower available. He and Smothers routinely saw 210 and 211 miles per hour on the Mulsanne Straight at Le Mans. Greenwood designed his own cross-ram magnesium intake manifolds.

suggested that a call to Enzo informing him that Goodyear had just withdrawn its sponsorship because Chinetti had refused to cooperate with a small favor might not be so well received. Chinetti backed down.

Dave Heinz and Bob Johnson started fourth in the English's four-year-old, once-wrecked former street car. They routinely saw 212 miles per hour along the Mulsanne Straight on their Goodyear radials. When the checkered flag fell, their Ferrari-red NART badge-bedecked L88 had covered 2,414.9 miles, averaging 100.6 miles per hour, good enough to finish fifteenth overall, first in the over five-liter class.

In all, Chevrolet sold 28,004 Corvettes in 1972, with 20,496 coupes delivered against 6,508 convertibles. It was a nice position for a new general manager to inherit, and that's what Jim McDonald found on October 1, 1972. Another Pontiac graduate, he knew the value of building a car in great demand. He increased production, but only slightly, understanding the drawbacks of too great supply.

GOING BACK TO ITS ROOTS

Ironically, as the car began its 21st season, a pendulum had begun to swing back toward the Corvette's roots. Some of this change came on Duntov, Winchell, Mitchell, McDonald, and Estes by federal regulations, rules that required Corvette to forsake its recent high-performance identity if it was to survive.

To satisfy its own standards for 1973, design revised front fender side vents and eliminated the cowl flap that too often left owners without working windshield wipers. Chevrolet discontinued the removable back window, carried over since its introduction in 1968. Engineering fitted radial-ply tires. The cast-aluminum lightweight wheels engineering planned for delivery were never available due to quality problems. Chevy carried over the 454-cubic-inch displacement engine but revised it to provide an additional 5 horsepower, now rated at 275 and renamed the LS4. The small-block, hydraulic-lifter L82 offered 250 horsepower from the 350-cubic-inch displacement cast-iron engine; however, Duntov's chassis engineer Walt Zetye and body engineer Bob Vogelei changed body and engine mounts and applied more sound insulation throughout the body, stiffening the car while decreasing road and mechanical noise.

Model year 1974 marked the end of high performance. It had been under serious attack for some time. In December 1970, Congress passed the Clean Air Bill in the National Environmental Policy Act. This established regulations specifying fuel economy and emissions standards. It set targets the big blocks could never meet, giving auto makers less than six years to develop engines that would emit 90 percent less toxic gases. After 1974, there was no 454 and the small blocks lost true dual exhausts to a two-into-one pipe that ran through a catalytic converter before returning to dual-looking exhausts.

Those who thought that the Clean Air Act meant the end of happiness as they knew it were in for a worse shock. In mid-January 1971, members of an 11-year-old group called the Organization of Petroleum Exporting Countries (OPEC) failed to negotiate polite price increases with 17 western oil companies. In frustration, OPEC members agreed to set prices by themselves, ending the previous courtesy of consulting their customers beforehand. Gas prices in the United States climbed

The box-section steel tube frame swings low through the cockpit, making driver changes quick and easy. Ear protection was essential with the 850-horsepower engine exhaust exiting just below the doors through 4-inch pipes. Greenwood preparation was meticulous.

steadily. In mid–March 1974, OPEC, now 13 members strong, settled with its western customers, and crude oil that had sold for $2.11 per barrel in January 1971 went to $14.08 38 months later. Lines formed at gas stations and fuel economy suddenly made a difference. The White House ordered a nationwide 55 mile per hour "energy conservation" speed limit.

Despite all this, Chevrolet sold 30,460 Corvettes in 1973, 25,521 coupes and 4,943 convertibles, with many more buyers preferring the T-topped cars to pure open air motoring. Barely a third purchased an optional engine, yet nearly two-thirds ordered the automatic. The nature of Corvette buyers was changing, and the car kept pace. For 1974, the trend away from convertibles continued. Some 32,028 coupes sold, while only 5,474 convertibles were delivered. Again, however, it set new production and sales records with 37,502 cars sold.

The RPO V54 luggage rack was designed to carry the T-top panels. Some 16,860 buyers paid $73 for the rack, which allowed them to make full use of the luggage area even when the tops were off.

THE L82 BITES THE DUST

On New Year's Day 1975, Zora Arkus-Duntov, Corvette's most devoted engineer (and its chief engineer since December 1967), retired. He was replaced by his heir apparent, Dave McLellan, a GM engineer since 1959. Model year 1975 marked the end of several other Corvette mainstays as well. Chevrolet could no longer offer the L82 engine because of its excessive emissions. James McDonald moved out as general manager and was replaced in December 1974 by Robert Lund, who came from Cadillac but who earlier had been sales manager at Chevrolet. Convertible sales dwindled to only 4,629 cars, less than one-eighth of another record total production of 38,469 cars. Management killed the open cars. This was not just a production decision based on poor showroom performance, but it was also the result of outside pressures. An increasingly intrusive federal government made loud noises about convertible roll-over safety as early as 1970. Congressional hearings and investigations led Detroit carmakers to expect a governmental mandate. That it was no longer an economically viable product made the decision easier, even though the legislation never appeared.

The new fastback introduced in 1978—though definitely not a hatchback—featured styling that nearly doubled rear storage capacity, making the car very useful for long road trips. The pace car replica package included removable glass roof panels and special leather seats.

GM's Corporate Average Fleet Economy requirements limited the 350-cubic-inch displacement L48 base engine to 185 horsepower (except in California where its own emissions standards pulled another 10 horsepower from the engine). The optional L82 offered 220 horsepower. Total production reached 46,776 cars, including the B2Z optional Silver Anniversary and the replica Indy 500 Pace Car, one produced for each Chevrolet dealer.

The 1979 models gained in horsepower due to across-the-board adoption of the twin-snorkel air cleaner from the L82, ingesting cooler outside air. This, plus adoption of the L82's lower back-pressure mufflers, gave the base L48 a 10-horsepower boost to 195 in all 50 states. The L82 also gained a 5 to 225 horsepower boost. Thinner, lighter seats from the pace car were standard for all Corvettes in 1979. The Indy pace car spoilers became a $265 option (D80) for all Corvettes. Base price settled in at $10,220.23, and Chevrolet set a new production record of 53,807 cars. This level of output made GM corporate management question the need to change something that was doing just fine.

Corvette had been enormously profitable for several years. Few people remained in the division who would

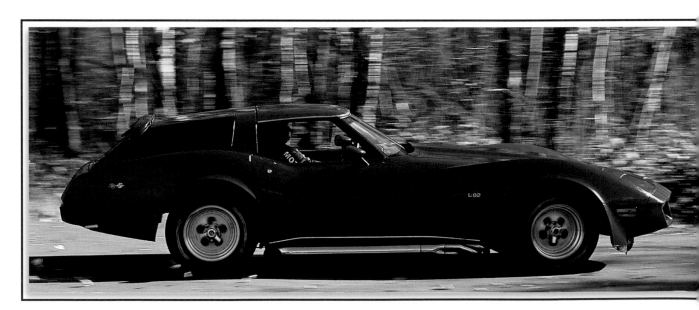

It's a distinctive appearance and clearly an acquired taste. John Greenwood produced the first two or three of these Sport Wagons, then turned the operation over to Corvette specialist American Custom Industries in Sylvania, Ohio, who completed perhaps another ten.

The gull-wing design of the rotary engine concept Corvette never made it into production, although this concept was also used in the 1977 Aerovette show car. All photos on this page 2002 General Motors Corporation. Used with permission of GM Media Archives.

buck the status quo. After Duntov left Chevrolet in January, Ed Cole soon followed him out the door, chased by Bill Mitchell, who retired in 1978. Chevrolet's newly named director of engineering, Lloyd Reuss, had no desire to make waves. David McLellan, Duntov's successor, resonated contentment, pronouncing his preference for front-engined Corvettes.

In 1980, buyers got cars with a newly revised, lower drag nose with a standard front chin spoiler. Between this more aerodynamically friendly front end and something like 250 pounds of weight removed from the car, 1980s cars weighed 3,179 pounds, a welcome improvement. One change inside the car was highly unwelcome. Federal standards that lowered national speed limits to 55 miles per hour required all speedometers to provide calibration no higher than 85 miles per hour no matter what the actual top speed of the car might be. In California, only the base 305-cubic-inch displacement engine would pass the state's stringent emissions requirements, so buyers in the Golden State had to be content with this lower-performance engine. Suggested retail price of the base Corvette rose by nearly $3,000, a result of countless federal safety and emissions requirements, to $13,140.24. Still, 40,614 buyers were undeterred by these facts and forked over the down payment or the first lease payment in a form of car financing that had steadily gained in popularity since the mid-1970s.

Improvements continued in fairly undramatic fashion in 1981 and 1982. The 49-state 350 was certified in California, but optional engines disappeared; 190 horsepower was all any buyer could get. Nationwide, under the hood, a new Computer Command Control (CCC) module managed fuel and air mixture in the carburetor and ignition timing to

The rear of the gull-wing followed the angled rear of the Mako Shark II.

The rotary Corvette explored mid-engine mounting for the first time.

(above) Everyone knows Chevrolet did not build a convertible Corvette between model years 1976 and 1986, but if you wanted one, American Custom Industries had just the thing for you. It was even engineered by none other than Zora Duntov. Even better, at Duntov's insistence, it was turbocharged.

(right) Exterior and interior colors respect the 1953 original, another homage to Corvette's history from ACI president Bob Schuller. But Schuller and Duntov moved into the 80s with digital readout instruments, an in-dash computerized telephone and rear stowage cooler. In the end, ACI sold fewer than 100 of these cars.

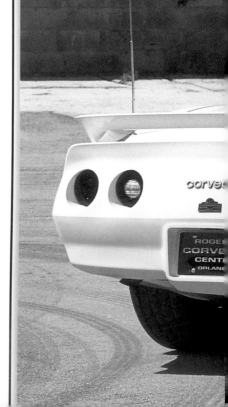

(right) The new nose and tail pieces, first introduced with the 1980 production models, incorporated fully integrated spoilers. These reduced air drag considerably, improved mileage slightly, and increased radiator air flow by 50 percent.

produce optimum exhaust emission performance and fuel economy, though the latter was a distant second in importance. This system first appeared in 1980 on California only 305s.

Complaints continued from magazine reviews and buyers alike about the car's fit and finish. Quality control still seemed to be elusive for Chevrolet's most expensive, most visible product. Finally, to control that problem, production began at a new high-tech assembly plant in Bowling Green, Kentucky, on June 1, 1981. Before GM acquired this plant, it had been Chrysler's air-temp division air-condition factory. Corvette assembly overlapped at the old St. Louis facility until model-year production ended on August 1. Bowling Green's new equipment offered not only tighter assembly standards but also new paint. Enamel base colors finished with clear topcoats came from Kentucky, while the remaining St. Louis cars finished up with the old standard lacquer.

Prices jumped another $3,100 as the standard car reached $16,258.52, about $1,660 more than Cadillac's El Dorado. The basic Corvette, however, was highly civilized, and the only remaining options just gilded the lily. Chevrolet sold 40,606 in all.

The existing Corvette body first appeared in 1968, assembled on a chassis that showed up underneath the 1963 Sting Rays. By 1982, Chevrolet certainly had paid off development and improvement costs. Still, mating Alfred Sloan's dictum to make last year's buyer dissatisfied to Ed Cole's philosophy of making a lame duck appealing, Chevrolet chose to make important introductions. Throttle-body fuel injection, which reappeared in a form called "Cross Fire Injection," bumped engine output to 200 horsepower for all 50 states. Engineering replaced the existing three-speed Turbo-Hydra-Matic with a new four-speed overdrive automatic transmission.

Chevrolet offered the final "Shark" for 1982, not only as a well-equipped base model at $18,290.07, but also as a special order Collector Edition. Product planners had watched sales of the 25th Anniversary model and the Indy Pace Car replica and produced a special exterior paint and interior trim option to honor the end of the longest production run and celebrate 30 years of Corvettes. Total production for 1982 was 25,407, anticlimactic after 15 years of production. Still, in 15 years Chevrolet sold more than half a million Sharks, 542,861 in all.

This was all the more remarkable considering the economy. Between 1973 and 1983, the average American salary topped $15,750 as inflation kept up its relentless 10 to 13.5 percent rate. In 1980, this took the prime rate up to 21 percent, making auto loans almost unaffordable at 24 percent. In 1981, GM announced its first loss since 1921, coming up $763 million short for the year. This forced the

It marked the end of the era. The 1982 model body began in 1968, and its chassis first appeared with the 1963 Sting Ray. Corvette enthusiasts expected an all-new car in 1983, so sales of this model year were barely half of those in 1981—25,407 compared to 40,606.

Striving for simplicity between two factories and 50 states, Chevrolet offered only one engine. This 190-horsepower 350-cubic-inch V-8 was all you could get in 1981. The four-speed manual was available nationwide but barely 10 percent of buyers wanted it.

The Cross Fire Injection, twin throttle-body fuel injection (TBI) system was shared by both Corvette and Camaro. The 350-cubic-inch small block was Corvette's first fuel-injected engine since 1965 and developed 200 horsepower.

The TBI engine and new transmission made for the best possible driving combination of performance and fuel economy. The 1982 models even had a cold-air induction system for full-throttle acceleration. The base car retailed for $18,290.07.

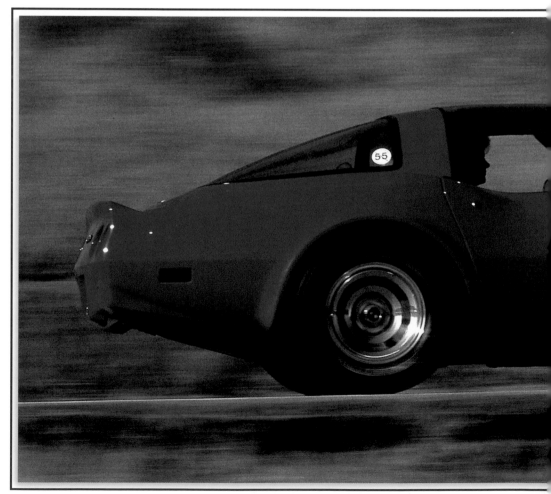

board to delay new projects a year or simply cancel them outright. Into this uninviting economy, former Chevrolet general manager John DeLorean introduced his stainless-steel, mid-engined, Irish-built sports car, priced at $25,000. His knowledge of manufacturing steel-bodied automobiles outside the United States would go for nothing, and his car would become a cult footnote once he was arrested for cocaine possession. In 1982, inflation dropped to 6 percent, but this hardly comforted the 9.7 percent of the population that was unemployed when the Shark approached the end of its scheduled life.

1983-1989

CHAPTER NINE

BETTERING THE BREED FOR THE ROAD AND THE TRACK

here was no 1983 Corvette. At least none were intended for the public. Chevrolet assembled 70 "engineering" cars and probably more than one has slipped out into private hands. But solid reasons led the company to skip the year completely. Historians can trace the decision to skip an entire production year as far back as 1977, when Chevrolet division first imagined the next model, the fourth-generation Corvette.

In 1977, Irwin W. Rybicki became GM's vice president of design when Bill Mitchell retired. Rybicki was very different from Mitchell; he was a conservative, modest man who had directed the Buick-Oldsmobile-Cadillac studios through countless folded-edge designs that sold cars like mad. Rybicki inherited Mitchell's legacy as well as his staff. Mitchell had nurtured Jerry Palmer, who had done Corvette show cars for him in 1969. Palmer began affecting the production cars with the 1973 model. In 1974, Mitchell named him chief designer of Chevrolet Studio 3, the home of the Corvette and Camaro, a job with high visibility and considerable influence.

Over in engineering, Dave McLellan was a veteran of similar training when he was Duntov's protégé. McLellan found himself in a similar position to Palmer in affecting what any new Corvette would become. Both Palmer and McLellan, who had worked well together on the second-generation Camaro in production from mid-1970 through 1980, learned the GM board had decided to replace the long-running and now highly profitable current model (it generated more than $100 million annually). The board author-ized a completely new model for 1983 to celebrate the car's 30th anniversary. Significantly, this would be the first Corvette designed, *(previous pages) The 1984 had the flattest-angle windshield to date at 64 degrees. The roof also divided into an openable hatchback—the largest compound surface glass formed until that time—and a removable glass roof panel over the seats.*

Chevrolet carried over the throttle-body, cross-ram induction V-8 introduced with the 1982 Shark, with a few improvements and modifications. It looked perfect under Cafaro's clamshell hood.

No production 1983 models were sold, but the 1984 went on sale in February 1983. 2002 General Motors Corporation. Used with permission of GM Media Archives.

developed, and sold without any link to Harley Earl and Ed Cole's 1953 model because Palmer and McLellan joined Chevrolet during the Mitchell/Duntov Sting Ray years.

Ideas emerged quickly. Experiments with Wankel's rotary engines had been disappointing, but engineering and design created the AeroVette with a transversely mounted 400-cubic-inch displacement reciprocating V-8 that restored promise for a new midengine configuration. GM had introduced Chevrolet's Citation X-11 and Pontiac's Phoenix, the X-body cars with transverse V-6 engines driving front axles. McLellan knew this technology was available, but Corvette's 205 horsepower was double what Citation/Phoenix 90- to 110-horsepower drivetrains could handle. It meant instant failure or long, costly development work. But these questions paled in contrast to a government challenge. Federal regulators proposed a gas-guzzler tax punishing fuel inefficiency. GM's fleet average for 1983 had to be 19 miles per gallon, no matter what performance the engineers developed for their Corvette. GM's board would never allow any of *their* cars to suffer that tax.

(opposite) Under the hood, production C4 featured a few subtle changes from this 1983 pilot prototype. 2002 General Motors Corporation. Used with permission of GM Media Archives.

While John DeLorean had been Chevrolet general manager, he had proposed downsizing the Corvette onto the smaller Camaro/Firebird F-body platform. Corvette could share chassis and development expenses, he argued. Palmer and McLellan both vigorously fought the idea because DeLorean's concept seemed less interested in improving the Corvette than increasing its profit.

Among engineering and design staffs, the debates continued over front-engine versus midplacement. When cast-iron big blocks skewed weight balance heavily to the front, mid engine placement provided better handling but sacrificed load carrying ability. Surveys told marketing that midengine high-performance cars often were the second or third cars in wealthy families. Corvette buyers often had only one car to carry groceries, golf clubs, or vacation luggage.

Heritage was on everyone's mind when McLellan and Palmer started their staffs brainstorming and sketching ideas. Marketing worried that Corvette buyers, generally traditionalists, would balk at anything radically different. The board, still smarting over the entire rear-engine Corvair adventure, had quietly dragged its feet against Zora Duntov's relentless arguments for a midengined Corvette. They knew he would retire in 1975. While he had championed the necessity of 50/50 weight balance, the board knew he had met that target on front-engine models. Despite Duntov's long-held objective of creating a sports car he could proudly drive in Europe, the Corvette was and always would be

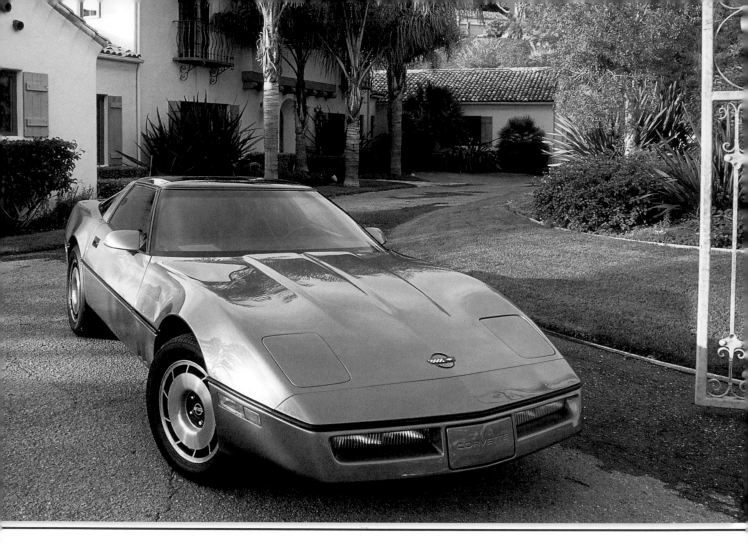

a car for American roads and drivers. What's more, McLellan favored the traditional front-engine rear-drive Corvette.

Outside support arrived unexpectedly. Porsche introduced its own Corvette, designed by a former Corvette stylist Tony Lapine, who had created Bill Mitchell's Corvette SS racing car in Studio X. After his promotion to GM's Opel operation in Russelsheim, Germany, Lapine left GM in 1969 to work for Porsche. In 1974, Porsche management feared U.S. regulations might legislate against the handling characteristics of their 911 model. They assigned design chief Lapine to create their first front-engined sports car, the V-8 Type 928. Porsche introduced the car in Germany in the fall of 1977. It was powerful, fast, sleek, and safe, and its arrival encouraged the configuration of the next Corvette.

HIGH-PERFORMANCE TIRES

When Dave McLellan sought performance targets for the 1983 Corvette, everyone agreed they wanted the new model to be the best-handling sports car in the world. To McLellan, that dictated fat low-profile tires on 10-inch-wide wheels. From the time of the Grand Sports, Corvettes introduced the highest performance tires. Furthermore, McLellan accepted Duntov's dictum that Corvette's suspension must remain compliant at full speed over uneven roads. This required vast suspension travel, but it ensured that no driver would be thrown out of control at top speed because the suspension bottomed out.

Design chief Jerry Palmer wanted 16-inch wheels for styling purposes. When McLellan's engineers set the first specifications on paper, they established minimum ground clearance at 5.25 inches, up 0.25 inches from the 1968 to 1982 car. They placed four squat tires at the corners. From there the car's design began, capitalizing on GM's relationship with Goodyear Tire & Rubber. Engineering wanted tires capable of 140 to 145 mile per hour speeds. Yet they also demanded crisp handling, quiet ride, efficient water shedding, an interesting appearance, and at least 10,000-mile tread life even with enthusiastic use. Goodyear based its efforts on its Formula One rain tire development. It developed the VR50 "Gatorback," which met Corvette's parameters with room to spare.

Room to spare was the consideration the tires missed. Fat front tires needed space to clear engine and suspension pieces under full-lock turning. Fitting the Gatorbacks inside the bodywork required McLellan and Palmer to widen the car by 2 inches over the existing model. (Even so, McLellan had to let go of his 10-inch wheel width target, settling for 8.5 inches when wider wheels stuck out beyond the new body.)

Owner surveys had told Chevrolet that the Corvette's Coke-bottle shape pinched shoulder room and created a claustrophobic cockpit. Widening the car helped remedy that. Still, McLellan and Palmer struggled to resolve other concerns. Safety, styling, and engineering improvements over 25 years had added weight and increased size, yet GM's board now ordered divisions to downsize each

(lower left) The large pad facing the passenger seat was part of a passive restraint system mandated by the federal government. It was nicknamed the "breadloaf."

(lower right) Digital readouts and liquid crystal displays filled the instrument panel. "Old-fashioned" analog gauges were not even available, a fact that frustrated magazine reviewers but never seemed to bother buyers.

(above) While the factory quoted 205-horsepower output from the 350-cubic-inch engine, racers knew they had closer to 350 horsepower under competition tune.

In order to lessen factory time spent finishing fiberglass panels, designers created a car body with all the body panel seams hidden under a rub molding that went around the entire car. The line also seemed to stretch the car's length visually.

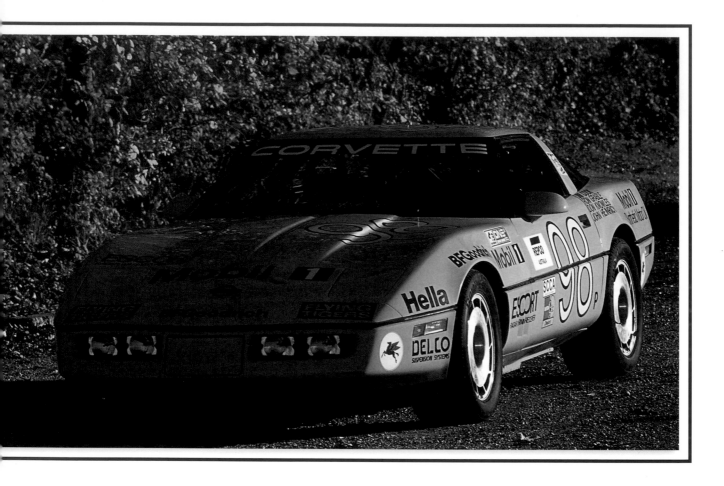

While Dick Guldstrand drove this one only briefly, the California influence extended not only to the Showroom Stock racing series but to the car itself. Its superb rear suspension was developed from existing successful Guldstrand Corvette racers.

(right) Guldstrand-Morrison-Cook racing won the SSGT championship with Corvette aces such as Ron Grable, John Heinricy, and Don Knowles at the wheel. The power, reliability, and antilock brake system frustrated the Porsche factory greatly.

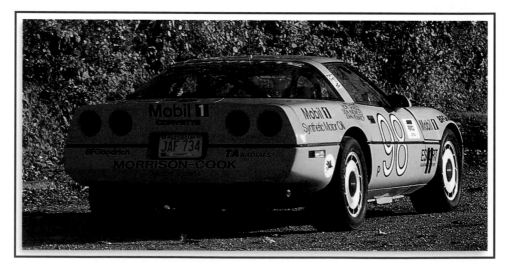

vehicle, yanking away the tightrope's safety net. The Corvette design team forged ahead and filled in the long-standing pinched waist. This added 6.5 inches to interior shoulder room.

Because shoulders are wider than waists, the designers adopted the backbone idea from Lotus car innovator Colin Chapman. He had introduced this central spine into his tiny fiberglass Elan model in 1963. This provided structural rigidity, crucial for a sports car that might go racing. McLellan's engineers widened their center tunnel enough to feed not only the driveshaft but also the exhaust, catalytic converter, plumbing, and wiring between the seats now instead of below them. Maintaining their minimum ground clearance, they still lowered the seating floor 2 inches, to the bottom of the chassis. This increased headroom yet lowered the roofline an inch. This in turn reduced frontal area, decreasing aerodynamic drag and improving fuel economy. With more efficient packaging of the mechanical necessities, McLellan and Palmer shortened overall length 8.4 inches from the existing model. It was wider, yes, but it was lower, shorter, and more fuel-efficient.

By early spring 1979, McLellan's engineering staff had a few development mules out testing. Palmer's Studio 3 design staff began creating the new car's look. Randy Wittine, called "Mr. Corvette" because of some 15 years of involvement with the car, worked alongside a new kid on the block, John Cafaro. Cafaro, the studio's youngest designer since Peter Brock, produced a rendering of the new car that incorporated an XK-E Jaguar-type hood that revealed the engine, front tires, suspension, and chassis. The hood opened like a clamshell, split along a seam that ran horizontally around the entire car, a styling element they adopted from Ferrari's midengined 308GTB. In this one drawing, Cafaro created two of the signature styling features. With this mammoth hood, Palmer saw an opportunity to make the engine and mechanical parts appear integrated. McLellan agreed and so both staffs coordinated engine castings, forged suspension pieces, and even spark plug wires for appearance as well as function, and they color coordinated pieces to add visual impact. Cafaro's clamshell seam simplified both molding and joining the fiberglass body panels. His design began to make possible tighter quality control in fit and finish.

Cafaro continued developing his body design. Roger Hughet, Palmer's chief assistant, worked with

With a 350-horsepower engine backbone frame, and Guldstrand-derived rear suspension, the car proved an unbeatable racer.

Charles Toner and his aerodynamics engineers to improve the body shape in wind tunnels at speeds up to 140 miles per hour. These confirmed that Cafaro's chin spoiler shoveled up enough ground-level air to reach the radiator behind his grille-less front end. High-speed experiments in the wind tunnels led to reintroducing fender-side "gills," the air extractor slots that vented the air-pressure buildup that popped hoods on Duntov's Grand Sports at speed.

As early as 1978, Palmer's interior designers began to mate the instrument panel and interior seating to the sleek, new exterior. The interior staff had other considerations to worry about, however. One was a cluster of federal regulations, Motor Vehicle Safety Standard (MVSS) 208, for driver and passenger safety in a front-end collision. The driver had the collapsible steering column in the event of a head-on crash; the passenger got a padded structure nicknamed the "breadloaf" because of its looks. Congress introduced MVSS 208 in 1977 to go into effect for model year 1982. It became a political issue, postponed eventually for 1985 introduction. Then in October 1981, President Reagan

Sports Car Club of America rules for the Showroom Stock Grand Touring class required a full roll cage and fire-suppression systems in the cockpit. Otherwise the interior had to remain as it came from the dealer.

revoked it altogether, but this was too late for designers to scrap it. The breadloaf was part of the car, and buyers found it where a glove box would have been.

Chevrolet carried over the throttle-body, cross-ram induction V-8 introduced with the 1982 model year Shark, adding improvements to engine management, a serpentine belt accessory drive, and an electric cooling fan in front of the radiator. It looked perfect under Cafaro's hood.

McLellan's engineers mated the engine to their innovative 4+3-speed manual transmission, a clever variation on the standard Warner Division gearbox re-engineered by Doug Nash. Coupled to the Delco Electronic Control Module (ECM), the Nash transmission provided what were essentially short shifts in second, third, and fourth gears. It was something like an automatic manual transmission, configured specifically to improve mileage for the EPA test. (When introduced, the car's window sticker stated 16 miles per gallon city mileage, 28 highway. The EPA balanced these figures 55/45 percent to arrive at Corvette's 19.8 miles per gallon, exceeding GM's 1984 CAFE number by 0.3 miles per gallon.) Engineering replaced the earlier heavy iron Delco-Moraine disc brakes with Australian Repco aluminum-and-iron versions, saving 70 pounds between the four brakes.

McLellan's people improved the suspension as well. They set out to accomplish 1.0 g of lateral-acceleration cornering power. Their chassis innovations, suspension configuration changes, and Goodyear's Gatorback tires made it possible.

The basic design of the C4 chassis allowed for a convertible version, which Chevrolet introduced during the second year of C4 production. 2002 General Motors Corporation. Used with permission of GM Media Archives.

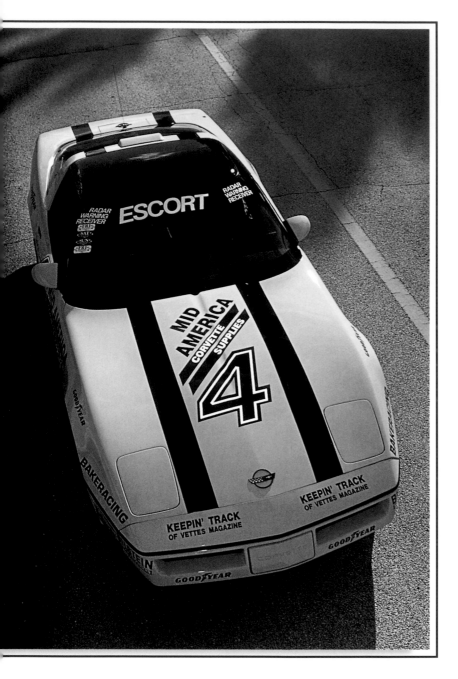

Engineering constructed the chassis from thin sheets of high-strength, low-alloy (HSLA) steel, spot welded into boxes and other shapes to support front and rear suspension, engine, differential, roof, doors, and windshield. Previous Corvette frames involved two separate elements, one chassis/frame and the other a "birdcage" of much smaller members fitted above the chassis/frame to support the body. With the new car, and unlike most other unit-frame cars where the body is a crucial structural element of the car, the fiberglass surface panels merely hid the frame and running gear. Past ladder frames had required cross members to tie outer frame rails together and add structural rigidity to the car, but engineers accomplished this with a single bolted-in cross member used as a front-engine support. The entire frame weighed just 351 pounds, yet it was rigid enough to allow a completely removable roof center section that no longer required the T-roof support.

Onto this chassis, suspension engineers hung all-aluminum forged suspension pieces. The independent rear suspension used a five-link system instead of the previous model's three links. This fixed the rear axle more positively in place, eliminating its tendency to steer the car from the back in certain suspension load-unload transitions. They mounted fiberglass leaf-type springs transversely on both front and rear suspensions. Fiberglass was not only lighter, but it was more resilient and it wouldn't sag after millions of jounce and rebound cycles. Engineers

It wasn't an outright champion in 1985, but Kim Baker's racer won the SSGT crown in 1986 and 1987. Chevrolet provided enormous technical assistance, but some of his most generous help came from Goodyear Tire & Rubber.

devised another use for the transverse springs, as antisway bars. It worked so well that engineers greatly decreased the diameter of the supplemental antisway bar.

McLellan's engineers raced against time and their perfectionists' desire to get everything right. Magazine stories told consumers a completely new Corvette was coming, and sales of the 1982 model fell off so dramatically that assembly-line engineers began dismantling the production line at Bowling Green in anticipation of the model changeover.

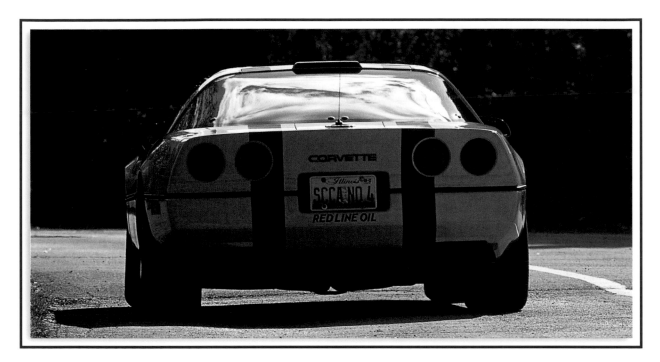

The board faced a dilemma. Engineering hadn't finished with the car. Did engineering and GM release a car that was not ready for production? Two other factors influenced the verdict. If GM waited until early spring, it ensured that Chevrolet had the first 1984 model available rather than the last 1983. It also meant Chevrolet would introduce the first automobile that met 1984 emissions and barrier impact standards. The board slowed engineers enough to conquer the 1984 regulations completely (thereby avoiding re-engineering a hastily completed car). Production fired up on January 3, 1983, and each of the cars bore a vehicle identification number (VIN) identifying it as a 1984 car (although there are reports that 11 cars appeared with 1983 VIN numbers as well).

This made the 1984 model year 17 months long. When it ended and GM completed count, 51,547 buyers drove Corvettes home. (GM kept the first 70 cars or so as continuing engineering development vehicles.) Two years after its introduction, Chevrolet's chief engineer Don Runkle talked to *Road & Track*'s John Lamm about the 1984 and 1985 cars.

"We more or less moved the Corvette away from the classic Corvette customer," Runkle said. "It was deliberate

Midway through 1985, Goodyear began offering $50,000 contingency purses to the SSGT winner. Kim Baker and his team won at Lime Rock and again at Mid-Ohio. $100,000 allowed him to get very serious about racing Corvettes.

The roll cage and window webbing are a giveaway that this interior belongs to an SSGT racer. The nozzle at the lower right belongs to the fire extinguisher required by SCCA rules.

With its 205 net horsepower, the Corvette was a bit below some of the other entries such as Nissan's 300ZX. But the chassis, suspension, and absolutely superior braking brought the car more wins than any other in its class.

The production-class rules dictate keeping a stock body. Hood scoops to accommodate engine modifications are permitted, and the roof "rails," the vertical air managers, are required. The parachute is essential.

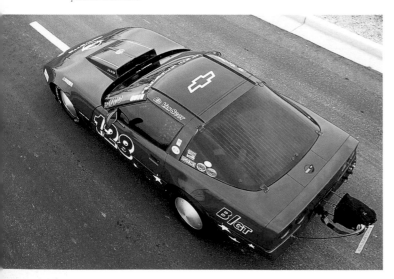

on our part, primarily because we wanted to make a technical statement with it, but we couldn't figure out how to keep it where it was price-wise and also make that statement.

"We didn't have to make the car cost as much as it does. But if we hadn't put all those features (aluminum front suspension arms, plastic springs, tuned port injection, etc.) into it, the car wouldn't be as good as it is right now. . . . I don't hear many people making fun of the Corvette anymore."

Racers took the car seriously too. As Gregory von Dare wrote in his book *Corvette Racers,* "In the 1980s, ABS brakes allowed Showroom Stock Corvettes to go at racing speeds in the rain where other fine cars such as the Porsche 944 Turbos were spinning all over the track." The factory openly helped teams like Morrison Motorsports, Bakeracing, Rippie Racing, and Powell Motorsports further the development of their racing cars that in turn fed back to the factory important wear and durability information about its chassis, drivetrain, and tires. Racetracks became two-way streets for information and cooperation, benefiting engineers, drivers, and enthusiasts.

"Even though Corvettes were able to beat every car that challenged them in the SCCA's Showroom Stock series," von Dare continued, "they still had to race each other. That's where the fun started."

The "fun" began outside Parkman, Ohio, at an older racetrack called Nelson Ledges, only 100 miles from Detroit. In 1979, the track staged its first 24-hour endurance race for showroom stock cars. They drew 19 entries but much more interest. Each year the entry list grew, and when Chevrolet brought out its new Camaro and Porsche had its first 944 in 1983, the organizers found they had to create a "prototype" class. Porsche's front suspensions proved too fragile for Nelson's city street-like surface. Then the new Corvettes arrived in 1984 and stunned their racing world. They won 19 races in 19 starts. For four years straight, they took every race in the series run first as the Playboy Challenge, then as SCCA Showroom Stock Grand Touring, and finally as the Escort GT Endurance series. Drivers in lesser cars recalled nursing their ailing entries into corners in

If speed gets your attention, then this car should grab you. August 2001: 223.051 miles per hour on the salt flats at Bonneville, Utah. It took Ed and Linda Van Scoy four years to crack the 220 miles per hour barrier.

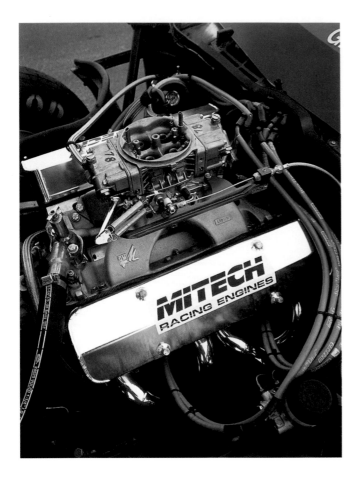

Ed and Linda Van Scoy had Mike LeFevers of Mitech build their engine. LeFevers gave them a 407-cubic-inch dry-sump V-8 that develops 750 horsepower (and 625 foot-pounds of torque). LeFevers linked it to the six-speed ZF transmission.

the rain, watching a Corvette storm past them implausibly fast, its driver adjusting the radio or the heater, then using the ABS to haul the car through the turn. Kim Baker, owner and co-driver of his yellow #4 Bakeracing Corvette, won the series in 1985 and 1986, and von Dare reported that Porsche bought Corvettes to take apart and study. At the end of 1987, Porsche and others hinted that they might withdraw if the SCCA didn't level the field. The SCCA banned Corvettes from its series beginning in 1988, but Corvette racers were not done.

THE 1985 PRODUCTION CARS

For 1985 production cars, Dave McLellan's engineers addressed complaints about ride harshness, adjusting shock valving on both the base shocks and the Z-51 Bilstein gas shocks and spring rates in the fiberglass transverse leaves. The rear wheels grew to 9.5-inch widths during the 1984 production run; the fronts were upsized as well for 1985.

Under the hood, Chevrolet continued meeting EPA numbers while improving performance. Fuel injection, Tuned Port Injection, replaced Cross Fire Throttle Body injection. The result was engine output up to 230 horsepower, a 0–60 mile per hour time of 6.6 seconds, and top speed nearer the magic 150 miles per hour. Production for the 1985 model year slipped relative to the long 1984 numbers, but the second year of C4 was a 12-month year, and the total reflected more accurately the continuing interest in the car. In all, 39,729 cars sold.

Model year 1986 brought patient enthusiasts a convertible Corvette near the middle of the year. While the chassis had easily accommodated the "Targa" type removable roof, the open car required substantial reinforcement. Engineers enlarged the bolt-in cross member ahead of the engine and the braces connecting that piece to the frame rails. In addition, they fitted a large X-brace below the passenger compartment and added two more crosspieces behind the seats. Convertible buyers could not get the stiff Z51 suspension, but the 9.5-inch wheels were part of the convertible's own dedicated Z52 suspension. Chevrolet introduced the convertible in bright yellow Indianapolis Pace Car replica trim, at a $4,000 premium over the coupes. Base convertible price was $32,507, while the base coupes retailed at $28,502. These "base" cars were nearly fully equipped, and prices reflected the addition of a number of mandatory options. One new standard item was an intelligent ignition key, the PASS-key with an identification sensor, part of an overall Vehicle Anti-Theft System (VATS). Any other key fit into the ignition except for the one coded to the car would fail to start, disabling the

Competing in Bonneville's production class requires a "non-gutted" interior, and of course, a full roll cage. Running with stock interior pieces adds considerable weight, but the rules are intended to create a "true stock" automobile for racing purposes.

Leather sport seats were a $1,025 option that 13,372 buyers selected. Chevrolet produced 7,319 convertibles, selling at a $5,005 premium over sport coupes, $32,032 compared to $27,027.

ignition for any attempt for three minutes. Performance improved once again with Z51-equipped coupes turning 0–60 in 5.8 seconds and registering top speeds of 154. The convertibles were good for nearly 140 miles per hour with the top down, aided in small part by new aluminum cylinder heads made standard for all production body styles when the convertibles appeared. For the 1986 model year, Chevrolet produced 7,315 convertibles and 27,794 coupes.

For 1987, engineering boosted the engine another 10 horsepower to 240 through, among other changes, roller-bearing hydraulic valve-lifters that lessened power lost to friction. In addition, they redesigned the heads to improve burn efficiency by centering the spark plugs in the combustion chamber. Engineering fitted the same stiffening measures used on 1986 convertibles to the 1987 coupes. Chevrolet continued to offer the Z51 suspension on the coupe (with manual transmissions), but the convertible carried over its own Z52 version. The convertible, in magazines tests, scored an impressive 0.87-gram lateral acceleration (the Z51 pulled 0.91 around the 216-feet-diameter circle).

Convertible sales increased to 10,625 (at $33,647), while coupes slipped to 20,007. This was a total of 30,632, down nearly 5,000 cars from 1986.

For 1988, engineers provided a new less-restrictive exhaust system, good for 5 horsepower, taking the performance axle–equipped engine to 245 horsepower. They fitted lower profile Goodyear Z-rated P255/50ZR-16 tires (to allow speeds above 149 miles per hour) on 16-inch "Cuisinart" wheels, nick-named because they looked like the food processor blades. An optional Z51 (for coupes only) and Z52 Performance Handling Package offered 12-slot "Cuisinart" 17 x 9.5-inch wheels with Goodyear 275/40ZR-17 tires. Engineering changed front disc-brake calipers to dual-piston versions that they wrapped around thicker rotors for more braking power and better brake cooling. They also increased rear-suspension rebound travel and reconfigured front-suspension geometry to improve directional control in severe braking conditions.

Because 1988 was the 35th anniversary, design and product planners created a commemorative edition of 2,000 coupes painted white with a white leather interior. Production for 1988 dipped despite the car's measurable improvements, and Chevrolet sold only 7,407 convertibles and barely twice that many coupes, 15,382, for a total of only 22,789 cars. The coupe base price crept up to $29,955, while the convertible sat at $35,295.

Chevrolet had scheduled the much-anticipated ZR-1 for 1989, but it wasn't quite ready so the division introduced two elements of the long-rumored car. One was its six-speed manual transmission, built

(below) Designer John Cafaro's "clamshell" hood represents a lot of real estate when it's lifted. But the access it provided to the entire front end was unlike anything else in the industry at the time.

(opposite bottom) Chevrolet brought back the Corvette convertible after a ten–model year absence. Because the 1986 model was the Indy 500 Pace Car, all the convertibles were designated as replicas and dealers received decal sets.

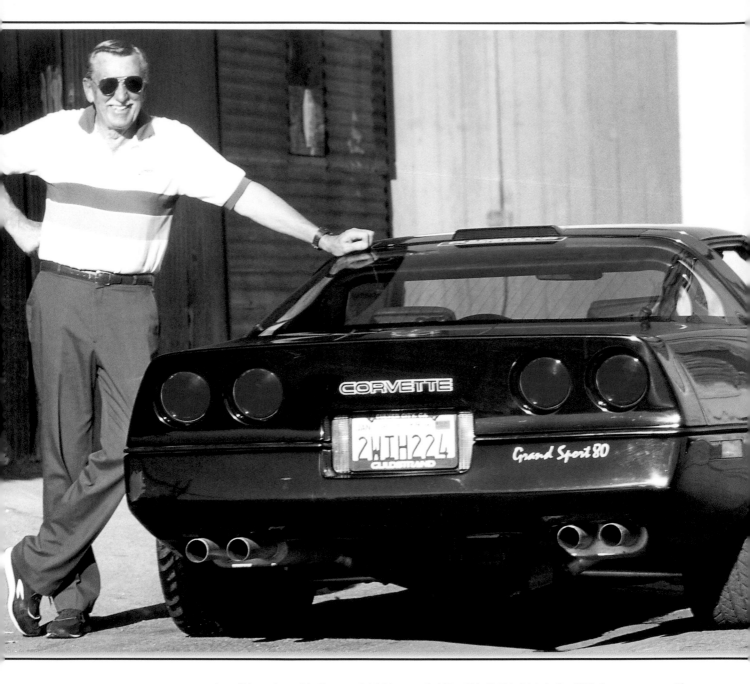

Former Corvette racer and current day performance and handling consultant/speed merchant Dick Guldstrand posed alongside his personal GS-80. He was photographed at his famous Thunder Alley shop on Jefferson Avenue in Culver City, California.

in collaboration with Germany's highly regarded Zandfabrik Friedrichshafen (ZF) that was operated by, or more accurately over-ruled by, its own computer, the Computer-Aided Gear Selection (CAGS). This was another engineering effort to satisfy the EPA and the performance lover. A driver, accelerating at one-third throttle or less at speeds below 20 miles per hour with a fully warmed engine, found the CAGS blocking the gates to second and third gear so the shift went straight from first to fourth. At 20 miles per hour in fourth, the engine idled along at 1,050 rpm. It was simpler than the previous much-

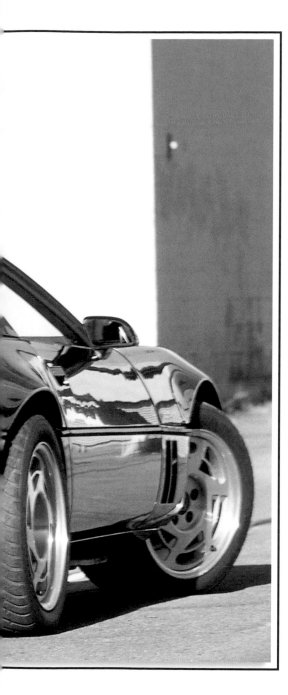

(top below) In all, Guldstrand produced about three dozen of these cars. He reacquired his tired warrior when Bridgestone finished its testing and development work.

(bottom below) Magazine reviewers at the time described the 400 horsepower, 400 foot-pounds torque GS-80 engine as a tire shredder. That was good enough for Bridgestone, which bought Dick's personal car from him to use for 200 miles per hour tire testing at Talladega.

Guldstrand was involved in the suspension engineering of the C4, ZR-1, and C5. Chevrolet provided prototype ZR-1 fenders that he fitted to his personal GS-80 to accommodate 17-inch wheels and tires for development testing.

maligned and mostly misunderstood Doug Nash–designed 4+3 speed, yet it accomplished the same kind of EPA numbers *and,* ultimately, the same kind of enthusiast disrespect. It did, however, make very clear the quality and quantity of torque that the 350-cubic-inch displacement L98 engine produced. While cruising at 65 miles per hour in sixth gear, the engine loafed at barely 1,600 rpm. Buyers who ordered the six-speed gearbox also got an engine oil cooler, heavy-duty radiator, and electric radiator cooling fan that were part of the Z51 package.

The other feature Corvette introduced for 1989 was the FX3 Selective Ride Control Delco-Bilstein electronic suspension. Chevrolet offered this only on Z51-equipped six-speed coupes. Drivers could change the four gas-filled Bilstein shock absorbers by a cockpit control that adjusted shock valving from "Touring"

The appearance of these cars was subdued in the first year. Graphics were designed by the series sponsors. In the view of many, this was too subtle.

When Corvettes proved indomitable, the SCCA catered to other competitor manufacturers and outlawed the cars. Quickly, Canadian racer John Powell and others created a plan to run a one-marque series, the Corvette Challenge.

The interior remained untouched except for the addition of a full roll cage, a fire-extinguishing system, and a racing seat for the driver. Air-conditioning and stereo radios still worked fine. Chevrolet built 56 of these.

No engine modifications were permitted except for removing the catalytic converters to prevent overheating. The cars were otherwise street legal. The engines, matched as closely as possible, were sealed at the Flint engine plant.

The Corvette badge evolved over the decades but from the beginning it has incorporated some kind of checkered flag motif to represent the car's dedication to racing.

The 35th Anniversary package also included a striking black and white interior with custom white leather sport seats and white leather–covered steering wheel. The rest of the interior was black, creating a stark contrast.

development manager Doug Robinson's support. Then he enlisted major sponsorship from parts supplier Mid-America Designs and its enthusiast owner Mike Yager, from Goodyear Tire & Rubber and from Exxon. Chevrolet's general manager Robert Berger approved lending the car's name to the series but made it clear GM had no money to fund it.

Within months, Powell had put together a series called the Million Dollar Corvette Challenge, and SCCA put 10 one-hour race dates on the calendar beginning May 1, 1988, at the Grand Prix of Dallas. Powell promoted the series well enough to entice some of the sport's better drivers, including Jeff Andretti, Bobby and Tommy Archer, Kim Baker, John Greenwood, Tommy Kendall, Scott Legase, Johnny Rutherford, Jimmy Vasser, and Desire Wilson. Chevrolet produced 56 matching C4s, removing catalytic converters but remaining otherwise completely stock, retaining air-conditioning and CD audio systems. Nine buyers never raced or converted their cars. For the rest, Powell lined up ProtoFab

Chevrolet built 60 Challenge racers, though only 30 of them ever saw competition.

Engineering in Wixom, Michigan, near Detroit, to add roll cages, on-board fire-extinguishing systems, racing seats, and Bilstein shocks. Racers drove the break-in miles on the way from Detroit to their own shops. Racers paid their dealers for the cars, then an additional $15,000 to Powell for ProtoFab's conversion and their 1988 season entry fee.

By midyear, the series was in serious trouble, coming up about half a million dollars shy of its target. Powell went back to Chevrolet and appealed to Mike Goodman, the division marketing manager who already knew Berger's terms to Powell. Goodman sensed that this series seemed to be selling cars; he not only found the funds but also signed a deal to continue the series through 1989. With that assurance, ESPN agreed to broadcast every Challenge race the second year.

Graphics on the 1988 cars were subtle and the muffled exhausts too quiet to attract attention. The Series and the SCCA modified their rules for 1989, allowing entrants to get their own spon-

(above) Spectators had made it clear to the SCCA that they wanted to hear these cars as well as see them. The rules for 1989, besides allowing modified but matched engines, permitted freer flowing exhaust. The cars began to sound like racers as well as look like them.

Two matched racing seats filled out the interior package, surrounded by a full competition roll cage and cockpit fire suppression system. Still, the cars retained stereo radios, functioning air-conditioning, and power windows.

sorships. This enhanced each car's visual appeal considerably. Engineering changed the exhausts so spectators could hear the cars coming as well as going. Chevrolet constructed 61 of the racers for 1989, although perhaps as many as 31 never got converted to racers.

GM hoped to attract its own co-sponsors for the series, but that never happened. The races provided great drama with entrants often qualifying within hundredths of seconds of each other. ESPN's coverage put viewers inside the cars with full-functioning gauge-readouts on screen. Chevrolet authorized assembly for 1990 even as regular production sales increased through 1989, validating

Goodman's suspicions. Chevy manufactured just 23 cars, coded R9G, before pulling the plug on its sponsorship. Meanwhile, the rest of the racing world had grown envious of the ESPN coverage and had caught up with Corvette's chassis and ABS brakes. The SCCA invited Corvette back into its general series for 1990.

At the end of the second season, Bill Cooper emerged Challenge champion, winning three events in a row and finishing well in most of the others. By late 1989, Porsche and others had mastered ABS systems and increased their horsepower. They let SCCA know they'd be willing to race against Corvettes again.

1990–1996

CHAPTER TEN

IT BECAME PERSONAL WITH EVERYONE

he very nature of Chevrolet's sports car has always been in question. From Harley Earl's dream to Ed Cole's tool to Zora Duntov's race car, the car has meant something different to each creator. From the beginning up through the two-seat personal luxury car that Dave McLellan and Jerry Palmer created, the decision makers have molded and directed the Corvette. Their goal has always been a vehicle they hoped each board chairman from Alfred Sloan through Roger Smith would bless with a production future.

In early 1986, Don Runkle, Chevrolet's chief engineer, talked with *Road & Track* editors about the future of Corvette. He made clear what he hoped the car might become. He described what in later years enthusiasts know the car became.

"We could obviously build a $100,000 Corvette and blow away the [Ferrari] Testarossa," Runkle said, "but I'm not sure what the point of that exercise is. That just shows that you can do it. Our goal is to do it at 25 percent of the price."

Runkle examined the battles between GM's board and those responsible for the character of the Corvette. Half the decision makers saw Chevrolet as GM's sales volume leader, and every Chevy product must do its part. Others argued that the Corvette is very profitable, and it contributes more than its share of publicity and prestige not only to Chevrolet but to GM as well. Any high-tech development—engine, chassis, suspension—further reinforced Chevrolet's technological stature in the car world. Runkle described a project involving engineering expertise from Lotus and Chevrolet, an engine producing perhaps 400 brake horsepower. This was the car that resurrected the Duntov code name ZR-1 and brought it to a much wider audience. It made Chevrolet division a *(previous spread) There were numerous arguments about how the car should appear. Subtlety won out and only a minor enlargement of the rear bodywork, square taillights, and understated badging marked the car for what it was.*

Once a buyer checked the ZR1 option, there were few choices left. ZR1s got leather everywhere and their own specially laminated windshield.

Developed at Lotus Engineering in Norwich, England, the dual-overhead camshaft, 4-valve per cylinder V-8 developed 375 horsepower yet operated efficiently enough to avoid paying the gas guzzler tax. Called the LT5, it was hand-assembled at Mercury Marine in Stillwater, Oklahoma.

In 1990, Chevrolet sold 7,630 convertible Corvettes and 16,016 coupes.

lot of money, and it definitely reiterated the high-tech nature of the car.

"It is so expensive," Runkle said at the time. "Some people at Chevrolet don't think the additional volume it would generate would be worth the investment. My position is that this project has nothing to do with volume. This is a different thing. This is to get the Corvette to be an unquestioned leader."

Within weeks of that dinner, Runkle's prediction moved toward reality. At about 2:30 A.M. on May 1, 1986, in Norwich, England, engineers at Lotus fired up the first LT5, Chevrolet's brand-new dual-overhead camshaft, four-valve per cylinder, small-block V-8. They ran it up to 3,000 rpm and held it for 30 minutes. Then they shut it off and uncorked champagne. That half hour culminated 18 months of discussion, design, and development. The LT5 was Chevrolet's first new V-8 for 21 years, since the Mark IV in 1965.

The RPO B2K Callaway Twin Turbo option started out in 1987 as a $19,995 option, and by 1990 the cost had increased to $26,895 plus the price of the car. At this price, it was $121 less than the ZR1. The Callaways raced ZR1s neck-and-neck to 60 miles per hour but outran them at the top end.

The ZR1 was an ideological turning point for Chevrolet. Half the decision makers argued against the car, suggesting its development costs were too high. The other half recognized it as a high-tech status symbol that would enhance not only Chevrolet's but GM's reputation.

The engine developed enough horsepower and torque that 5th gear was a 0.60 overdrive. This was "long" enough gearing to see the car to more than 191 miles per hour.

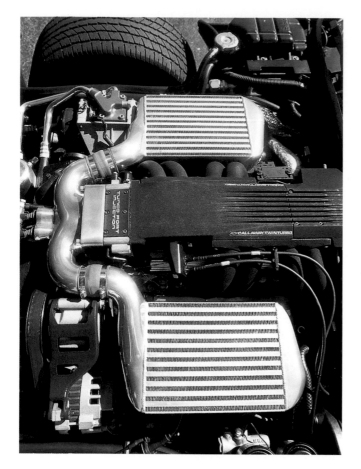

Getting it done required some unusual alliances, the recognition of values beyond costs, and the identification of who Corvette's next generation of competitors would be and what they would do. Whether anyone went back and read Alfred Sloan and Donaldson Brown, the decision to launch the ZR-1 demanded faith that great ideas need time to pay off.

McLellan's and Palmer's improved Corvette attracted attention from German and Japanese car builders who believed they could build one better. Porsche had used the car as its benchmark for engineering the 944, and if SCCA's Showroom Stock racing series was any indication, Porsche gained respect for Corvette's engineers. Nissan engineers who produced their legendary Z-cars used Corvettes as CAD-CAM computer screen savers. Honda made it clear they produced their high-tech, midengined Acura NSX to show how much technology Japanese engineers had learned from America's automakers.

Anthony Young, an excellent historian on the development of a variety of high-performance engines in recent years, wrote in great detail about the LT5 in his 1994 book *The Heart of the Beast: History of the LT5 V-8 and ZR-1 Corvette.*

This was an official factory option, though it was not factory installed. Called RPO B2K, Chevrolet introduced it for model year 1987. Callaway shipped fully assembled Corvettes from the Bowling Green assembly plant to his facilities in Old Lyme, Connecticut, for modification. By 1990, the Twin-Turbo developed 390 horsepower.

The rear-end styling of the standard 1991 Corvette matched the special ZR-1 model. 2002 General Motors Corporation. Used with permission of GM Media Archives.

Russ Gee, a director of powertrain engineering at Chevrolet-Pontiac-Canada (CPC) continued alternate powerplant research for the Corvette, following in the footsteps of Wankel developers and others. Inside Chevrolet and out, engineers knew Corvette's engine was its only shortcoming. They had steadily improved the small-block V-8 since its introduction in 1955. Gee tried turbo charging V-6 engines, reconsidering midengine installations. He encountered critical vibration problems and fatal philosophical ones: Corvette owners perceived any engine with fewer than eight cylinders as un-Corvette-like. Early experiments with turbo charging Chevy V-8 engines yielded unacceptable fuel economy (though Reeves Callaway later worked through those).

When the SCCA suspended the Corvette Challenge series at the end of 1989, Chevrolet already had begun creating successor cars for 1990. These "World Challenge" cars, RPO R9G, gave buyers a car with more deletions than additions.

The World Challenge cars got stronger springs with the FX3 electronic Selective Ride and Handling Package. With its very few options, this R9G retailed for $35,539.

As chief engineer, Lloyd Reuss had overseen the Cosworth four-valve head development for the Vega. He wondered about the V-8. Russ Gee began work in October 1984. In November, Tony Rudd, managing director of Lotus (owned by GM at this time), offered his firm's engineering services. Runkle, Reuss, Gee, and Rudd formed a plan to create four-valve, dual-overhead camshaft heads to fit Chevrolet's small block.

Car assembly realities stopped the design. The Bowling Green assembly line installed L98 engines from the bottom. Any proposed engine had to slip between the frame rails. By April 1985, Rudd and Gee accepted that the taller, wider heads could not fit. Changing the assembly line was enormously expensive; changing the frame rails was unthinkable, since that changed the entire car. Engineers and project managers concluded it made the best sense to create an entire new engine.

Lloyd Reuss went before GM Chairman Roger Smith and presented the benefits this engineering offered, over time, to other products throughout GM's entire product line. He emphasized the Japanese threat. The Corvette was significant in Japan because it was the Japanese car manufacturers' target.

Smith agreed. Reuss, Gee, and Roy Midgley, chief engineer of the 90-degree V-type engines at CPC, understood that all days off were canceled, since any change in GM's financial condition or the economy threatened projects. Engine development at GM sometimes took as long as six years. Smith's funding could disappear at any moment. Reuss knew the further the project progressed, however, the more difficult it might be to kill it. Engineering designated the project the LT5; Runkle named it the King of the Hill.

Dave McLellan studied the performance characteristics of every exotic car Corvette owners might consider if they won the lottery. He concluded the LT5 must get the Corvette to 60 miles per hour in four to five seconds. He knew that required at least 360 horsepower, but 400 had a better ring to it. It could not be a gas guzzler. They would design it from scratch, adopting no parts from any existing GM

As with the Corvette Challenge, these cars would have been fitted with full roll cages and on-board fire-suppression systems that sprayed the cockpit and engine compartment with fire-extinguishing materials.

Chevrolet reportedly manufactured just 23 of these coupes in 1990. Chip Miller, of Corvettes of Carlisle fame, fell in love with the Corvette Challenge series, and when he learned of these models, he bought one just to put in mothballs.

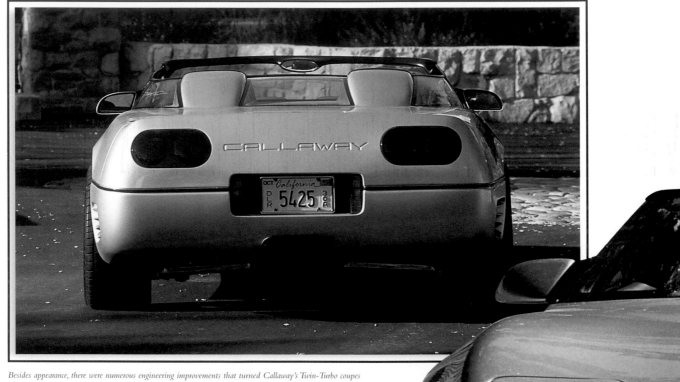

Besides appearance, there were numerous engineering improvements that turned Callaway's Twin-Turbo coupes into the Speedster. While the Twin-Turbo option added $33,000 to the price of the Corvette, the Speedsters checked in at $150,000.

engine just as Cole and Harry Barr had done with Cadillac's V-8 more than 30 years before. Then came the tough part: McLellan wanted a prototype engine running by May 1986 and one in a car three months later. CPC made it clear to Lotus that this engine, which might only have a total production run of 6,000 units, would be treated the same as any engine GM expected to go into 6 million automobiles, subject to every test, analysis, and second-guess.

Once Smith approved the LT5, Chevrolet had to find a plant to manufacture it in. It was too small a run for any GM facility, which meant outside vendors. Roy Midgley selected Mercury Marine in Stillwater, Oklahoma. Mercury's sophisticated computer-controlled manufacturing technology could engineer aluminum castings. After months of meetings, Mercury learned in mid-March 1986 that it was the builder.

At this same time in 1986, Lotus began gathering prototype parts from suppliers throughout Europe and the United States with which to build the prototype engine. Jerry Palmer's staff in Chevrolet Studio 3 made sure that if owners raised John Cafaro's large hood, they saw an engine that looked like 400 horsepower. Some features had to be obvious. Lotus engineers concluded that dual-injection intake ports per cylinder were the best way to ensure optimum fuel mix for performance and economy. On partial throttle below 3,000 rpm, each cylinder used one inlet runner, one injector, and one inlet valve. The cam lobe for that valve provided mild timing with little overlap. A heavier foot signaled the electronic control module (ECM) to open the butterflies in the second runners and turn on their injectors. Cam timing for the second intake valves was wilder. Palmer's designers created 16 distinct tubes running from

By his fifth year producing cars under license with Chevrolet, Reeves Callaway let his designer Paul Deutschman have more creative freedom. The result was Callaway's Speedster of which ultimately only 11 were manufactured.

the injection system's main plenum to the cylinders below. They outlined the dual overhead camshafts in sculpted cam covers. The result was an industrial designer's dream: Function dictated form that resulted in something beautiful to see.

By early 1987, Lotus ran brutal durability tests on the development engines. One trial ran alternately at peak horsepower speed for five minutes and then at peak torque speed for five minutes continuously for 200 hours. Cracks appeared in the cast crankshaft that forced an expensive specification change to nitrided forged steel. From there on the LT5 tested flawlessly.

Other problems threatened the LT5. Engineers fretted the details while Reuss fought for its very existence. GM cut budgets throughout CPC, yet Roger Smith let it slip through. On Christmas Eve 1987, Mercury Marine ran the first preproduction prototype LT5 on their dynamometer.

Starting in January 1988, Lotus prepared to assemble an engine with production parts. There was still testing to do. The LT5 would never make a September 1988 introduction. Reuss and Runkle wanted to provide a warranty that demanded they have it right. If the engine broke, GM would replace it. That kind of reliability required some 2,000 design changes. They balanced every moving part within the engine to tolerances common to Formula One racing engines capable of 14,000 rpm, far beyond the LT5's 7,000. At a press demonstration, Terry Stinson, LT5 project engineer at Mercury Marine, balanced a nickel on its edge on the engine plenum in a completed running car. It remained there, on edge, until he retrieved it.

HANDLING AND ROAD HOLDING

When Dave McLellan matched his vision of this new Corvette to the competition, he recognized the car needed not only exceptional power but also extraordinary handling and road holding. Prior to GM's purchasing Lotus, the small car maker had startled the Formula One world with its active suspension system. With it, drivers Elio de Angelis and others set lap records at circuits that stand to this day. Like Corvettes in Showroom Stock, the FIA, Formula One's sanctioning body, outlawed it. Lotus' system used heavy hydraulic pumps and cylinders, and sometimes the system didn't keep up with the speed of the car, causing unsettling changes. Once it was outlawed, Lotus set it aside.

Active suspension next appeared in Porsche's 959, shown in racing trim as early as 1984 and as a $200,000+ road car in 1986. The electronic system, developed with assistance from Bosch, performed flawlessly. Active suspension intrigued McLellan and others when it was Lotus' project and later when it appeared on a Chevrolet-sponsored racer in the International Motor Sports Association (IMSA) series.

In the early 1980s, rumors circulated that NASCAR would change engine regulations to require V-6s rather than V-8s by the middle of the decade. Indianapolis engine wizard Ryan Falconer worked on Chevy V-6s and routinely pulled nearly 1,200 horsepower from turbocharged versions. That

Both Chevrolet's ZR1 and Callaway's turbos have exercised restraint in design. The integrated ellipsoid rearview mirror is an example of letting astronomical performance speak louder than outrageous wings and flares.

Acceleration was quoted as less than 4 seconds to 60, and top speeds were above 185 miles per hour. Owners have described the power as "like a rocket-propelled locomotive, smooth and unimaginably fast."

Despite its striking looks and its awe-inspiring power, the Callaway Speedster is a comfortable and user-friendly open car. The glass-enclosed cockpit almost totally eliminates wind buffeting at any speed.

Since the ZR-1s reappeared as press prototypes in 1989, racers like Tommy Morrison wondered how they would hold up as racers. At the end of the 1991 Daytona 24 Hours he knew, with one finishing 12th overall and this one coming in 21st.

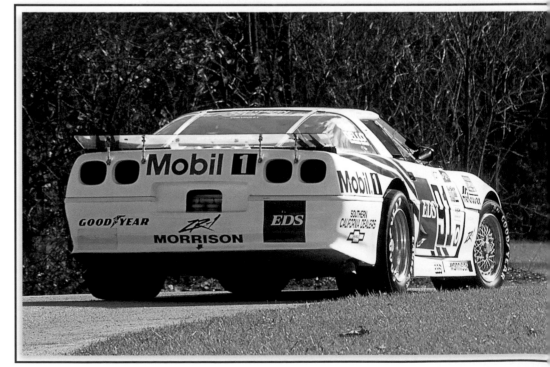

Electrical problems and a major impact with another racer slowed the overall progress of this ZR-1. The carbon-fiber bodywork saved nearly 600 pounds. Its teammate, car #92, is on permanent display at the Smithsonian Institution in Washington, D.C.

intrigued NASCAR team owner Rick Hendrick, who looked for another racing series in which to hide his own development efforts. Back in 1980, IMSA had created a grand touring prototype (GTP) class to encourage European teams to compete in their modified 250 mile per hour Group C cars on American circuits. Chevrolet let Hendrick know in late 1985 that it could support his effort. Hendrick hired IMSA GTP veteran Ken Howes to run it. Howes knew of Lotus' suspension and promoted its use. He believed that while the system was troublesome in ultralight F1 cars, the greater room and weight allowance of a GTP car offered the system great potential. As the effort came together, Corvette designer Randy Wittine sketched the body that became the Corvette GTP.

The car first raced in August 1985 at Road America in Wisconsin, with about 800 horsepower in a chassis built for Chevrolet by England's Eric Broadley. The Lotus active suspension used dozens of sensors to register road surface traction and chassis dynamics. It flexed the suspension to eliminate body roll on cornering, rear squat on acceleration, and nosedive on braking. This kept the tires flat on the roadway without transferring unwanted dynamics back to the passenger compartment.

Competition at Daytona usually includes purpose-built prototypes of featherweight and astonishing power. Mercury Marine balanced and blueprinted this engine and ported the cylinder heads. Rumors put its output at 550 horsepower.

Morrison built new cars based on two street-driven models with nearly 10,000 miles on each. Ohio Corvette "tuner" Chuck Mallett fabricated full tube frame chassis and bumper-to-bumper roll cages. Toledo Pro produced carbon-fiber bodies for car #91 and #92.

Exterior body modifications were minimal. The biggest change for 1992 was under the big clamshell hood, an all new engine. Chevrolet sold 14,604 coupes at a base price of $33,635 and 5,875 convertibles starting at $40,145.

The car proved spectacularly fast, qualifying on the pole for dozens of events between mid-1985 and the end of the program in late 1988. Corvette GTPs won outright at West Palm Beach, Florida, and at Road Atlanta. The highly stressed V-6 failed sometimes, and the suspension challenged engineers. Yet Chevrolet continued its support because the engines offered promise for its Camaro production models and the suspension offered what Dave McLellan envisioned for the ZR1. He built at least one prototype with the GTP system. It fit crab-like over the LT5 engine, its plumbing adding 200 pounds to the car, about 6 inches to the hood height, and immeasurable uncertainty to the reliability the car had to have. The GTP proved that active suspension was worth the effort. McLellan sent his engineers off to work with Bosch on a modified version of Porsche's electronic system.

INTRODUCING THE LT5

The worldwide introduction took place in Geneva, Switzerland, in March 1989. Journalists raced the cars through mountains and praised the crews at Lotus, Mercury Marine, and Corvette. But that was routine compared to the press launch at Riverside Raceway in September 1988, described by Anthony Young. While the project managers spoke during the media introduction, two Mercury engineers, Chris Allen and Ron Opszynski, started assembling an LT5.

"They had been rehearsing this for weeks," Young wrote, "performing like a two-man pit crew. They put their tools down just as Midgley finished his last sentence. Midgley asked Allen and Opszynski if the engine would start. Both gave a thumbs up. Midgley said, 'Gentlemen, start your engine.'

"Ron flipped the switch and the engine turned over. [Chris] pulled the throttle linkage and when those throttle

(top left) In 1989, GM replaced the Doug Nash–designed 4+3-speed transmission shown here with a six-speed Zandfabrik Friedrichshafen (ZF) unit.

(left) The LT2 remained at 350-cubic-inch displacement, yet due to computer optimized ignition timing, a higher compression ratio, new camshafts, redesigned intake manifolds, cylinder heads, and a muiltiport fuel-injection system, Chevrolet boosted power to 300 net horsepower at 5,000 rpm.

plates opened and everyone heard the engine roar to life, that was the moment. In that dark amphitheater camera flashes started going off, people started clapping and whistling—it was amazing."

First production engines built by Mercury employees came off their line on July 13, 1989. The engines developed 380 horsepower. The new Corvettes reached 60 miles per hour in 4.2 seconds and a top speed of 172 miles per hour. They had met McLellan's target.

Midgley and his crew worked to get more power. Subtly modifying and improving air intakes, revising cam timing, and reducing exhaust back pressure helped them reach 405 horsepower for 1993. Even more impressively, they cleared the EPA gas guzzler mark of 22.5 miles per gallon. With 405 horsepower and 180 miles per hour capability, it returned 23.1 miles per gallon on the test cycle.

Option Z25 was the 40th Anniversary package that colored the car Ruby Red inside and out. The commemorative option added $1,455 to the price. Chevrolet produced 6,749 commemorative editions.

A car running 170 to 180 miles per hour needed brakes capable of hauling down this 3,000-pound-plus missile. During early days of development before engines were ready, development mules were still narrow-body Corvettes, not wide versions needed to accommodate Goodyear's new tires. Engineering built a 400-horsepower V-8 with nitrous oxide injection added to it. This would get the car to its top speed in the least distance to allow more runoff in case the brakes failed. Chevrolet hired Corvette Challenge racers Kim Baker and John Powell to do handling and brake testing. In Powell's first test, he targeted a 0.50g deceleration test from maximum speed to get a feel for the car. The calibration was incorrect, however. When Powell got on the brakes, he hauled the car down to a standstill at nearly 1.0g without any problem.

One troubling question Chevrolet faced was whether it should adorn the body with wings, spoilers, or scoops. Reuss wanted visual significance; Palmer disagreed. "The differences should be subtle," he told Anthony Young. "The only ones who really care are the Corvette people. They'll know." Palmer's staff mocked up Reuss' ideas, eventually incorporating many of them in the whole Corvette lineup for 1991. Only Palmer's understated widening of the car's rear end and its squarish taillights distinguished the LT5. The back end enlargement, 1.5 inches on each side, started with new outer door panels feathering in the additional size. It accommodated Goodyear's first 35-series Eagle road tire, P315/35ZR-17 rears, mounted in 11-inch-wide wheels.

It became a costly package. The base coupe started at $34,595. Adding the ZR1 alone boosted the price another $31,683. Chevrolet produced only 448 ZR-1s, and no one complained about the extra 30 horsepower.

Corvettes have often served as pace cars for the Indianapolis 500. 2002 General Motors Corporation. Used with permission of GM Media Archives.

The pace car replicas used Corvette's 300-horsepower LT2 V-8. The package, RPO Z4Z, sold for $2,816, and Chevrolet ultimately manufactured 527 of the cars.

While the hotter car still wore wider bodywork, 1990 owners had expressed pleasure when others recognized the subtle distinction, and 1991 buyers made their discontent known when that uniqueness was taken away.

Following the land speed record run in March 1990, Tommy Morrison went to Daytona in February 1991 with two freshly converted ZR1s (one completed just hours before practice began; both cars already had at least 9,800 miles on them). Morrison, wary of using Daytona to debut the ZR1 as a race car against some of the world's toughest competitors, was a realist. "The Corvette has an important place as the American flagship car," he said at the time. "What we have to do is outlast the other guys." When the rain-soaked race ended, his car #92 finished 12th overall, 4th in GTO class. Car #91, piloted by Stu Hayner and John Heinricy as well as Scott Legase and Morrison, suffered several delays with electrical problems early and an off-road excursion late at night that damaged front bodywork and broke the oil cooler. Still, it finished 21st overall, 6th in GTO. Morrison gave both cars bumper-to-bumper roll cages and carbon-fiber bodywork that cut nearly 600 pounds off each car's weight. Car #92 also ran a special Mercury Marine–produced LT5 engine that reportedly developed 520 horsepower. That car then finished 6th in class at Sebring a month later. Because #91 honorably represented American racing efforts and outlasted the others, Morrison retired it to its permanent display at the Smithsonian Institution's National Museum of American History.

More than three decades after the first Grand Sport racing prototypes snuck out of Zora Duntov's shops, Chevrolet commemorated the efforts with these non-racing versions. Offered as a coupe and convertible, Chevrolet produced just 1,000.

CHANGES FOR 1992

Model year 1992 brought numerous changes, including a new LT1 small-block powerplant, an electronic traction control to more successfully get its power to the ground and keep it there, another production offshoot of the GTP racers between 1986 and 1988, and a new Goodyear tire to further aid that task. When the new LT1 reached showrooms 20 years after the original 370-horsepower LT1 disappeared in 1972, it produced 300 net horsepower and provided 0–60 miles per hour times of four seconds, three full seconds faster than the 1972 model. While the old LT1 consumed 12 miles per gallon, the new engine with 50 horsepower more than the L98, returned 17 miles per gallon city and 25 highway.

The Bosch Acceleration Slip Regulation (ASR) performed like its ABS (antilock braking system) in reverse, controlling wheel spin under acceleration, not braking. Meant to limit those "Oh my God!" moments, the ASR worked liked an instantaneously reactive, very intelligent limited-slip differential. Coupled with Goodyear's new Eagle directional, asymmetrical GS-C P275/40Z–17 tires front and rear, Formula One and Indy race car technology for wet and damp and dry racing came to the street.

On July 2, 1992, many of the principals responsible for making the Corvette into what it had become gathered in Bowling Green for a celebration. The one millionth car, a white convertible, drove off the line. It went just a few blocks into storage, where it would await completion of its new home about a quarter-mile from the end of the Bowling Green assembly line.

Board members of the National Corvette Restorers Society voted in November 1988 to establish a national Corvette museum. Setting a budget of $6 million, they raised funds, acquired a site, and selected building architects and exhibit designers. They opened their 68,000-square-foot structure, constructed alongside Interstate 65, in 1994. Now they routinely display as many as 80 Corvettes at a time. The ever-changing exhibits usually include equal numbers of cars on loan from GM's own collection and from private collectors around the world as well as Corvettes the museum owns from generous donations made possible by the museum nonprofit tax-exempt status. The museum hosts numerous events each year, including Pace Car reunions, and publishes its own monthly magazine, *America's Sports Car,* and it is home to the National Corvette Hall of Fame, a registry for designers, engineers, planners, managers, racers, and owners of significance to the history of the car. One popular feature is the museum's in-house delivery program where buyers of new model Corvettes who select option R8C can pick up their cars under the golden 140-foot-diameter, 100-foot-tall Skydome in the midst of Corvette's history. Following its opening, the National Corvette Museum quickly became a mecca for Corvette enthusiasts.

MORE POWER UNDER THE HOOD

The big news for 1993 was that Midgley's and McLellan's goal of 400+ horsepower under the hood of the ZR1 got to the dealerships. Engineering subtly changed intake valve head shape and the valve seat to improve fuel flow and overall breathing. This micro-tinkering brought output to 405 horsepower. Goodyear's asymmetrical GS-C's improved wet-weather maneuverability over the Gatorbacks at the modest cost of dry-pavement acceleration. Zero-to-60 miles per hour times slipped from 4.2 to 4.5 seconds.

Production was split with 810 coupes and just 190 convertibles. The cars came from the factory with black-painted wheels. Many owners later had them polished or replaced them with brushed or polished chrome.

Outside and inside the car, Chevrolet division celebrated the 40th anniversary with an appearance option, Z25 for $1,455, providing Ruby Red exterior paint and interior leather but no effect on performance. Some 6,749 were produced. Total production crept up slightly to 21,590, with 5,692 convertibles (at $41,195 base) and 15,898 coupes (at $34,595). Only 448 were ZR-1 options, still at $31,683 extra, despite the new engine.

Chevrolet upgraded the PASS-key system introduced in 1986 with the addition of the new Passive Keyless Entry (PKE). Engineering imbedded a tiny transmitter in the key fob that signaled one of two receivers in the car body to open one or both doors and light the interior. As owners walked away with their keys in pocket or purse, the PKE automatically locked their car and set the alarm, confirmed by a brief toot of the horn. With the key fob still in the car while walking away, nothing happened. No horn sounding was a reminder to return for the keys.

For 1994, Corvette engineers replaced the recently reintroduced glove compartment with a passenger-side air bag, and this provided the opportunity for an interior makeover. The interior studio redesigned the seats making them more comfortable to a wider variety of bodies.

Goodyear introduced Extended Mobility Tires (EMTs), essentially run-flat rubber useful at zero air pressure for up to 200 miles as fast as 55 miles per hour. An instrument panel monitor alerted the driver of low—or no—pressure. For a driver alone at night or in foul weather on a freeway in rush hour, there was no longer any risk. Corvettes still carried spare tires, jacks, and tire irons, and the EMT option was available only on about 5,000 of the 1994 model year cars with either the FX3 option (with slightly softer springs) or the base suspension, but not the Z01 or ZR-1.

Engineering and electronics engineers replaced the Engine Control Module (ECM) with a new powertrain control module (PCM) to control not only the transmission but also the new sequential-port fuel injection. In this system, the injectors worked simultaneously with the engine-firing order, offering smoother idle, quicker throttle response, and reduced exhaust emissions.

Production numbers for 1994 inched up again. Total Bowling Green output was 23,330 cars, of which 17,984 were coupes and 5,346 convertibles. Chevrolet sold only 448 ZR1s, though the price of $67,443 dropped a few dollars from the previous year as more equipment on the base car was made standard equipment. The bleed-through of engineering from the ZR-1 to the LT1 had produced a car so good that with few options (the G92 performance axle at only $50 and the FX3 electronic ride and handling option at $1,695), a buyer had as close to a ZR-1 as most customers could measure. The ZR-1's supplemental 105 horsepower made the biggest difference in speed ranges few owners ever saw, and insurance companies began to react to the ZR-1 code as they had to muscle cars in the late 1960s and early 1970s.

The Indianapolis Motor Speedway chose the 1995 Corvette as the 500-mile pace car. Palmer's designers developed a wild dark purple and white scheme and Chevrolet offered replicas to the public. They sold only 527; the two-tone combination put off more people than it attracted. In total, 4,971 convertibles sold, and Chevrolet repeated 1994 ZR-1 production with just 448 cars, making total 1995 coupe sales of 15,771. In anticipation of the C5 introduction, earlier scheduled for 1996, Chevrolet discontinued the ZR-1 package at the end of production of 1995 cars. Even when management

Chevrolet engineers never stopped tinkering with the venerable 350-cubic-inch V-8s. This latest version, LT4, used new aluminum heads, Crane roller rocker arms, revised cams, and other improvements to squeak out 330 net horsepower. It was standard with the Grand Sport Package.

Painted in Admiral Blue and emblazoned with a wide white racing stripe, the other subtle distinction was the pair of red stripes on the left fender.

The new Grand Sport also marked the end of the C4 chassis, fitted with options such as RPO F45 Selective Real-Time Damping. This suspension system read shock absorber loads 75 to 100 times a second and adjusted any one shock to improve handling instantly.

acknowledged that C5 would not be available until 1997, they let the ZR1 disappear. Mercury Marine assembled the last LT5 engine in November 1993. The total ZR1 count was 6,939 from 1990 through 1995.

GOODBYE TO THE C4

Spy photos confirmed that C5 was coming and that 1996 was the final year for C4; once again customers wrestled with waiting for the unknown new car or buying the familiar. To give them something to consider, Chevrolet released its new 330-horsepower LT4. Engineering used a new aluminum-head design, new camshaft, and Crane roller bearing rocker arms.

Externally, designers and product planners created two packages with visual appeal. The first was a silver-painted Collector Edition, the Z15, for $1,250. Besides color and special trim, it used ZR1 wheels (but not the tires), also painted silver. More exciting visually was the Grand Sport Package Z16. Chevrolet produced only 1,000 of these in coupe or convertible form ($2,880 for the convertible option, $3,250 for the coupe). Coupes used the full ZR1 wheel and tire option, including the fat, squat P315/35ZR-

17 rears, barely contained by fender flares (not, however, body panels like the ZR-1). Convertible Grand Sports took advantage of the tire package for the Collector Edition. Chevrolet painted the cars Admiral Blue with twin white racing stripes centered on the car and bright red slashes across the left front fender.

Dick Guldstrand's long racing and engineering relationship with Chevrolet saw him involved with improving the suspension of the C1 during its development. But Chevrolet didn't go far enough, so he took on the project himself with his 6590.

Guldstrand's Nassau Roadsters now boast 400 horsepower out of Chevrolet's LT1 through the use of a Vortech belt-driven supercharger. As always, Guldstrand's work not only performs exceptionally well, it is handsomely done.

This third completed Nassau Roadster carried on the styling cues introduced in Guldstrand's first GS-90 coupe. Huge vents aid in cooling front and rear brakes.

Chevrolet replaced the previous FX3 suspension with F45, "Selective Real-Time Damping," a new active system that took road surface and suspension load inputs 60 times per second, revising shock characteristics with equal frequency. Chevrolet produced 21,536 1996 models, including the Grand Sports and 5,412 Collector Editions. The new $1,695 LT4 engine option went into nearly a third of all the cars.

Chevrolet carried on its fourth-edition Corvette for 13 years, another long run for a popular car. It sold 368,180 of them, earning GM nearly $100 million in profit. The car withstood attacks from Nissan's 300ZX, Acura's NSX, Mitsubishi's 3000GT VR-4, Porsche's 959, 944, and 968, and from Dodge's 10-cylinder Viper. Lamborghini replaced its Countach with its Diablo, which for all its bravado represented only a slight movement of the benchmark. Only Ferrari, with its racecar-like F40 and F50, and England's Gordon Murray, with his $1 million McLaren three-seat F1, moved off into such rarified space that few could come close. Corvette's competitors came and went. They kept on coming, and to their chagrin, so did Corvette.

Guldstrand's lines put the Coke-bottle taper back into the middle of the car. He flared front and rear wheel houses to allow better brake cooling.

1997-2003

CHAPTER ELEVEN

THE ULTIMATE CORVETTE

I t first emerged in the imaginations of a few dedicated individuals as early as August 1988. They hoped it would be released four years later, as a 1993 model, the 40th Anniversary Corvette. Between then and its eventual introduction as a 1997 car, the next generation C5 Corvette endured a Shakespearean saga performed by a cast of characters that included some of the most brilliant and dedicated people in modern automotive history. Like any great story, it also included some characters whose ideas and actions were dubious enough to cause later observers to wonder whose side they really were on. The protagonists broke rules or they rewrote them. They worked and connived to get designs approved, to gather personnel and garner funding, to get prototypes built and development cars to run until they stopped breaking. They produced the C5 seemingly despite diligent efforts by antagonists determined to make new rules, challenge and obstruct the car-building process, and stop this car every chance they found.

The late author James Schefter recorded the dramas that yielded the C5 in his book, *All Corvettes Are Red*. Its title comes from a quote from John Heinricy, Corvette racer, endurance record holder, and supervisor of the C4 until the end of the program. Heinricy maintains that all other colors are just mistakes. (Some Corvette collectors, for example, judge green as suitable only for primer.) Schefter's history takes readers deep inside GM to explain how the C5 came to be.

Titanic egos played roles in this story. Titanic describes their size and, in a few cases, their end. During the car's eight-year gestation—the darkest days of the automobile industry's economy—thousands of employees left the industry. GM lost hundreds of employees, including key engineers. So many engineers had left that during some critical periods of the C5's development, barely enough remained to do the work. Engineering staffs at Ford and (previous spread) Among the Z06's unique cosmetic touches are the black air scoops for the rear brakes and the split-spoke wheels with a chrome finish.

The C5's reversed air scoop behind the front wheel echoes Corvette designs of the past, while the car's aerodynamic shape pushes the modern wedge silhouette of recent Corvettes even further into the future.

Chrysler swelled during this period as these companies took their pick from among hundreds of experienced, qualified individuals who left their jobs because of worries that GM may go bankrupt. As Chevrolet reinvented its Corvette, General Motors, which had reorganized before C5 development started, would reorganize itself a second and then a third time.

Corvette's competition had changed by 1988. Porsche's "affordable" front-engine cars had four-cylinder engines that matched the Corvette's top speed but not its acceleration or, initially, its braking. But Porsche's cars started at $45,000, beyond the price range most Corvette buyers would consider. Japanese cars were Corvette's biggest competition, cars in the Corvette's price range, cars like Mazda's RX-7, Nissan's 300ZX, Mitsubishi's 3000, and its Dodge Stealth twin. Toyota had a new Supra. Acura's NSX, while wildly different from the street-fighter-in-a-suit image of the ZR1, sold for $10,000 less. GM gave Chevrolet division $250 million to develop a car to meet any competition until at least the year 2000. Lloyd Reuss, GM executive vice-president, shared with Corvette Chief Engineer Dave McLellan and Chevrolet Design Studio Chief Jerry Palmer the goal of making a car that would *beat* all comers, in the marketplace or on a race track. Whatever had been good in 1988 must be great in 1993. They would accept only improvements in performance, handling, body design, interior comfort, and baggage space. In 1989, Jim Perkins directed Chevrolet as division general manager and GM vice president. His love for automobiles and the Corvette rivaled Ed Cole's 35 years before him, and few in his business were more enthusiastic.

To the outside world, GM's profit statements looked healthy. Inside, the picture was bleak and drawn in red ink. Worse yet, an offhand remark by GM Chairman Roger Smith, who had previously been something of a friend to the car, wasted a year. Made during a body styling review of

Corvette ideas, Smith's comment set design's development and experimentation chasing after midengine/transaxle configurations.

Worse, Smith's intentional message to the board cost Corvette an additional year. Cost containment realities slipped the 1993 launch back to 1994, and it would be a traditional front-engine, rear-drive Corvette. By midyear, more bad financial news forced the C5 back to 1995.

A SIX-YEAR CAR

Each reschedule led to new design directives. Chuck Jordan, GM's vice president of design since 1986, delivered the messages to his increasingly impatient designers. Jordan rewarded John Cafaro, who had created the C4's basic shape and its signature clamshell hood, with primary design authority for the C5. As each quarter's financial statements brought another year's delay to introduction, however, Jordan beleaguered anyone who'd listen that the Japanese, Corvette's target competitors, were not standing still and they could bring out their cars in three years. The C5 was on the way to being a six-year car.

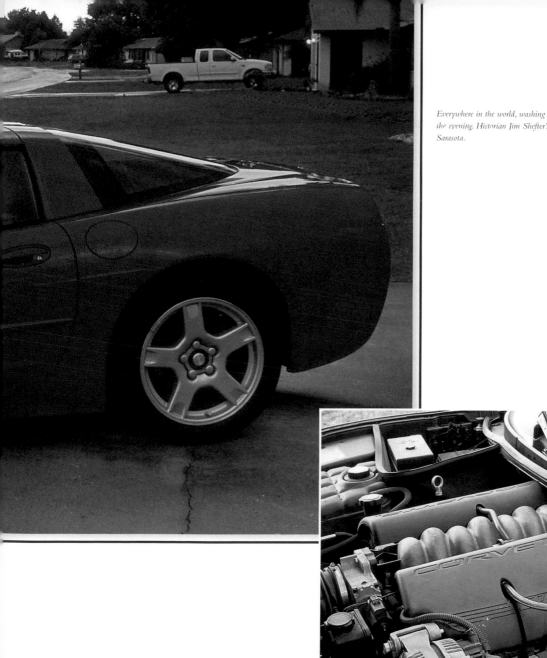

Everywhere in the world, washing a car in the afternoon guarantees rain in the evening. Historian Jim Shefter's red C5 has found a good home in Sarasota.

Everything about the C5 was new, including its LS1 engine. This freshly designed 346-cubic-inch pushrod V-8 engine produced 345 horsepower at 5,600 rpm. The engine weighed 44 pounds less than the 1996 Grand Sport LT4.

The C5 appeared in convertible form a year after coupe introduction. Design provided the rear deck with a built-in tonneau, operable by a single button, to hide the cloth top.

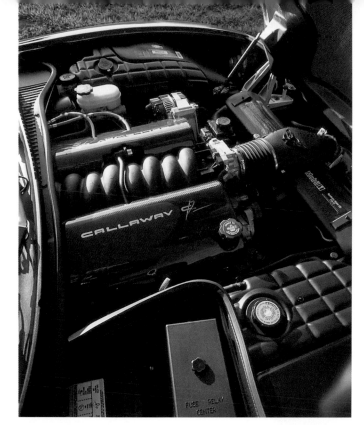

Callaway's tweaks to the 346-cubic-inch V-8 yields 440 horsepower at 6300 rpm and a pavement shredding 420 pounds feet torque at 4800 rpm. The entire package weighs about 3,380 pounds.

(opposite) From the fertile minds that created the Callaway Speedster came this C12 coupe. Its lines—to say nothing of its engine rumble—confuse everyone as to its origin.

(below) Callaway's wizard body designer Paul Deutschman produced something barely resembling the car from which it was derived. He and Callaway composed its body of carbon fiber, Kevlar, and fiberglass.

There are more options for Callaway's C12 interior than Chevrolet offered during the heydays of muscle cars. Carbon fiber peeks out from many panels.

Smith's midengine misdirection forced engineering and design to work side by side for the first time to meet their goal. The two sides created a car with nearly five times as much resistance to twisting and flexing as the C4. This was another benefit to this collaborative working arrangement and to the hydroformed chassis. This backbone chassis encouraged them to use a transaxle, a one-piece transmission-differential they bolted directly to the rear axle. Moving this weight rearward allowed the nearly 50/50 front-to-rear weight balance that midengines offered. With the transmission bulk out of the cockpit foot well, designers and engineers moved the entire compartment forward slightly, opening up rear space for a luggage compartment. Golf was the game of business. Japanese cars accommodated two golf bags. Now so did the Corvette.

In summer 1990, GM's board named Bob Stempel, a former engineer and former general manager of Chevrolet, as its chairman, and Lloyd Reuss became president. While they were longtime

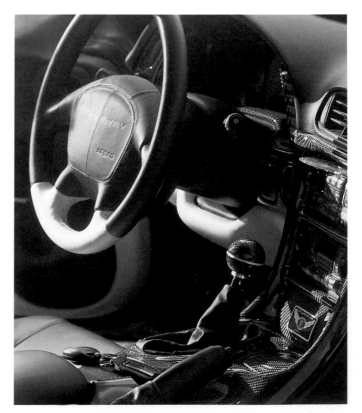

This is the first product of Callaway Cars Europe GmbH though the title registers it as a Corvette. The Borg-Warner six-speed and a switchable traction control give the C12 the versatility to spin rear tires in 1st through 4th gears.

Corvette supporters, they had a corporation to save. GM was in deep trouble. The Corvette took another big hit.

James Schefter reported that instead of a C5 for 1995, the board ordered a thorough reskin for the C4, slipping the C5 back to 1998. Yet all passenger cars sold in the United States for 1997 had to have side-impact protection requiring a structure engineering could not incorporate into the C4. At this point, some directors suggested that the Corvette was superfluous; no other American car maker produced a sports car, and GM could no longer afford the luxury of this exclusive product. Others felt that Chevrolet, GM's car maker for the masses, was the wrong parent for such exclusivity. GM definitely needed it, they argued, but the car ought to be its own division entirely. Jim Perkins protested that making the car its own product line would confuse and destroy customer loyalty. What's more, killing off GM's showcase product would damage its image irrevocably. Corvettes generated more than half the GM-related stories in newspapers or magazines except for disheartening financial analyses at that time. If the board killed the Corvette, writers would dig deeply into how GM foundered so badly that it would kill its profit leader.

Stempel's board gave Perkins a small budget to re–skin the C4, leaving the C5 with a 1998 introduction deadline. Then Lloyd Reuss spoke; recognizing the side-impact requirements, he reinstated the

Testers reached 60 miles per hour in 4.2 seconds, but the real strength of this machine is its long-legged running. A quarter-mile happens in 12.8 seconds at 116 miles per hour. Top speed is better than 188 miles per hour.

This was the third body incarnation that Chevrolet General Manager Jim Perkins conceived when he approved the C5 project. With its fixed hardtop welded in place, it weighed 80 pounds less than the coupe and was 12 percent stiffer.

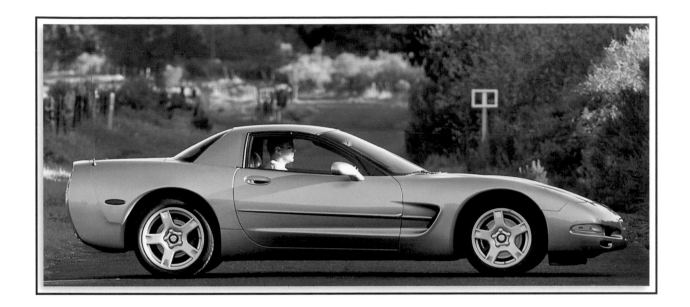

budget for the C5 for a new body, backbone chassis, and, now, for a 1996 launch. The C5 would be introduced first as a Targa-roof coupe. A full convertible would appear for 1997 as well as an entry-level hardtop, a $25,000 to $30,000 concept close to Perkins' heart, a boy-racer he nicknamed "Billy Bob."

Jim Perkins conceived the body style as a boy racer, a car he lovingly nicknamed "Billy Bob." When accountants realized he was going to remove profit-producing options, they vetoed his idea but approved the bodystyle.

Then profit and loss statements for the corporation arrived. CPC lost $3.3 billion, not the 2.6 predicted. Projections for 1991 hinted that GM could be bankrupt sometime in 1991. Roger Smith had relied on separate plants for separate vehicles much like Billy Durant's uncontrolled product lineup 75 years earlier. Worse, he had replaced low-tech but generally adaptable people with high-tech difficult-to-relocate-and-reprogram robots that now left profitable lines suffering from insufficient capacity. The board cut Corvette's budget and the car slipped to 1997. In 1991, GM lost $4.5 billion; John Smith, GM's new president, relieved Lloyd Reuss of his duties. Bob Stempel, the "car guy" engineer never trained in the financial tricks required to drive a stalled leviathan out of someone else's quagmire, resigned in October 1992. John Smale replaced Stempel as board chairman. Corvette remained in Chevrolet, but the board warned engineering to find a way to retrofit side-impact protection to the C4 as a worst case 1997 scenario.

Dave McLellan followed Stempel and Reuss out the door, retiring the next August. Dave Hill, Cadillac's chief engineer,

Because this was essentially the convertible's optional hardtop welded on, the new bodystyle kept the convertible's trunk. It provided about 14 cubic feet of storage capacity.

(top opposite) Lingenfelter Performance Engineering is another of the super tuners who believe that Chevrolet offers nowhere near enough horsepower from the Bowling Green factory. Lingenfelter has options up to 725 horsepower from a twin-turbocharged LS6 package, costing $49,995 on top of the purchase price of the C5.

The hardtop got Chevrolet's new LS1 345-horsepower 346-cubic-inch engine and was only available with the manual transmission. Buyers got the Z51 sport suspension as standard equipment.

replaced him. Hill had McLellan's brilliance with better management and performance skills. Chuck Jordan retired in October, replaced by European design boss Wayne Cherry as administrative boss and by Chevy design chief Jerry Palmer as director of design for North American operations, now incorporating CPC, Oldsmobile, Buick, and Cadillac divisions.

According to Schefter, the first driveable C5 test vehicle was a $1.2 million mule called CERV-4. Soon after, there was a half-price copy, the CERV-4b. Engineering set 1993 C4 bodies on C5 frames and ran them around Milford and GM's Desert Proving Ground in Mesa, Arizona. They were indistinguishable from C4s, except that they had a trunk. There was scarcely any money available from the board to create these most necessary first cars, so Jim Perkins discretely funneled other division funds into the Corvette program he'd fought so hard to preserve.

After the CERVs came "alpha" and then "beta" test cars, each wearing close-to-correct C5 bodies that they heavily disguised, engineering assembled these two, closely matching production specifications. Then came prototypes, nearly perfect from an engineering and design point of view, fabricated from preproduction versions of production parts. As testers devoured these, prepilot cars began to appear, the first ones actually assembled in Bowling Green starting August 1996. Chevrolet command had changed by this time. John Middlebrook took over to replace Perkins, who retired feeling fairly certain the C5 would appear. "Pilot" cars, the first saleable production vehicles, began a month later.

The two CERVs used C4 engines and existed primarily to examine the chassis. They got cobbled-together interiors to test heating, ventilation, and air-conditioning. Engineering created a new powerplant for the C5, known as Gen III. It was an all-new, third-generation version of the decades-old Chevy small block. Responses from thousands of owner and customer surveys reinforced another ZR1 lesson. Corvette owners wanted torque, not turbos or superchargers. They didn't want the added expense of four-valve heads with dual-overhead camshafts. Engineer Dave Hill liked the ZR1 LT5 and Cadillac's 32-valve Northstar, but he was a realist. He knew pushrod engines were not as tall as overhead cam and multivalve engines. A low hood improved forward visibility, a longtime customer complaint, and this was essential to achieve their aerodynamic drag coefficient targets, which were crucial to meeting fuel-consumption goals.

Black leather seats were the only interior option. Sport seats could not be fitted and other colors were not offered.

John Lingenfelter is as well known a driver as he is an engine builder. Lingenfelter Performance Engineering produced the 1,200-horsepower engine for Reeves Callaway's famous "Sledgehammer" speed record car, and John drove the machine to 254 miles per hour on the 7.5-mile course at East Liberty, Ohio.

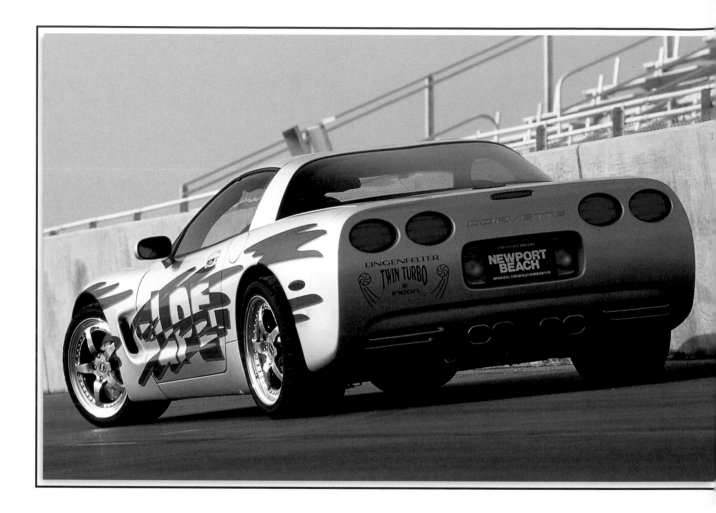

Body modifications range from mild and subtle to more extensive aerodynamic fairings. Lingenfelter quotes 0–60 miles per hour times in the 3.9 second range and top speeds above 190 for the C5 500TT.

Engineering cast the Gen III engine in aluminum to save weight. The aim was to get the car below 3,500 pounds with full tanks, two passengers, and luggage. Every pound of weight increased fuel consumption, and tire, brake, and engine wear. Excess weight decreased shock absorber life, added strain to chassis and driveline, and detracted from performance. Engineering developed research figures equating improved acceleration time with increased sales. Weight became an obsession.

John Cafaro's sleek body had gotten aerodynamic adjustments from engineer Kurt Romberg, who shaved its shape. The C5 measured 0.293 coefficient of drag in the wind tunnel, the lowest of any production vehicle made anywhere except for GM's EV1 electric vehicle. With its twin gas tanks straddling the rear axle, and new Goodyear run-flat extended mobility tires requiring no spare (the rears measured 1 inch wider than 1996 C4s), the C5 offered 23.8 cubic feet of trunk space, more than Cadillac's largest full-size sedans. Engineering found ways to eliminate more than 1,400 separate parts from the previous car, each piece costing from fractions of a cent to many dollars. Eliminating these parts also cut 69 pounds from the 1996 C4 weight. The body, formed in plastic, not fiberglass, saved weight as well. The C5 uses sheet-molded compound-plastic (SMC) and reaction injection-molded plastic (RIM). These technologies produced lighter, stronger, and more rigid panels.

In creating the C5, engineering examined not only the cost to buy the car but also ongoing costs of ownership. The huge clamshell hood was removed from the C4 because insurance companies factored in replacement parts and labor charges when establishing premium rates. The large hood with its bonded fenders made the C4 expensive to repair. Engineering bolted the C5 fenders onto the frame.

The rear suspension no longer relied on the half-axles to perform suspension duties. Upper control arms locked the rear wheels into place much more accurately. As a by-product of the C5's stiffer backbone frame, engineers softened the transverse fiberglass springs technology adapted from the C4. This allowed a better ride and kept the tires in contact despite road surface changes.

The GEN III LS1 engine produced 345 horsepower, 15 more than the C4 LT4. This moved the car from 0–60 miles per hour in 4.7 seconds with the six-speed manual gearbox. Yet EPA fuel economy numbers were published as 18 city/29 highway miles per gallon. Chevy quoted top speed at 172 miles per hour.

While magazine reviewers loved the car, buyers barely sauntered to dealerships. With only a fastback coupe available, Chevrolet produced just 9,752 of the coupes, at a base price of $37,495. But the pace accelerated throughout model year 1998 when Jim Perkins' convertible appeared. While it weighed 114 pounds less than the 1996 convertible, it was four times stiffer. While its trunk, the first in a Corvette since 1962, measured 13.8 cubic feet (just over half the coupe's capacity), it still held two full golf bags. And while it sold for $44,425, Chevrolet produced more of them than it had 1997 coupes, 11,849 in all, as well as 19,235 coupes. Of the 31,084 Corvettes manufactured, 5,356 featured the optional active handling system, a $500 version of the earlier racing GTP's immensely complicated suspension. Fewer buyers selected the $5,408 Indy Pace Car replica option. Its vivid purple

(lower left) John Lingenfelter offers modification packages for the C3, C4, and C5. Most impressive is this 500TT twin-turbocharged model with 500 horsepower and 500 foot-pounds of torque. He mounts the turbos low, flanking the oil pan.

(lower right) For those to whom information is important, LPE pays attention. A small, lighted boost gauge mounted on the driver's A-pillar is an optional part of the package for an additional $339.

After interviewing other "tuners," the owners went to Chuck Mallett of Berea, Ohio, looking for a 50-state legal, street-drivable car that could run 200 miles per hour in order to win a Nevada open road race. Only Mallett could deliver a car that could also pass California's stringent smog tests.

exterior, wild graphics, yellow wheels, and yellow and black leather interior spoke to only 1,163 souls. The Corvette itself, however, spoke clearly again to the automotive media, which named the 1998 model the North American Car of the Year during the North American International Auto Show in Detroit.

GOING RACING

On November 4, 1998, Chevrolet division's general manager John Middlebrook made a startling announcement. Chevrolet was going sports car racing, and not just in some clandestine Zora Duntov manner in which various engineers coincidentally took vacations during race weekends at Daytona, Sebring, or Le Mans. This was a full-on and very public effort. The program would be overseen by

Mallett's options include lowering the car 1.5 inches, fitting Fikse three-piece forged alloy wheels, and a catalog full of other things. Basic conversion to the Mallett 435 cost $34,650, though nothing about the result is basic.

That's not low altitude flight velocity. That's all four wheels on the ground during the Silver State 100, an unlimited speed open road race over Nevada highways. This car won the 2001 event by 2 seconds.

GM's motorsports manager, Herb Fischel, and racing program manager, Doug Fehan. They intended to compete internationally in FIA's category GT2, where the racer car's chassis must be production-based, engines production-derived, and bodies only slightly modified. The Corvette would race head-to head against twin-turbo Porsche 911 GTs and V-10 Vipers among others. Their C5-R would debut at the January 30 to 31, 1999, 24 Hours of Daytona, then move on to the Sebring 12 Hours and through several of the Petit Le Mans series events in preparation to attempt the full 24-hour French race in June 2000.

Fischel and Fehan tagged Ken Brown, the engineer who had designed the C5's chassis and suspension for Corvette chief engineer Dave Hill, to design the C5-R. Corvette brand manager Jim Campbell told them their "primary focus was to improve the breed," and "to squeeze valuable engineering information from each lap Corvette turns on the racetrack." They reduced the weight from the production car's 3,245 pounds to 2,510 pounds. John Cafaro's production body, reproduced in carbon fiber, helped save weight. It needed only minor attention from aerodynamicist Brian Miller, who developed front underbody ducting to assist with engine cooling, down force, and drag. He also added a rear wing and

Before trials and tribulation, before dirt, and before victory, the GTS class-winning C5-R Corvette pitted for tires, fuel, and a driver change. Hyper-efficient pit stops helped hold its lead, even after a spin put it into the gravel traps. Photo copyright Peter Brock

Mallett's technicians offer a "four-point chassis stiffener," and created this eight-point roll cage and other required safety equipment to meet race rules. The owners added the navigation and timing devices.

(below) Moments from sweet victory, both team cars had spent most of an exceptionally wet race running on rain tires, avoiding disasters on the track, and making up time from frustrating parts failures. At the end of 24 hours, none of it mattered. Photo copyright Peter Brock

From its introduction at Road Atlanta in mid-December 1998, through the 1999 racing season, the C5-R ran silver and black Mr. Goodwrench colors before going to all yellow. Here, in late afternoon during the American LeMans Series, called Petit LeMans, its headlights announce a fast qualifying run was underway. Photo copyright Peter Brock

The 2nd place finisher at Sebring 2001 sits beside a spare engine before the start of the 12-hour race. Mechanics tie-wrapped a spare oil-pump drive belt to an engine mount, a preparation that saved the entry during the 24 Hours of Le Mans four months later. Photo copyright Peter Brock

rear diffusers. FIA rules strictly prescribed horsepower output based on vehicle weight, increasing the technical challenges. To meet the formula, Joe Negri, GM's motorsports engine director, revised engine dimensions from the production Gen III LS1's 346-cubic-inch displacement to 365-cubic-inch displacement. Chevrolet published output as 600 horsepower at 7,200 rpm. By the end of the 24-hour Daytona race, drivers Ron Fellows, John Paul Jr., and Chris Kniefel had nursed their silver and black C5-R #2 through a time-consuming and position-sacrificing morning oil leak to finish 3rd in GT2 and 18th overall, having climbed as high as 5th overall through much of the night. The second car, #4, finished well back after breaking a rear suspension upright. While everyone had hoped for better results, racing is an alchemist's blend of preparation and luck. By season end, Fehan and his crew had learned lessons about parts and tracks. They committed to run at least four events in 2000.

Production numbers for 1999 road-going cars were strong, with a total of 33,270 produced, including 4,031 of the new hardtop that Jim

A who's who of great race drivers has crawled in past the roll cage to drive the C5-R. Throughout 1999, the interior configuration remained vaguely stock, though the beefy white shift lever has yet to appear on any parts option list. Photo copyright Peter Brock

Perkins first envisioned. His plan was to provide privateer racers an "option deleted" fixed-roof version, with cloth seats, no air-conditioning, power steering, brakes, windows, door locks, no radio, and rubber mats in place of interior carpeting. Weekend hobbyists could trailer these to parking lot Auto Cross or SCCA Solo I events. When cost accountants examined Perkins' first proposal, they revised the description because losing the profitable options would cost the division too much. When the hardtop arrived it was well equipped.

CORVETTE HITS LE MANS

Model year 2000 was one of refinements, improvements, revisions, increases, and continuing healthy sales. While the hardtop production dipped almost in half to just 2,090, overall figures totaled 33,682, and Corvette's racing effort officially reached Le Mans. Following a February second-place overall finish behind a French-entered Viper GTS-R, Chevrolet prepared to go abroad. Already plans were floating to promote and sell the C5 in Europe and in Great Britain. European journalists told *Corvette Quarterly* editor John Stein that they considered the Corvette more a touring car than a sports car. That was before the race. When it ended on June 18, one of the Corvettes, #63, having had its racing transmission replaced in 16 minutes, set the quickest laps in GTS class, ahead of every Porsche and faster than the Vipers. With two hours to go, the #64 car lost its starter in the pits, consuming another 12 minutes for the replacement. Then the checkered flag fell. The Corvettes finished 10th and 11th overall, 3rd and 4th in GTS class. Dave Hill, who admitted Le Mans was always in his plans for the C5, told John Stein that he was "very glad we came."

The Corvette has a long served as a platform for the introduction of new technologies, and the C5 is no exception. A heads-up instrument display, drive-by-wire throttle, and a stability control system are all part of the leading-edge C5.

Only the hardtop body was stiff enough to handle the potential of the new LS6 engine and Z06 package. Both numbers harkened back to higher performance times (the LS6 was Chevrolet's monstrous 454-cubic-inch muscle engine in the early 1970s.)

In the fall of 2000, Chevrolet resurrected the Z06 racing model designation that brought wide grins and wild eyes even to Corvette buyers who only wanted to grand tour. Available only in the hardtop body, the 2001 model car reminded historians and racers alike of the ZR-1 models from 1990 and even Duntov's first production racers from 1963. With 385 horsepower in a 3,115-pound car, the Z06 achieved 0–60 miles per hour in 4.0 seconds flat, half a second quicker than the ZR-1s. The car's interior was slightly less refined than the convertibles or coupes, but its nature was performance at the expense of grand touring. Stronger valve springs allowed its LS6 engine to reach 6,500 rpm where the standard LS1 was limited to 6,000 rpm. Under the hood, design and engineering fitted red engine

The Z06 got its own suspension designation for 2002 in the FE45 system. It included a stiffer rear leaf monospring, a larger diameter front stabilizer bar, and revised front camber settings to improve cornering.

The original LS6 Z06 option provided buyers with 385 horsepower. Several internal modifications brought that output up to 405 horsepower for this 2002 model. The original Z06 was a racer's package available in 1963.

The Spartan interior remains. The car is strictly business and that business is 3.9 second 0–60 miles per hour times and quarter miles consumed in 12.4 seconds at 116 miles per hour.

covers, while red-disc brake calipers peeked through the wheels and functional ventilation cooled the rear brake rotors. It arrived as Corvette's highest priced variant, at $47,500, just $500 more than the convertible. Production finished at 5,773 copies for its first year.

On February 1, at Daytona International Speedway, Ron Fellows, Chris Kniefel, Frank Freon, and Johnny O'Connell brought their C5-R home in first place, first overall, and first in class. They were soon followed by the late Dale Earnhardt, his son Dale Jr., Andy Pilgrim, and Kelly Collins, who finished in fourth overall, second in GTS class. The two Corvettes were split by a pair of GT1 Porsches, identical to models that had won Le Mans in 1998. Fellow's car covered 2,335.4 miles averaging 97.3 miles per hour. The results humbled project manager Doug Fehan, who told *Corvette Quarterly* editorial director Jerry Burton, "The fact that we can compete with them at all is testimony to how far we've come and how great a car the Corvette is." Just four-and-a-half months later, Corvettes proved Daytona was no fluke, finishing first and second in GTS class at the 24 Hours of Le Mans and establishing the car's reputation worldwide.

For model year 2002, Chevrolet continued to improve its production Corvettes, boosting Z06 output to a muscle car–era 405 horsepower by fitting slightly softer piston rings, using a well-known NASCAR engine–builder's trick that allows even higher engine speeds. Chevrolet designers and engineers in Detroit and assemblers in Bowling Green did such a good job refining the car that J. D. Power named it the best premium sports car in their Initial Quality Study. Yet the future and time wait for no one.

In a design studio in Pasadena, clay modelers fashion concepts of the C6. Conceived at one time to be the 50th Anniversary model, it has been slipped back like many before it. Those who have been privileged to see the shapes have struggled for words, and then finally, haltingly, concluded that "if they build that one, they'll blow everybody else off the road. Everybody!"

Whether Chevrolet will select one of the Pasadena designs or one of the Warren versions is a question perhaps best left to Las Vegas odds makers, or certainly to GM's new chief executive officer Bob Lutz. The visual lineage of the car has evolved more subtly through the C4 into the C5, while changes from the C1 through the C2 to the C3 were more radical. But these design and engineering decisions are based on money and courage and faith and optimism. The Europeans say that winning at Le Mans is not a one-time thing. They rebuke Audi, which won outright in 1999 but then went into Formula 1. Yet racing is staggeringly expensive and no corporation will continue when

Both the 50th Anniversary logo and the wheel were distinctive and different. The wheel had a unique warmer, more golden color than stock wheels and was only available for the commemorative package. 2002 General Motors Corporation. Used with permission of GM Media Archives.

In a striking departure from the past, the Anniversary models were delivered with a shale—khaki—interior rather than the traditional all-black Corvette interior.

All photos this spread 2002 General Motors Corporation. Used with permission of GM Media Archives.

money gets tight or priorities change or other products need massive infusions. Before year-end 2001, Chevrolet announced it will not sell Corvettes directly in England in 2002. Yet the car has made money and it has made converts. The C4 brought us the ZR1 and world distance records, and the C5 brought us the Z06 and world-class, headline-making racing victories. It is tantalizing to slip into a new Corvette, squint past the heads-up information display, and try to imagine the road ahead for America's sports car.

Getting a jump on its anniversary, the 50th Anniversary Package debuted at the 2002 Indy 500 as the official pace car. Chevrolet had no plans to offer replicas (though it considered offering a pace car graphics package as a dealer option) and only three pace cars were built.

INDEX

GIOVANNI'S

ROOM

James Baldwin

Giovanni's
Room

THE MODERN LIBRARY

NEW YORK

LIBRARY OF CONGRESS CATALOGING-IN-PUBLICATION DATA
Baldwin, James.
Giovanni's room / James Baldwin.
p.   cm.
ISBN 0-679-64219-6
1. Americans—France—Fiction.   2. Sexual orientation—Fiction.
3. Paris (France)—Fiction.   4. Bisexuals—Fiction.   I. Title.
PS3552.A45 G5 2001
813'.54—dc21   00-066205

Modern Library website address: www.modernlibrary.com

Printed in the United States of America
on acid-free paper

2 4 6 8 9 7 5 3 1

JAMES BALDWIN

James Baldwin was born on August 2, 1924, and educated in New York. His first novel, *Go Tell It on the Mountain*, appeared in 1953 to excellent reviews and immediately was recognized as establishing a profound and permanent new voice in American letters. It made him, *The Nation* noted, "read and awaited by perhaps a wider range of people than any other major American writer." The (Chicago) *Sun-Times* called *Go Tell It on the Mountain* "extraordinary," the *Times* of London called it "passionately eloquent," and *Harper's* magazine praised its "poetic intensity and great narrative skill." Arthur Schlesinger wrote that Baldwin "drew himself into the agony he saw around him and charged it with the force of an electric and passionate personality."

Baldwin's play *The Amen Corner* was first performed at Howard University in 1955 (it was staged commercially in the 1960s), and his acclaimed collection of essays *Notes of a Native Son* was published the same year. A second collection of essays, *Nobody Knows My Name*, was published in

1961 between his novels *Giovanni's Room* (1956) and *Another Country* (1961).

The appearance of *The Fire Next Time* in 1963, just as the civil rights movement was exploding across the American South, galvanized the nation. It became a national bestseller, and Baldwin was featured on the cover of *Time* magazine. In 1964 *Blues for Mister Charlie*, his drama based on the murder of a young black man in Mississippi, was produced by the Actors Studio in New York. That same year, Baldwin was made a member of the National Institute of Arts and Letters and collaborated with the photographer Richard Avedon on *Nothing Personal*, a series of portraits of America intended as a eulogy for the slain Medgar Evers. A collection of short stories, *Going to Meet the Man*, was published in 1965, and in 1968 *Tell Me How Long the Train's Been Gone*, his last novel of the 1960s, appeared.

In the 1970s he wrote two more collections of essays and cultural criticism: *No Name in the Street* (1972) and *The Devil Finds Work* (1976). He produced two novels, the bestselling *If Beale Street Could Talk* (1974) and *Just Above My Head* (1979), and also a children's book, *Little Man, Little Man: A Story of Childhood* (1976). He collaborated with Margaret Mead on *A Rap on Race* (1971) and with the poet-activist Nikki Giovanni on *A Dialogue* (1973). He also adapted Alex Haley's *The Autobiography of Malcolm X* into *One Day When I Was Lost*.

In the remaining years of his life, Baldwin produced a volume of poetry, *Jimmy's Blues* (1983), and a final collection of essays, *The Price of the Ticket*. Baldwin's last work, *The Evidence of Things Not Seen* (1985), was prompted by a series of child murders in Atlanta. Baldwin was made a Commander of the French Legion of Honor in June 1986.

Among the other awards he received are a Eugene F. Saxon Memorial Trust Award, a Rosenwald fellowship, a Guggenheim fellowship, a *Partisan Review* fellowship, and a Ford Foundation grant.

James Baldwin died at his home in Saint-Paul-de-Vence in France on December 1, 1987.

FOR LUCIEN

I am the man, I suffered, I was there.

—WHITMAN

PART ONE

ONE

I stand at the window of this great house in the south of France as night falls, the night which is leading me to the most terrible morning of my life. I have a drink in my hand, there is a bottle at my elbow. I watch my reflection in the darkening gleam of the window pane. My reflection is tall, perhaps rather like an arrow, my blond hair gleams. My face is like a face you have seen many times. My ancestors conquered a continent, pushing across death-laden plains, until they came to an ocean which faced away from Europe into a darker past.

I may be drunk by morning but that will not do any good. I shall take the train to Paris anyway. The train will be the same, the people, struggling for comfort and, even, dignity on the straight-backed, wooden, third-class seats will be the same, and I will be the same. We will ride through the same changing countryside northward, leaving behind the olive trees and the sea and all of the glory of the stormy southern sky, into the mist and rain of Paris. Someone will offer to share a sandwich with me, someone will offer me a sip of wine, someone will ask me for a match. People will be roaming the corridors outside, looking out of windows, looking in at us. At each stop, recruits in their baggy brown uniforms and colored hats will open the compartment door to ask *Complet?* We will all nod Yes, like conspirators, smiling faintly at each other as they continue through the train. Two or three of them will end up before our compartment door, shouting at each other in their heavy, ribald voices, smoking their dreadful army cigarettes. There will be a girl sitting opposite me who will wonder why I have not been flirting with her, who will be set on edge by the presence of the recruits. It will all be the same, only I will be stiller.

And the countryside is still tonight, this countryside reflected through my image in the pane. This house is just outside a small summer resort—which is still empty, the season has not yet begun. It is on a small hill, one can look down on the lights of the town and hear the thud of the sea. My girl, Hella, and I rented it in Paris, from photographs, some months ago. Now she has been gone a week. She is on the high seas now, on her way back to America.

I can see her, very elegant, tense, and glittering, surrounded by the light which fills the salon of the ocean liner, drinking rather too fast, and laughing, and watching the men. That was how I met her, in a bar in Saint-Germain-des-Prés, she was drinking and watching, and that was why I liked her, I thought she would be fun to have fun with. That was how it began, that was all it meant to me; I am not sure now, in spite of everything, that it ever really meant more than that to me. And I don't think it ever really meant more than that to her—at least not until she made that trip to Spain and, finding herself there, alone, began to wonder, perhaps, if a lifetime of drinking and watching the men was exactly what she wanted. But it was too late by that time. I was already with Giovanni. I had asked her to marry me before she went away to Spain; and she laughed and I laughed but that, somehow, all the same, made it more serious for me, and I persisted; and then she said she would have to go away and think about it. And the very last night she was here, the very last time I saw her, as she was packing her bag, I told her that I had loved her once and I made myself believe it. But I wonder if I had. I was thinking, no doubt, of our nights in bed, of the peculiar innocence and confidence, which will never come again, which had made those nights so delightful, so unrelated to past, present, or anything to come, so unrelated, finally, to my life since it was not necessary for me to take any but the most mechanical responsibility for them. And these nights were being acted out under a foreign sky, with no one to watch, no penalties attached—it was this last fact which was our undoing, for nothing is more unbearable, once one has it, than freedom. I suppose this was why I asked her to marry me: to give myself something to be moored to. Perhaps this was why, in Spain, she decided that she wanted to marry me. But people can't, unhappily, invent their mooring posts, their lovers and their friends, anymore than they can invent their parents. Life gives these and also takes them away and the great difficulty is to say Yes to life.

I was thinking, when I told Hella that I had loved her, of those days before anything awful, irrevocable, had happened to me, when an affair was nothing more than an affair. Now, from this night, this coming morning, no matter how many beds I find myself in between now and my final bed, I shall never be able to have any more of those boyish, zestful affairs—which are, really, when one thinks of it, a kind of higher, or, anyway, more pretentious masturbation.

People are too various to be treated so lightly. I am too various to be trusted. If this were not so I would not be alone in this house tonight. Hella would not be on the high seas. And Giovanni would not be about to perish, sometime between this night and this morning, on the guillotine.

———

I repent now—for all the good it does—one particular lie among the many lies I've told, told, lived, and believed. This is the lie which I told to Giovanni but never succeeded in making him believe, that I had never slept with a boy before. I had. I had decided that I never would again. There is something fantastic in the spectacle I now present to myself of having run so far, so hard, across the ocean even, only to find myself brought up short once more before the bulldog in my own backyard—the yard, in the meantime, having grown smaller and the bulldog bigger.

I have not thought of that boy—Joey—for many years; but I see him quite clearly tonight. It was several years ago. I was still in my teens, he was about my age, give or take a year. He was a very nice boy, too, very quick and dark, and always laughing. For a while he was my best friend. Later, the idea that such a person *could* have been my best friend was proof of some horrifying taint in me. So I forgot him. But I see him very well tonight.

It was in the summer, there was no school. His parents had gone someplace for the weekend and I was spending the weekend at his house, which was near Coney Island, in Brooklyn. We lived in Brooklyn too, in those days, but in a better neighborhood than Joey's. I think we had been lying around the beach, swimming a little and watching the near-naked girls pass, whistling at them and laughing. I am sure that if any of the girls we whistled at that day had shown any signs of responding, the ocean would not have been deep enough to drown our shame and terror. But the girls, no doubt, had some intimation of this, possibly from the way we whistled, and they ignored us. As the sun was setting we started up the boardwalk towards his house, with our wet bathing trunks on under our trousers.

And I think it began in the shower. I know that I felt something—as we were horsing around in that small, steamy room, stinging each other with wet towels—which I had not felt before, which mysteriously, and yet aimlessly, included him. I remember in myself a heavy reluctance to get dressed: I blamed it on the heat. But we did get dressed, sort of, and we ate cold things out of his icebox and drank a lot of beer. We must have gone to the movies. I can't think of any other reason for our going out and I remember walking down the dark, tropical Brooklyn streets with heat coming up from the pavements and banging from the walls of houses with enough force to kill a man, with all the world's grownups, it seemed, sitting shrill and dishevelled on the stoops and all the world's children on the sidewalks or in the gutters or hanging from fire escapes, with my arm around Joey's shoulder. I was proud, I think, because his head came just below my ear. We were walking along and Joey was making dirty wisecracks and we were laughing. Odd to remember, for the first time in so long, how good I felt that night, how fond of Joey.

When we came back along those streets it was quiet; we were quiet too. We were very quiet in the apartment and sleepily got undressed in Joey's bedroom and went to bed. I fell asleep—for quite a while, I think. But I woke up to find the light on and Joey examining the pillow with great, ferocious care.

"What's the matter?"

"I think a bedbug bit me."

"You slob. You got bedbugs?"

"I think one bit me."

"You ever have a bedbug bite you before?"

"No."

"Well, go back to sleep. You're dreaming."

He looked at me with his mouth open and his dark eyes very big. It was as though he had just discovered that I was an expert on bedbugs. I laughed and grabbed his head as I had done God knows how many times before, when I was playing with him or when he had annoyed me. But this time when I touched him something happened in him and in me which made this touch different from any touch either of us had ever known. And he did not resist, as he usually did, but lay where I had pulled him, against my chest. And I realized that my heart was beating in an awful way and that Joey was trembling against me and the light in the room was very bright and hot. I started to move and to make some kind of joke but Joey mumbled something and I put my head down to hear. Joey raised his head as I lowered mine and we kissed, as it were, by accident. Then, for the first time in my life, I was really aware of another person's body, of another person's smell. We had our arms around each other. It was like holding in my hand some rare, exhausted, nearly doomed bird which I had miraculously happened to find. I was very frightened; I am sure he was frightened too, and we shut our eyes. To remember it so clearly, so painfully tonight tells me that I have never for an instant truly forgotten it. I feel in myself now a faint, a dreadful stirring of what so overwhelmingly stirred in me then, great thirsty heat, and trembling, and tenderness so painful I thought my heart would burst. But out of this astounding, intolerable pain came joy; we gave each other joy that night. It seemed, then, that a lifetime would not be long enough for me to act with Joey the act of love.

But that lifetime was short, was bounded by that night— it ended in the morning. I awoke while Joey was still sleeping, curled like a baby on his side, toward me. He looked like a baby, his mouth half open, his cheek flushed, his curly hair darkening the pillow and half hiding his damp round forehead and his long eyelashes glinting slightly in the summer sun. We were both naked and the sheet we had used as a cover was tangled around our feet. Joey's body was brown, was sweaty, the most beautiful creation I had ever seen till then. I would have touched him to wake him up but something stopped me. I was suddenly afraid. Perhaps it was because he looked so innocent lying there, with such perfect trust; perhaps it was because he was so much smaller than me; my own body suddenly seemed gross and crushing and the desire which was rising in me seemed monstrous. But, above all, I was suddenly afraid. It was borne in on me: *But Joey is a boy.* I saw suddenly the power in his thighs, in his arms, and in his loosely curled fists. The power and the promise and the mystery of that body made me suddenly afraid. That body suddenly seemed the black opening of a cavern in which I would be tortured till madness came, in which I would lose my manhood. Precisely, I wanted to know that mystery and feel that power and have that promise fulfilled through me. The sweat on my back grew cold. I was ashamed. The very bed, in its sweet disorder, testified to vileness. I wondered what Joey's mother would say when she saw the sheets. Then I thought of my father, who had no one in the world but me, my mother having died when I was little. A cavern opened in my mind, black, full of rumor, suggestion, of half-heard, half-forgotten, half-understood stories, full of dirty words. I thought I saw my future in that cavern. I was afraid. I could have cried, cried for shame and terror, cried for not understanding how this could have happened to me, how this could have happened *in* me. And I made my decision. I got out of bed and took a shower and was dressed and had breakfast ready when Joey woke up.

I did not tell him my decision; that would have broken my will. I did not wait to have breakfast with him but only drank some coffee and made an excuse to go home. I knew the excuse did not fool Joey; but he did not know how to protest or insist; he did not know that this was all he needed to have done. Then I, who had seen him that summer nearly every day till then, no longer went to see him. He did not come to see me. I would have been very happy to see him if he had, but the manner of my leave-taking had begun a constriction, which neither of us knew how to arrest. When I finally did see him, more or less by accident, near the end of the summer, I made up a long and totally untrue story about a girl I was going with and when school began again I picked up with a rougher, older crowd and was very nasty to Joey. And the sadder this made him, the nastier I became. He moved away at last, out of the neighborhood, away from our school, and I never saw him again.

I began, perhaps, to be lonely that summer and began, that summer, the flight which has brought me to this darkening window.

And yet—when one begins to search for the crucial, the definitive moment, the moment which changed all others, one finds oneself pressing, in great pain, through a maze of false signals and abruptly locking doors. My flight may, indeed, have begun that summer—which does not tell me where to find the germ of the dilemma which resolved itself, that summer, into flight. Of course, it is somewhere before me, locked in that reflection I am watching in the window as the night comes down outside. It is trapped in the room with me, always has been, and always will be, and it is yet more foreign to me than those foreign hills outside.

We lived in Brooklyn then, as I say; we had also lived in San Francisco, where I was born, and where my mother lies buried, and we lived for awhile in Seattle, and then in New York—for me, New York is Manhattan. Later on, then, we moved from Brooklyn back to New York and by the time I came to France my father and his new wife had graduated to Connecticut. I had long been on my own by then, of course, and had been living in an apartment in the east sixties.

We, in the days when I was growing up, were my father and his unmarried sister and myself. My mother had been carried to the graveyard when I was five. I scarcely remember her at all, yet she figured in my nightmares, blind with worms, her hair as dry as metal and brittle as a twig, straining to press me against her body; that body so putrescent, so sickening soft, that it opened, as I clawed and cried, into a breach so enormous as to swallow me alive. But when my father or my aunt came rushing into my room to find out what had frightened me, I did not dare describe this dream, which seemed disloyal to my mother. I said that I had dreamed about a graveyard. They concluded that the death of my mother had had this unsettling effect on my imagination and perhaps they thought that I was grieving for her. And I may have been, but if that is so, then I am grieving still.

My father and my aunt got on very badly and, without ever knowing how or why I felt it, I felt that their long battle had everything to do with my dead mother. I remember when I was very young how, in the big living room of the house in San Francisco, my mother's photograph, which stood all by itself on the mantelpiece, seemed to rule the room. It was as though her photograph proved how her spirit dominated that air and controlled us all. I remember the shadows gathering in the far corners of that room, in which I never felt at home, and my father washed in the gold light which spilled down on him from the tall lamp which stood beside his easy chair. He would be reading his newspaper, hidden from me behind his newspaper, so that, desperate to conquer his attention, I sometimes so annoyed him that our duel ended with me being carried from the room in tears. Or I remember him sitting bent forward, his elbows on his knees, staring towards the great window which held back the inky night. I used to wonder what he was thinking. In the eye of my memory he always wears a grey, sleeveless sweater and he has loosened his tie, and his sandy hair falls forward over a square, ruddy face. He was one of those people who, quick to laugh, are slow to anger; so that their anger, when it comes, is all the more impressive, seeming to leap from some unsuspected crevice like a fire which will bring the whole house down.

And his sister Ellen, a little older than he, a little darker, always overdressed, overmade-up, with a face and figure beginning to harden, and with too much jewelry everywhere, clanging and banging in the light, sits on the sofa, reading; she read a lot, all the new books, and she used to go to the movies a great deal. Or she knits. It seems to me that she was always carrying a great bag full of dangerous-looking knitting needles, or a book, or both. And I don't know what she knitted, though I suppose she must, at least occasionally, have knitted something for my father, or me. But I don't remember it, anymore than I remember the books she read. It might always have been the same book and she might have been working on the same scarf, or sweater, or God knows what, all the years I knew her. Sometimes she and my father played cards—this was rare; sometimes they talked together in friendly, teasing tones, but this was dangerous. Their banter nearly always ended in a fight. Sometimes there was company and I was often allowed to watch them drink their cocktails. Then my father was at his best, boyish and expansive, moving about through the crowded room with a glass in his hand, refilling people's drinks, laughing a lot, handling all the men as though they were his brothers, and flirting with the women. Or no, not flirting with them, strutting like a cock before them. Ellen always seemed to be watching him as though she were afraid he would do something awful, watched him and watched the women and, yes, she flirted with the men in a strange, nerve-wracking kind of way. There she was, dressed, as they say, to kill, with her mouth redder than any blood, dressed in something which was either the wrong color, or too tight, or too young, the cocktail glass in her hand threatening, at any instant, to be reduced to shards, to splinters, and that voice going on and on like a razor blade on glass. When I was a little boy and I watched her in company, she frightened me.

But no matter what was happening in that room, my mother was watching it. She looked out of the photograph frame, a pale, blonde woman, delicately put together, dark-eyed, and straight-browed, with a nervous, gentle mouth. But something about the way the eyes were set in the head and stared straight out, something very faintly sardonic and knowing in the set of the mouth suggested that, somewhere beneath this tense fragility was a strength as various as it was unyielding and, like my father's wrath, dangerous because it was so entirely unexpected. My father rarely spoke of her and when he did he covered, by some mysterious means, his face; he spoke of her only as my mother and, in fact, as he spoke of her, he might have been speaking of his own. Ellen spoke of my mother often, saying what a remarkable woman she had been, but she made me uncomfortable. I felt that I had no right to be the son of such a mother.

Years later, when I had become a man, I tried to get my father to talk about my mother. But Ellen was dead, he was about to marry again. He spoke of my mother, then, as Ellen had spoken of her and he might, indeed, have been speaking of Ellen.

They had a fight one night when I was about thirteen. They had a great many fights, of course; but perhaps I remember this one so clearly because it seemed to be about me.

I was in bed upstairs, asleep. It was quite late. I was suddenly awakened by the sound of my father's footfalls on the walk beneath my window. I could tell by the sound and the rhythm that he was a little drunk and I remember that at that moment a certain disappointment, an unprecedented sorrow entered into me. I had seen him drunk many times and had never felt this way—on the contrary, my father sometimes had great charm when he was drunk—but that night I suddenly felt that there was something in it, in him, to be despised.

I heard him come in. Then, at once, I heard Ellen's voice.

"Aren't you in bed yet?" my father asked. He was trying to be pleasant and trying to avoid a scene, but there was no cordiality in his voice, only strain and exasperation.

"I thought," said Ellen, coldly, "that someone ought to tell you what you're doing to your son."

"What I'm doing to my son?" And he was about to say something more, something awful; but he caught himself and only said, with a resigned, drunken, despairing calm: "What are you talking about, Ellen?"

"Do you really think," she asked—I was certain that she was standing in the center of the room, with her hands folded before her, standing very straight and still—"that you're the kind of man he ought to be when he grows up?" And, as my father said nothing: "He *is* growing up, you know." And then, spitefully, "Which is more than I can say for you."

"Go to bed, Ellen," said my father—sounding very weary.

I had the feeling, since they were talking about me, that I ought to go downstairs and tell Ellen that whatever was wrong between my father and myself we could work out between us without her help. And, perhaps—which seems odd—I felt that she was disrespectful of *me*. For I had certainly never said a word to her about my father.

I heard his heavy, uneven footfalls as he moved across the room, towards the stairs.

"Don't think," said Ellen, "that I don't know where you've been."

"I've been out—drinking—" said my father, "and now I'd like to get a little sleep. Do you mind?"

"You've been with that girl, Beatrice," said Ellen. "That's where you always are and that's where all your money goes and all your manhood and self-respect, too."

She had succeeded in making him angry. He began to stammer. "If you think—if you *think*—that I'm going to stand—stand—stand here—and argue with *you* about my private life—*my* private life!—if you think I'm going to argue with *you* about it, why, you're out of your mind."

"I certainly don't care," said Ellen, "what you do with yourself. It isn't *you* I'm worried about. It's only that you're the only person who has any authority over David. I don't. And he hasn't got any mother. And he only listens to me when he thinks it pleases you. Do you really think it's a good idea for David to see you staggering home drunk all the time? And don't fool yourself," she added, after a moment, in a voice thick with passion, "don't fool yourself that he doesn't know where you're coming from, don't think he doesn't know about your women!"

She was wrong. I don't think I did know about them—or I had never thought about them. But from that evening, I thought about them all the time. I could scarcely ever face a woman without wondering whether or not my father had, in Ellen's phrase, been "interfering" with her.

"I think it barely possible," said my father, "that David has a cleaner mind than yours."

The silence, then, in which my father climbed the stairs was by far the worst silence my life had ever known. I was wondering what they were thinking—each of them. I wondered how they looked. I wondered what I would see when I saw them in the morning.

"And listen," said my father suddenly, from the middle of the staircase, in a voice which frightened me, "all I want for David is that he grow up to be a man. And when I say a man, Ellen, I don't mean a Sunday school teacher."

"A man," said Ellen, shortly, "is not the same thing as a bull. Good-night."

"Good-night," he said, after a moment.

And I heard him stagger past my door.

From that time on, with the mysterious, cunning, and dreadful intensity of the very young, I despised my father and I hated Ellen. It is hard to say why. I don't know why. But it allowed all of Ellen's prophecies about me to come true. She had said that there would come a time when nothing and nobody would be able to rule me, not even my father. And that time certainly came.

It was after Joey. The incident with Joey had shaken me profoundly and its effect was to make me secretive and cruel. I could not discuss what had happened to me with anyone, I could not even admit it to myself; and, while I never thought about it, it remained, nevertheless, at the bottom of my mind, as still and as awful as a decomposing corpse. And it changed, it thickened, it soured the atmosphere of my mind. Soon it was I who came staggering home late at night, it was I who found Ellen waiting up for me, Ellen and I who wrangled night in and night out.

My father's attitude was that this was but an inevitable phase of my growing up and he affected to take it lightly. But beneath his jocular, boys-together air, he was at a loss, he was frightened. Perhaps he had supposed that my growing up would bring us closer together—whereas, now that he was trying to find out something about me, I was in full flight from him. I did not *want* him to know me. I did not want anyone to know me. And then, again, I was undergoing with my father what the very young inevitably undergo with their elders: I was beginning to judge him. And the very harshness of this judgment, which broke my heart, revealed, though I could not have said it then, how much I had loved him, how that love, along with my innocence, was dying.

My poor father was baffled and afraid. He was unable to

believe that there could be anything seriously wrong between us. And this was not only because he would not then
have known what to do about it; it was mainly because he
would then have had to face the knowledge that he had left
something, somewhere, undone, something of the utmost
importance. And since neither of us had any idea of what
this so significant omission could have been, and since we
were forced to remain in tacit league against Ellen, we took
refuge in being hearty with each other. We were not like
father and son, my father sometimes proudly said, we were
like buddies. I think my father sometimes actually believed
this. I never did. I did not want to be his buddy; I wanted to
be his son. What passed between us as masculine candor
exhausted and appalled me. Fathers ought to avoid utter
nakedness before their sons. I did not want to know—not,
anyway, from his mouth—that his flesh was as unregener-
ate as my own. The knowledge did not make me feel more
like his son—or buddy—it only made me feel like an in-
terloper, and a frightened one at that. He thought we were
alike. I did not want to think so. I did not want to think that
my life would be like his, or that my mind would ever grow
so pale, so without hard places and sharp, sheer drops. He
wanted no distance between us; he wanted me to look on
him as a man like myself. But I wanted the merciful distance of father and son, which would have permitted me to
love him.

One night, drunk, with several other people on the way
back from an out-of-town party, the car I was driving
smashed up. It was entirely my fault. I was almost too
drunk to walk and had no business driving; but the others
did not know this, since I am one of those people who can
look and sound sober while practically in a state of col-
lapse. On a straight, level piece of highway something

weird happened to all my reactions, and the car sprang suddenly out of my control. And a telephone pole, foam-white, came crying at me out of the pitch darkness; I heard screams and then a heavy, roaring, tearing sound. Then everything turned absolutely scarlet and then as bright as day and I went into a darkness I had never known before.

I must have begun to wake up as we were being moved to the hospital. I dimly remember movement and voices, but they seemed very far away, they seemed to have nothing to do with me. Then, later, I woke up in a spot which seemed to be the very heart of winter, a high, white ceiling and white walls, and a hard, glacial window, bent, as it seemed, over me. I must have tried to rise, for I remember an awful roaring in my head, and then a weight on my chest and a huge face over me. And as this weight, this face, began to push me under again, I screamed for my mother. Then it was dark again.

When I came to myself at last, my father was standing over my bed. I knew he was there before I saw him, before my eyes focused and I carefully turned my head. When he saw that I was awake, he carefully stepped closer to the bed, motioning to me to be still. And he looked very old. I wanted to cry. For a moment we just stared at each other.

"How do you feel?" he whispered, finally.

It was when I tried to speak that I realized I was in pain and immediately I was frightened. He must have seen this in my eyes, for he said in a low voice, with a pained, a mar-vellous intensity, "Don't worry, David. You're going to be all right. You're going to be all right."

I still could not say anything. I simply watched his face.

"You kids were mighty lucky," he said, trying to smile. "You're the one got smashed up the most."

"I was drunk," I said at last. I wanted to tell him everything—but speaking was such agony.

"Don't you know," he asked, with an air of extreme bafflement—for this was something he could allow himself to be baffled about—"better than to go driving around like that when you're drunk? You know better than that," he said, severely, and pursed his lips. "Why you could all have been killed." And his voice shook.

"I'm sorry," I said, suddenly. "I'm sorry." I did not know how to say what it was I was sorry for.

"Don't be sorry," he said. "Just be careful next time." He had been patting his handkerchief between his palms; now he opened his handkerchief and reached out and wiped my forehead. "You're all I've got," he said then, with a shy, pained grin. "Be careful."

"Daddy," I said. And began to cry. And if speaking had been agony, this was worse and yet I could not stop.

And my father's face changed. It became terribly old and at the same time absolutely, helplessly young. I remember being absolutely astonished, at the still, cold center of the storm which was occurring in me, to realize that my father had been suffering, was suffering still.

"Don't cry," he said, "don't cry." He stroked my forehead with that absurd handkerchief as though it possessed some healing charm. "There's nothing to cry about. Everything's going to be all right." He was almost weeping himself. "There's nothing wrong, is there? I haven't done anything wrong, have I?" And all the time he was stroking my face with that handkerchief, smothering me.

"We were drunk," I said. "We were drunk." For this seemed, somehow, to explain everything.

"Your Aunt Ellen says it's my fault," he said. "She says I

never raised you right." He put away, thank heaven, that handkerchief, and weakly straightened his shoulders. "You got nothing against me, have you? Tell me if you have?"

My tears began to dry, on my face and in my breast. "No," I said, "no. Nothing. Honest."

"I did the best I could," he said. "I really did the best I could." I looked at him. And at last he grinned and said, "You're going to be on your back for awhile but when you come home, while you're lying around the house, we'll talk, huh? and try to figure out what the hell we're going to do with you when you get on your feet. OK?"

"OK," I said.

For I understood, at the bottom of my heart, that we had never talked, that now we never would. I understood that he must never know this. When I came home he talked with me about my future but I had made up my mind. I was not going to go to college, I was not going to remain in that house with him and Ellen. And I maneuvered my father so well that he actually began to believe that my finding a job and being on my own was the direct result of his advice and a tribute to the way he had raised me. Once I was out of the house of course, it became much easier to deal with him and he never had any reason to feel shut out of my life for I was always able, when talking about it, to tell him what he wished to hear. And we got on quite well, really, for the vision I gave my father of my life was exactly the vision in which I myself most desperately needed to believe.

For I am—or I was—one of those people who pride themselves on their willpower, on their ability to make a decision and carry it through. This virtue, like most virtues, is ambiguity itself. People who believe that they are strong-willed and the masters of their destiny can only continue to believe this by becoming specialists in self-deception. Their decisions are not really decisions at all—a real decision makes one humble, one knows that it is at the mercy of more things than can be named—but elaborate systems of evasion, of illusion, designed to make themselves and the world appear to be what they and the world are not. This is certainly what my decision, made so long ago in Joey's bed, came to. I had decided to allow no room in the universe for something which shamed and frightened me. I succeeded very well—by not looking at the universe, by not looking at myself, by remaining, in effect, in constant motion. Even constant motion, of course, does not prevent an occasional mysterious drag, a drop, like an airplane hitting an air pocket. And there were a number of those, all drunken, all sordid, one very frightening such drop while I was in the Army which involved a fairy who was later court-martialed out. The panic his punishment caused in me was as close as I ever came to facing in myself the terrors I sometimes saw clouding another man's eyes.

What happened was that, all unconscious of what this ennui meant, I wearied of the motion, wearied of the joyless seas of alcohol, wearied of the blunt, bluff, hearty, and totally meaningless friendships, wearied of wandering through the forests of desperate women, wearied of the work, which fed me only in the most brutally literal sense. Perhaps, as we say in America, I wanted to find myself. This is an interesting phrase, not current as far as I know in the language of any other people, which certainly does not mean what it says but betrays a nagging suspicion that something has been misplaced. I think now that if I had had any intimation that the self I was going to find would turn out to be only the same self from which I had spent so much time in flight, I would have stayed at home. But, again, I think I knew, at the very bottom of my heart, exactly what I was doing when I took the boat for France.

TWO

I met Giovanni during my second year in Paris, when I had no money. On the morning of the evening that we met I had been turned out of my room. I did not owe an awful lot of money, only around six thousand francs, but Parisian hotel-keepers have a way of smelling poverty and then they do what anybody does who is aware of a bad smell; they throw whatever stinks outside.

My father had money in his account which belonged to me but he was very reluctant to send it because he wanted me to come home—to come home, as he said, and settle down, and whenever he said that I thought of the sediment at the bottom of a stagnant pond. I did not, then, know many people in Paris and Hella was in Spain. Most of the people I knew in Paris were, as Parisians sometimes put it, of *le milieu* and, while this milieu was certainly anxious enough to claim me, I was intent on proving, to them and to myself, that I was not of their company. I did this by being in their company a great deal and manifesting toward all of them a tolerance which placed me, I believed, above suspicion. I had written to friends for money, of course, but the Atlantic Ocean is deep and wide and money doesn't hurry from the other side.

So I went through my address book, sitting over a tepid coffee in a boulevard cafe, and decided to call up an old acquaintance who was always asking me to call, an aging, Belgian-born, American businessman named Jacques. He had a big, comfortable apartment and lots of things to drink and lots of money. He was, as I knew he would be, surprised to hear from me and before the surprise and the charm wore off, giving him time to become wary, he had invited me for supper. He may have been cursing as he hung up, and reaching for his wallet, but it was too late. Jacques is not too bad. Perhaps he is a fool and a coward but almost everybody is one or the other and most people are both. In some ways I liked him. He was silly but he was so lonely; anyway, I understand now that the contempt I felt for him involved my self-contempt. He could be unbelievably generous, he could be unspeakably stingy. Though he wanted to trust everybody, he was incapable of trusting a living soul; to make up for this, he threw his money away on people; inevitably, then, he was abused. Then he buttoned his wallet, locked his door, and retired into that strong self-pity which was, perhaps, the only thing he had which really belonged to him. I thought for a long while that he, with his big apartment, his well-meant promises, his whiskey, his marijuana, his orgies, had helped to kill Giovanni. As, indeed, perhaps he had. But Jacques' hands are certainly no bloodier than mine.

I saw Jacques, as a matter of fact, just after Giovanni was sentenced. He was sitting bundled up in his greatcoat on the terrace of a cafe, drinking a *vin chaud*. He was alone on the terrace. He called me as I passed.

He did not look well, his face was mottled, his eyes, behind his glasses, were like the eyes of a dying man who looks everywhere for healing.

"You've heard," he whispered, as I joined him, "about Giovanni?"

I nodded yes. I remember the winter sun was shining and I felt as cold and distant as the sun.

"It's terrible, terrible, terrible," Jacques moaned. "Terrible."

"Yes," I said. I could not say anything more.

"I wonder why he did it," Jacques pursued, "why he didn't ask his friends to help him." He looked at me. We both knew that the last time Giovanni had asked Jacques for money, Jacques had refused. I said nothing. "They say he had started taking opium," Jacques said, "that he needed the money for opium. Did you hear that?"

I had heard it. It was a newspaper speculation which, however, I had reasons of my own for believing, remembering the extent of Giovanni's desperation, knowing how far this terror, which was so vast that it had simply become a void, had driven him. "Me, I want to escape," he had told me, "*Je veux m'evader*—this dirty world, this dirty body. I never wish to make love again with anything more than the body."

Jacques waited for me to answer. I stared out into the street. I was beginning to think of Giovanni dying—where Giovanni had been there would be nothing, nothing forever.

"I hope it's not my fault," Jacques said at last. "I didn't give him the money. If I'd known—I would have given him everything I had."

But we both knew this was not true.

"You two together," Jacques suggested, "you weren't happy together?"

"No," I said. I stood up. "It might have been better," I said, "if he'd stayed down there in that village of his in Italy and planted his olive trees and had a lot of children and beaten his wife. He used to love to sing," I remembered suddenly, "maybe he could have stayed down there and sung his life away and died in bed."

Then Jacques said something that surprised me. People are full of surprises, even for themselves, if they have been stirred enough. "Nobody can stay in the garden of Eden," Jacques said. And then: "I wonder why."

I said nothing. I said goodbye and left him. Hella had long since returned from Spain and we were already arranging to rent this house and I had a date to meet her.

I have thought about Jacques' question since. The question is banal but one of the real troubles with living is that living is so banal. Everyone, after all, goes the same dark road—and the road has a trick of being most dark, most treacherous, when it seems most bright—and it's true that nobody stays in the garden of Eden. Jacques' garden was not the same as Giovanni's, of course. Jacques' garden was involved with football players and Giovanni's was involved with maidens—but that seems to have made so little difference. Perhaps everybody has a garden of Eden, I don't know; but they have scarcely seen their garden before they see the flaming sword. Then, perhaps, life only offers the choice of remembering the garden or forgetting it. Either, or: it takes strength to remember, it takes another kind of strength to forget, it takes a hero to do both. People who remember court madness through pain, the pain of the perpetually recurring death of their innocence; people who forget court another kind of madness, the madness of the denial of pain and the hatred of innocence; and the world is mostly divided between madmen who remember and madmen who forget. Heroes are rare.

Jacques had not wanted to have supper in his apartment because his cook had run away. His cooks were always running away. He was always getting young boys from the provinces, God knows how, to come up and be cooks; and they, of course, as soon as they were able to find their way around the capital, decided that cooking was the last thing they wanted to do. They usually ended up going back to the provinces, those, that is, who did not end up on the streets, or in jail, or in Indochina.

I met him at a rather nice restaurant on the rue de Grenelle and arranged to borrow ten thousand francs from him before we had finished our aperitifs. He was in a good mood and I, of course, was in a good mood too, and this meant that we would end up drinking in Jacques' favorite bar, a noisy, crowded, ill-lit sort of tunnel, of dubious— or perhaps not dubious at all, of rather too emphatic— reputation. Every once in a while it was raided by the police, apparently with the connivance of Guillaume, the *patron,* who always managed, on the particular evening, to warn his favorite customers that if they were not armed with identification papers they might be better off elsewhere.

I remember that the bar, that night, was more than ordinarily crowded and noisy. All of the habitués were there and many strangers, some looking, some just staring. There were three or four very chic Parisian ladies sitting at a table with their gigolos or their lovers or perhaps simply their country cousins, God knows; the ladies seemed extremely animated, their males seemed rather stiff; the ladies seemed to be doing most of the drinking. There were the usual paunchy, bespectacled gentlemen with avid, sometimes despairing eyes, the usual, knife-blade lean, tight-trousered boys. One could never be sure, as concerns these latter, whether they were after money or blood or love. They moved about the bar incessantly, cadging cigarettes and drinks, with something behind their eyes at once terribly vulnerable and terribly hard. There were, of course, *les folles,* always dressed in the most improbable combinations, screaming like parrots the details of their latest love affairs—their love affairs always seemed to be hilarious. Occasionally one would swoop in, quite late in the evening, to convey the news that he—but they always called each other "she"—had just spent time with a celebrated movie star, or boxer. Then all of the others closed in on this newcomer and they looked like a peacock garden and sounded like a barnyard. I always found it difficult to believe that they ever went to bed with anybody, for a man who wanted a woman would certainly have rather had a real one and a man who wanted a man would certainly not want one of *them.* Perhaps, indeed, that was why they screamed so loud. There was the boy who worked all day, it was said, in the post office, who came out at night wearing makeup and earrings and with his heavy blond hair piled high. Sometimes he actually wore a skirt and high heels. He usually stood alone unless Guillaume walked over to tease him. People said that he was very nice, but I confess that his utter grotesqueness made me uneasy; perhaps in the same way that the sight of monkeys eating their own excrement turns some people's stomachs. They might not mind so much if monkeys did not—so grotesquely— resemble human beings.

This bar was practically in my *quartier* and I had many

times had breakfast in the nearby workingman's cafe to which all the nightbirds of the neighborhood retired when the bars closed. Sometimes I was with Hella; sometimes I was alone. And I had been in this bar, too, two or three times; once very drunk, I had been accused of causing a minor sensation by flirting with a soldier. My memory of that night was, happily, very dim, and I took the attitude that no matter how drunk I may have been, I could not possibly have done such a thing. But my face was known and I had the feeling that people were taking bets about me. Or, it was as though they were the elders of some strange and austere holy order and were watching me in order to discover, by means of signs I made but which only they could read, whether or not I had a true vocation.

Jacques was aware, I was aware, as we pushed our way to the bar—it was like moving into the field of a magnet or like approaching a small circle of heat—of the presence of a new barman. He stood, insolent and dark and leonine, his elbow leaning on the cash register, his fingers playing with his chin, looking out at the crowd. It was as though his station were a promontory and we were the sea.

Jacques was immediately attracted. I felt him, so to speak, preparing himself for conquest. I felt the necessity for tolerance.

"I'm sure," I said, "that you'll want to get to know the barman. So I'll vanish anytime you like."

There was, in this tolerance of mind, a fund, by no means meagre, of malicious knowledge—I had drawn on it when I called him up to borrow money. I knew that Jacques could only hope to conquer the boy before us if the boy was, in effect, for sale; and if he stood with such arrogance on an auction block he could certainly find bidders richer and more attractive than Jacques. I knew that Jacques knew this. I knew something else: that Jacques' vaunted affection for me was involved with desire, the desire, in fact, to be rid of me, to be able, soon, to despise me as he now despised that army of boys who had come, without love, to his bed. I held my own against this desire by pretending that Jacques and I were friends, by forcing Jacques, on pain of humiliation, to pretend this. I pretended not to see, although I exploited it, the lust not quite sleeping in his bright, bitter eyes and, by means of the rough, male candor with which I conveyed to him his case was hopeless, I compelled him, endlessly, to hope. And I knew, finally, that in bars such as these I was Jacques' protection. As long as I was there the world could see and he could believe that he was out with me, his friend, he was not there out of desperation, he was not at the mercy of whatever adventurer chance, cruelty, or the laws of actual and emotional poverty might throw his way.

"You stay right here," said Jacques. "I'll look at him from time to time and talk to you and that way I'll save money— and stay happy, too."

"I wonder where Guillaume found him," I said.

For he was so exactly the kind of boy that Guillaume always dreamed of that it scarcely seemed possible that Guillaume could have found him.

"What will you have?" he now asked us. His tone conveyed that, though he spoke no English, he knew that we had been speaking about him and hoped we were through.

"Une fine à l'eau," I said; and *"un cognac sec,"* said Jacques, both speaking too quickly, so that I blushed and realized by a faint merriment on Giovanni's face as he served us that he had seen it.

Jacques, wilfully misinterpreting Giovanni's nuance of a smile, made of it an opportunity. "You're new here?" he asked in English.

Giovanni almost certainly understood the question, but it suited him better to look blankly from Jacques to me and then back again at Jacques. Jacques translated his question.

Giovanni shrugged. "I have been here a month," he said.

I knew where the conversation was going and I kept my eyes down and sipped my drink.

"It must," Jacques suggested, with a sort of bludgeoning insistence on the light touch, "seem very strange to you."

"Strange?" asked Giovanni. "Why?"

And Jacques giggled. I was suddenly ashamed that I was with him. "All these men"—and I knew that voice, breathless, insinuating, high as no girl's had ever been, and hot, suggesting, somehow, the absolutely motionless, deadly heat which hangs over swamp ground in July—"all these men," he gasped, "and so few women. Doesn't that seem strange to you?"

"Ah," said Giovanni, and turned away to serve another customer, "no doubt the women are waiting at home."

"I'm sure one's waiting for you," insisted Jacques, to which Giovanni did not respond.

"Well. That didn't take long," said Jacques, half to me, half to the space which had just held Giovanni. "Aren't you glad you stayed? You've got me all to yourself."

"Oh, you're handling it all wrong," I said. "He's mad for you. He just doesn't want to seem too anxious. Order him a drink. Find out where he likes to buy his clothes. Tell him about that cunning little Alfa Romeo you're just dying to give away to some deserving bartender."

"*Very* funny," said Jacques.

"Well," I said, "faint heart never won fair athlete, that's for sure."

"Anyway, I'm sure he sleeps with girls. They always do, you know."

"I've heard about boys who do that. Nasty little beasts."

We stood in silence for awhile.

"Why don't *you* invite him to have a drink with us?" Jacques suggested.

I looked at him.

"Why don't *I*? Well, you may find this hard to believe, but, actually, I'm sort of queer for girls myself. If that was his sister looking so good, I'd invite *her* to have a drink with us. I don't spend money on men."

I could see Jacques struggling not to say that I didn't have any objection to allowing men to spend money on *me;* I watched his brief struggle with a slight smile, for I knew he couldn't say it; then he said, with that cheery, brave smile of his:

"I was not suggesting that you jeopardize, even for a moment, that"—he paused—"that *immaculate* manhood which is your pride and joy. I only suggested that *you* invite him because he will almost certainly refuse if *I* invite him."

"But man," I said, grinning, "think of the confusion. He'll think that *I'm* the one who's lusting for his body. How do we get out of that?"

"If there should be any confusion," said Jacques, with dignity, "I will be happy to clear it up."

We measured each other for a moment. Then I laughed. "Wait till he comes back this way. I hope he orders a magnum of the most expensive champagne in France."

I turned, leaning on the bar. I felt, somehow, elated.

Jacques, beside me, was very quiet, suddenly very frail and old, and I felt a quick, sharp, rather frightened pity for him. Giovanni had been out on the floor, serving the people at tables, and he now returned with a rather grim smile on his face, carrying a loaded tray.

"Maybe," I said, "it would look better if our glasses were empty."

We finished our drinks. I set down my glass.

"Barman?" I called.

"The same?"

"Yes." He started to turn away. "Barman," I said, quickly, "we would like to offer you a drink, if we may."

"Eh, bien!" said a voice behind us, *"c'est fort ça!* Not only have you finally—thank heaven!—corrupted this great American football player, you use him now to corrupt *my* barman. *Vraiment, Jacques! At your age!"*

It was Guillaume standing behind us, grinning like a movie star, and waving that long white handkerchief which he was never, in the bar at any rate, to be seen without. Jacques turned, hugely delighted to be accused of such rare seductiveness, and he and Guillaume fell into each other arms like old theatrical sisters.

"Eh bien, ma chérie, comment vas-tu? I have not seen you for a long time."

"But I have been awfully busy," said Jacques.

"I don't doubt it! Aren't you ashamed, *vieille folle?"*

"Et toi? You certainly don't seem to have been wasting your time."

And Jacques threw a delighted look in the direction of Giovanni, rather as though Giovanni were a valuable race-horse or a rare bit of china. Guillaume followed the look and his voice dropped.

"Ah, ça, mon cher, c'est strictement du business, *comprends-tu?"*

They moved a little away. This left me surrounded, abruptly, with an awful silence. At last I raised my eyes and looked at Giovanni, who was watching me.

"I think you offered me a drink," he said.

"Yes," I said. "I offered you a drink."

"I drink no alcohol while I work, but I will take a Coca-Cola." He picked up my glass. "And for you—it is the same?"

"The same." I realized that I was quite happy to be talking with him and this realization made me shy. And I felt menaced since Jacques was no longer at my side. Then I realized that I would have to pay, for this round anyway; it was impossible to tug Jacques' sleeve for the money as though I were his ward. I coughed and put my ten thousand franc note on the bar.

"You are rich," said Giovanni, and set my drink before me.

"But no. No. I simply have no change."

He grinned. I could not tell whether he grinned because he thought I was lying or because he knew I was telling the truth. In silence he took the bill and rang it up and carefully counted out my change on the bar before me. Then he filled his glass and went back to his original position at the cash register. I felt a tightening in my chest.

"*À la votre,*" he said.

"*À la votre.*" We drank.

"You are an American?" he asked at last.

"Yes," I said. "From New York."

"Ah! I am told that New York is very beautiful. Is it more beautiful than Paris?"

"Oh, no," I said, "*no* city is more beautiful than Paris—"

"It seems the very suggestion that one *could* be is enough to make you very angry," grinned Giovanni. "Forgive me. I was not trying to be heretical." Then, more soberly and as though to appease me, "You must like Paris very much."

"I like New York, too," I said, uncomfortably aware that my voice had a defensive ring, "but New York is very beautiful in a very different way."

He frowned. "In what way?"

"No one," I said, "who has never seen it can possibly imagine it. It's very high and new and electric—exciting." I paused. "It's hard to describe. It's very—twentieth century."

"You find that Paris is *not* of this century?" he asked with a smile.

His smile made me feel a little foolish. "Well," I said, "Paris is *old*, is many centuries. You feel, in Paris, all the time gone by. That isn't what you feel in New York—" He was smiling. I stopped.

"What do you feel in New York?" he asked.

"Perhaps you feel," I told him, "all the time to come. There's such power there, everything is in such movement. You can't help wondering—*I* can't help wondering—what it will all be like—many years from now."

"Many years from now? When we are dead and New York is old?"

"Yes," I said. "When everyone is tired, when the world—for Americans—is not so new."

"I don't see why the world is so new for Americans," said Giovanni. "After all, you are all merely emigrants. And you did not leave Europe so very long ago."

"The ocean is very wide," I said. "We have led different lives than you; things have happened to us there which have never happened here. Surely you can understand that this would make us a different people?"

"Ah! If it had only made you a different people!" he laughed. "But it seems to have turned you into another species. You are not, are you, on another planet? For I suppose that would explain everything."

"I admit," I said with some heat—for I do not like to be laughed at—"that we may sometimes give the impression that we think we are. But we are not on another planet, no. And neither, my friend, are you."

He grinned again. "I will not," he said, "argue that most unlucky fact."

We were silent for a moment. Giovanni moved to serve several people at either end of the bar. Guillaume and Jacques were still talking. Guillaume seemed to be recounting one of his interminable anecdotes, anecdotes which invariably pivoted on the hazards of business or the hazards of love, and Jacques' mouth was stretched in a rather painful grin. I knew that he was dying to get back to the bar.

Giovanni placed himself before me again and began wiping the bar with a damp cloth. "The Americans are funny. You have a funny sense of time—or perhaps you have no sense of time at all, I can't tell. Time always sounds like a parade *chez vous*—a *triumphant* parade, like armies with banners entering a town. As though, with enough time, and that would not need to be so very much for Americans, *n'est-ce pas?*" and he smiled, giving me a mocking look, but I said nothing. "Well then," he continued, "as though with enough time and all that fearful energy and virtue you people have, everything will be settled, solved, put in its place. And when I say everything," he added, grimly, "I mean all the serious, dreadful things, like pain and death and love, in which you Americans do not believe."

"What makes you think we don't? And what do you believe?"

"I don't believe in this nonsense about time. Time is just common, it's like water for a fish. Everybody's in this water, nobody gets out of it, or if he does the same thing happens to him that happens to the fish, he dies. And you know what happens in this water, time? The big fish eat the little fish. That's all. The big fish eat the little fish and the ocean doesn't care."

"Oh, please," I said. "I don't believe *that*. Time's hot water and we're not fish and you can choose to be eaten and also not to eat—not to eat," I added quickly, turning a little red before his delighted and sardonic smile, "the little fish, of course."

"To choose!" cried Giovanni, turning his face away from me and speaking, it appeared, to an invisible ally who had been eavesdropping on this conversation all along. "To *choose*!" He turned to me again. "Ah, you are really an American. *J'adore votre enthousiasme!*"

"I adore yours," I said, politely, "though it seems to be a blacker brand than mine."

"Anyway," he said mildly, "I don't see what you can do with little fish except eat them. What else are they good for?"

"In my country," I said, feeling a subtle war within me as I said it, "the little fish seem to have gotten together and are nibbling at the body of the whale."

"That will not make them whales," said Giovanni. "The only result of all that nibbling will be that there will no longer be any grandeur anywhere, not even at the bottom of the sea."

"Is *that* what you have against us? That we're not grand?"

He smiled—smiled like someone who, faced with the

total inadequacy of the opposition, is prepared to drop the argument. *"Peut-être."*

"You people are impossible," I said. "You're the ones who killed grandeur off, right here in this city, with paving stones. Talk about little fish—!" He was grinning. I stopped.

"Don't stop," he said, still grinning. "I am listening."

I finished my drink. "You people dumped all this *merde* on us," I said, sullenly, "and now you say we're barbaric because we stink."

My sullenness delighted him. "You're charming," he said. "Do you always speak like this?"

"No," I said, and looked down. "Almost never."

There was something in him of the coquette. "I am flattered then," he said, with a sudden, disconcerting gravity, which contained, nevertheless, the very faintest hint of mockery.

"And you," I said, finally, "have you been here long? Do you like Paris?"

He hesitated a moment and then grinned, suddenly looking rather boyish and shy. "It's cold in the winter," he said. "I don't like that. And Parisians—I do not find them so very friendly, do you?" He did not wait for my answer. "They are not like the people I knew when I was younger. In Italy we are friendly, we dance and sing and make love—but these people," and he looked out over the bar, and then at me, and finished his Coca-Cola, "these people, they are cold, I do not understand them."

"But the French say," I teased, "that the Italians are too fluid, too volatile, have no sense of measure—"

"Measure!" cried Giovanni, "ah, these people and their measure! They measure the gram, the centimeter, these people, and they keep piling all the little scraps they save, one on top of the other, year in and year out, all in the stocking or under the bed—and what do they get out of all this measure? A country which is falling to pieces, measure by measure, before their eyes. Measure. I do not like to offend your ears by saying all the things I am sure these people measure before they permit themselves any act whatever. May I offer you a drink now," he asked suddenly, "before the old man comes back? Who is he? Is he your uncle?"

I did not know whether the word "uncle" was being used euphemistically or not. I felt a very urgent desire to make my position clear but I did not know how to go about it. I laughed. "No," I said, "he is not my uncle. He is just somebody I know."

Giovanni looked at me. And this look made me feel that no one in my life had ever looked at me directly before. "I hope he is not very dear to you," he said, with a smile, "because I think he is silly. Not a bad man, you understand—just a little silly."

"Perhaps," I said, and at once felt like a traitor. "He's not bad," I added quickly, "he's really a pretty nice guy." That's not true, either, I thought, he's far from being a nice guy. "Anyway," I said, "he's certainly not very dear to me," and felt again, at once, this strange tightening in my chest and wondered at the sound of my voice.

Carefully now, Giovanni poured my drink. *"Vive l'Amérique,"* he said.

"Thank you," I said, and lifted my glass, *"vive le vieux continent."*

We were silent for a moment.

"Do you come in here often?" asked Giovanni suddenly.

"No," I said, "not very often."

"But you will come," he teased, with a wonderful, mocking light on his face, "more often *now*?"

I stammered: "Why?"

"Ah!" cried Giovanni. "Don't you know when you have made a friend?"

I knew I must look foolish and that my question was foolish too: "So soon?"

"Why no," he said, reasonably, and looked at his watch, "we can wait another hour if you like. We can become friends then. Or we can wait until closing time. We can become friends *then*. Or we can wait until tomorrow, only that means that you must come in here tomorrow and perhaps you have something else to do." He put his watch away and leaned both elbows on the bar. "Tell me," he said, "what is this thing about time? Why is it better to be late than early? People are always saying, we must wait, we must wait. What are they waiting for?"

"Well," I said, feeling myself being led by Giovanni into deep and dangerous water, "I guess people wait in order to make sure of what they feel."

"In order to make *sure*!" He turned again to that invisible ally and laughed again. I was beginning, perhaps, to find his phantom a little unnerving but the sound of his laughter in that airless tunnel was the most incredible sound. "It's clear that you are a true philosopher." He pointed a finger at my heart. "And when you have waited—has it made you sure?"

For this I could simply summon no answer. From the dark, crowded center of the bar someone called *"Garçon!"* and he moved away from me, smiling. "You can wait now. And tell me how sure you have become when I return."

And he took his round metal tray and moved out into

the crowd. I watched him as he moved. And then I watched their faces, watching him. And then I was afraid. I knew that they were watching, had been watching both of us. They knew that they had witnessed a beginning and now they would not cease to watch until they saw the end. It had taken some time but the tables had been turned; now I was in the zoo, and they were watching.

I stood at the bar for quite a while alone, for Jacques had escaped from Guillaume but was now involved, poor man, with two of the knife-blade boys. Giovanni came back for an instant and winked.

"Are you sure?"

"You win. You're the philosopher."

"Oh, you must wait some more. You do not yet know me well enough to say such a thing."

And he filled his tray and disappeared again.

Now someone whom I had never seen before came out of the shadows toward me. It looked like a mummy or a zombie—this was the first, overwhelming impression—of something walking after it had been put to death. And it walked, really, like someone who might be sleepwalking or like those figures in slow motion one sometimes sees on the screen. It carried a glass, it walked on its toes, the flat hips moved with a dead, horrifying lasciviousness. It seemed to make no sound; this was due to the roar of the bar, which was like the roaring of the sea, heard at night, from far away. It glittered in the dim light; the thin, black hair was violent with oil, combed forward, hanging in bangs; the eyelids gleamed with mascara, the mouth raged with lipstick. The face was white and thoroughly bloodless with some kind of foundation cream; it stank of powder and a gardenia-like perfume. The shirt, open coquettishly to the navel, revealed a hairless chest and a silver crucifix; the shirt was covered with round, paper-thin wafers, red and green and orange and yellow and blue, which stormed in the light and made one feel that the mummy might, at any moment, disappear in flame. A red sash was around the waist, the clinging pants were a surprisingly sombre grey. He wore buckles on his shoes.

I was not sure that he was coming towards me, but I could not take my eyes away. He stopped before me, one hand on his hip, looked me up and down, and smiled. He had been eating garlic and his teeth were very bad. His hands, I noticed, with an unbelieving shock, were very large and strong.

"*Eh bien,*" he said, "*il te plaît?*"

"*Comment?*" I said.

I really was not sure I had heard him right, though the bright, bright eyes, looking, it seemed, at something amusing within the recess of my skull, did not leave much room for doubt.

"You like him—the barman?"

I did not know what to do or say. It seemed impossible to hit him; it seemed impossible to get angry. It did not seem real, he did not seem real. Besides—no matter what I said, those eyes would mock me with it. I said, as drily as I could:

"How does that concern you?"

"But it concerns me not at all, darling. *Je m'en fou.*"

"Then please get the hell away from me."

He did not move at once, but smiled at me again. "*Il est dangereux, tu sais.* And for a boy like you—he is *very* dangerous."

I looked at him. I almost asked him what he meant. "Go to hell," I said, and turned my back.

"Oh, no," he said—and I looked at him again. He was

laughing, showing all his teeth—there were not many. "Oh, no," he said, "I go not to hell," and he clutched his crucifix with one large hand. "But you, my dear friend—I fear that you shall burn in a very hot fire." He laughed again. "Oh, such fire!" He touched his head. "Here." And he writhed, as though in torment. "Every*where.*" And he touched his heart. "And here." And he looked at me with malice and mockery and something else; he looked at me as though I were very far away. "Oh, my poor friend, so young, so strong, so handsome—will you not buy me a drink?"

"Va te faire foutre."

His face crumpled in the sorrow of infants and of very old men—the sorrow, also, of certain, aging actresses who were renowned in their youth for their fragile, childlike beauty. The dark eyes narrowed in spite and fury and the scarlet mouth turned down like the mask of tragedy. *"T'aura du chagrin,"* he said. "You will be very unhappy. Remember that I told you so."

And he straightened, as though he were a princess and moved, flaming, away through the crowd.

Then Jacques spoke, at my elbow. "Everyone in the bar," he said, "is talking about how beautifully you and the barman have hit it off." He gave me a radiant and vindictive smile. "I trust there has been no confusion?"

I looked down at him. I wanted to do something to his cheerful, hideous, worldly face which would make it impossible for him ever again to smile at anyone the way he was smiling at me. Then I wanted to get out of this bar, out into the air, perhaps to find Hella, my suddenly so sorely menaced girl.

"There's been no confusion," I snapped. "Don't you go getting confused, either."

"I think I can safely say," said Jacques, "that I have

scarcely ever been less confused than I am at this moment."
He had stopped smiling; he gave me a look which was dry,
bitter, and impersonal. "And, at the risk of losing forever
your so remarkably candid friendship, let me tell you
something. Confusion is a luxury which only the very, very
young can possibly afford and you are not that young anymore."

"I don't know what you're talking about," I said. "Let's
have another drink."

I felt that I had better get drunk. Now Giovanni went
behind the bar again and winked at me. Jacques' eyes never
left my face. I turned rudely from him and faced the bar
again. He followed me.

"The same," said Jacques.

"Certainly," said Giovanni, "that's the way to do it." He
fixed our drinks. Jacques paid. I suppose I did not look too
well, for Giovanni shouted at me playfully, "Eh? Are you
drunk already?"

I looked up and smiled. "You know how Americans
drink," I said. "I haven't even started yet."

"David is far from drunk," said Jacques. "He is only
reflecting bitterly that he must get a new pair of sus-
penders."

I could have killed Jacques. Yet it was only with difficulty that I kept myself from laughing. I made a face to sig-
nify to Giovanni that the old man was making a private
joke, and he disappeared again. That time of evening had
come when great batches of people were leaving and great
batches were coming in. They would all encounter each
other later anyway, in the last bar, all those, that is, unlucky
enough to be searching still at such an advanced hour.

I could not look at Jacques—which he knew. He stood
beside me, smiling at nothing, humming a tune. There was

nothing I could say. I did not dare to mention Hella. I could not even pretend to myself that I was sorry she was in Spain. I was glad. I was utterly, hopelessly, horribly glad. I knew I could do nothing whatever to stop the ferocious excitement which had burst in me like a storm. I could only drink, in the faint hope that the storm might thus spend itself without doing any more damage to my land. But I was glad. I was only sorry that Jacques had been a witness. He made me ashamed. I hated him because he had now seen all that he had waited, often scarcely hoping, so many months to see. We had, in effect, been playing a deadly game and he was the winner. He was the winner in spite of the fact that I had cheated to win.

I wished, nevertheless, standing there at the bar, that I had been able to find in myself the force to turn and walk out—to have gone over to Montparnasse perhaps and picked up a girl. Any girl. I could not do it. I told myself all sorts of lies, standing there at the bar, but I could not move. And this was partly because I knew that it did not really matter anymore; it did not even matter if I never spoke to Giovanni again; for they had become visible, as visible as the wafers on the shirt of the flaming princess, they stormed all over me, my awakening, my insistent possibilities.

That was how I met Giovanni. I think we connected the instant that we met. And remain connected still, in spite of our later *séparation de corps,* despite the fact that Giovanni will be rotting soon in unhallowed ground near Paris. Until I die there will be those moments, moments seeming to rise up out of the ground like Macbeth's witches, when his face will come before me, that face in all its changes, when the exact timbre of his voice and tricks of his speech will nearly burst my ears, when his smell will overpower my nostrils. Sometimes, in the days which are coming—God grant me the grace to live them—in the glare of the grey morning, sour-mouthed, eyelids raw and red, hair tangled and damp from my stormy sleep, facing, over coffee and cigarette smoke, last night's impenetrable, meaningless boy who will shortly rise and vanish like the smoke, I will see Giovanni again, as he was that night, so vivid, so winning, all of the light of that gloomy tunnel trapped around his head.

THREE

At five o'clock in the morning Guillaume locked the door of the bar behind us. The streets were empty and grey. On a corner near the bar a butcher had already opened his shop and one could see him within, already bloody, hacking at the meat. One of the great, green Paris buses lumbered past, nearly empty, its bright electric flag waving fiercely to indicate a turn. A *garçon de cafe* spilled water on the sidewalk before his establishment and swept it into the gutter. At the end of the long, curving street which faced us were the trees of the boulevard and straw chairs piled high before cafes and the great stone spire of Saint-Germain-des-Prés—the most magnificent spire, as Hella and I believed, in Paris. The street beyond the *place* stretched before us to the river and, hidden beside and behind us, meandered to Montparnasse. It was named for an adventurer who sowed a crop in Europe which is being harvested until today. I had often walked this street, sometimes, with Hella, towards the river, often, without her, towards the girls of Montparnasse. Not very long ago either, though it seemed, that morning, to have occurred in another life.

We were going to Les Halles for breakfast. We piled into a taxi, the four of us, unpleasantly crowded together, a circumstance which elicited from Jacques and Guillaume, a series of lewd speculations. This lewdness was particularly revolting in that it not only failed of wit, it was so clearly an expression of contempt and self-contempt; it bubbled upward out of them like a fountain of black water. It was clear that they were tantalizing themselves with Giovanni and me and this set my teeth on edge. But Giovanni leaned back against the taxi window, allowing his arm to press my shoulder lightly, seeming to say that we should soon be rid of these old men and should not be distressed that their dirty water splashed—we would have no trouble washing it away.

"Look," said Giovanni, as we crossed the river. "This old whore, Paris, as she turns in bed, is very moving."

I looked out, beyond his heavy profile, which was grey— from fatigue and from the light of the sky above us. The river was swollen and yellow. Nothing moved on the river. Barges were tied up along the banks. The island of the city widened away from us, bearing the weight of the cathedral; beyond this, dimly, through speed and mist, one made out the individual roofs of Paris, their myriad, squat chimney stacks very beautiful and varicolored under the pearly sky. Mist clung to the river, softening that army of trees, softening those stones, hiding the city's dreadful corkscrew alleys and dead-end streets, clinging like a curse to the men who slept beneath the bridges—one of whom flashed by beneath us, very black and lone, walking along the river.

"Some rats have gone in," said Giovanni, "and now other rats come out." He smiled bleakly and looked at me; to my surprise, he took my hand and held it. "Have you ever slept under a bridge?" he asked. "Or perhaps they have soft beds with warm blankets under the bridges in your country?"

I did not know what to do about my hand; it seemed better to do nothing. "Not yet," I said, "but I may. My hotel wants to throw me out."

I had said it lightly, with a smile, out of a desire to put myself, in terms of an acquaintance with wintry things, on an equal footing with him. But the fact that I had said it as he held my hand made it sound to me unutterably helpless and soft and coy. But I could not say anything to counteract this impression: to say anything more would confirm it. I pulled my hand away, pretending that I had done so in order to search for a cigarette.

Jacques lit it for me.

"Where do you live?" he asked Giovanni.

"Oh," said Giovanni, "out. Far out. It is almost not Paris."

"He lives in a dreadful street, near *Nation*," said Guillaume, "among all the dreadful bourgeoisie and their piglike children."

"You failed to catch the children at the right age," said Jacques. "They go through a period, all too brief, *hélas!* when a pig is perhaps the *only* animal they do not call to mind." And, again to Giovanni: "In a hotel?"

"No," said Giovanni, and for the first time he seemed slightly uncomfortable. "I live in a maid's room."

"With the maid?"

"No," said Giovanni, and smiled, "the maid is I don't know where. You could certainly tell that there was no maid if you ever saw my room."

"I would love to," said Jacques.

"Then we will give a party for you one day," said Giovanni.

This, too courteous and too bald to permit any further questioning, nearly forced, nevertheless, a question from my lips. Guillaume looked briefly at Giovanni, who did not look at him but out into the morning, whistling. I had been making resolutions for the last six hours and now I made another one: to have this whole thing "out" with Giovanni as soon as I got him alone at Les Halles. I was going to have to tell him that he had made a mistake but that we could still be friends. But I could not be certain, really, that it might not be I who was making a mistake, blindly misreading everything—and out of necessities, then, too shameful to be uttered. I was in a box for I could see that, no matter how I turned, the hour of confession was upon me and could scarcely be averted; unless, of course, I leaped out of the cab, which would be the most terrible confession of all.

Now the cabdriver asked us where we wanted to go, for we had arrived at the choked boulevards and impassable sidestreets of Les Halles. Leeks, onions, cabbages, oranges, apples, potatoes, cauliflowers, stood gleaming in mounds all over, on the sidewalks, in the streets, before great metal sheds. The sheds were blocks long and within the sheds were piled more fruit, more vegetables, in some sheds, fish, in some sheds, cheese, in some whole animals, lately slaughtered. It scarcely seemed possible that all of this could ever be eaten. But in a few hours it would all be gone and trucks would be arriving from all corners of France— and making their way, to the great profit of a beehive of middlemen, across the city of Paris—to feed the roaring multitude. Who were roaring now, at once wounding and charming the ear, before and behind, and on either side of our taxi—our taxi driver, and Giovanni, too, roared back. The multitude of Paris seems to be dressed in blue every day but Sunday, when, for the most part, they put on an unbelievably festive black. Here they were now, in blue, disputing, every inch, our passage, with their wagons, handtrucks, camions, their bursting baskets carried at an angle steeply self-confident on the back. A red-faced woman, burdened with fruit, shouted—to Giovanni, the driver, to the world—a particularly vivid *cochonnerie*, to which the driver and Giovanni, at once, at the top of their lungs, responded, though the fruit lady had already passed beyond our sight and perhaps no longer even remembered her precisely obscene conjectures. We crawled along, for no one had yet told the driver where to stop, and Giovanni and the driver, who had, it appeared, immediately upon entering Les Halles, been transformed into brothers, exchanged speculations, unflattering in the extreme, concerning the hygiene, language, private parts, and habits, of the citizens of Paris. (Jacques and Guillaume were exchanging speculations, unspeakably less good-natured, concerning every passing male.) The pavements were slick with leavings, mainly cast-off, rotten leaves, flowers, fruit, and vegetables which had met with disaster natural and slow, or abrupt. And the walls and corners were combed with *pissoirs,* dull-burning, make-shift braziers, cafes, restaurants, and smoky yellow bistros—of these last, some so small that they were little more than diamond-shaped, enclosed corners holding bottles and a zinc-covered counter. At all these points, men, young, old, middle-aged, powerful, powerful even in the various fashions in which they had met, or were meeting, their various ruin; and women, more than making up in shrewdness and patience, in an ability to count and weigh—and shout—whatever they might lack in muscle; though they did not, really, seem to lack much. Nothing here reminded me of home, though Giovanni recognized, revelled in it all.

"I know a place," he told the driver, *"très bon marché"*—and told the driver where it was. It developed that it was one of the driver's favorite rendezvous.

"Where is this place?" asked Jacques, petulantly. "I thought we were going to"—and he named another place.

"You are joking," said Giovanni, with contempt. "That place is *very* bad and *very* expensive, it is only for tourists. We are not tourists," and he added, to me, "When I first came to Paris I worked in Les Halles—a long time, too. *Nom de Dieu, quel boulot!* I pray always never to do that again." And he regarded the streets through which we passed with a sadness which was not less real for being a little theatrical and self-mocking.

Guillaume said, from his corner of the cab: "Tell him who rescued you."

"Ah, yes," said Giovanni, "behold my savior, my *patron.*" He was silent a moment. Then: "You do not regret it, do you? I have not done you any harm? You are pleased with my work?"

"Mais oui," said Guillaume.

Giovanni sighed. *"Bien sûr."* He looked out of the window again, again whistling. We came to a corner remarkably clear. The taxi stopped.

"Ici," said the driver.

"Ici," Giovanni echoed.

I reached for my wallet but Giovanni sharply caught my hand, conveying to me with an angry flick of his eyelash the intelligence that the least these dirty old men could do was *pay.* He opened the door and stepped out into the street. Guillaume had not reached for his wallet and Jacques paid for the cab.

"Ugh," said Guillaume, staring at the door of the cafe

before which we stood, "I am sure this place is infested with vermin. Do you want to poison us?"

"It's not the outside you're going to eat," said Giovanni. "You are in much more danger of being poisoned in those dreadful, chic places you always go to, where they always have the face clean, *mais, mon Dieu, les fesses!*" He grinned. "*Fais-moi confiance.* Why would I want to poison you? Then I would have no job and I have only just found out that I want to live."

He and Guillaume, Giovanni still smiling, exchanged a look which I would not have been able to read even if I had dared to try; and Jacques, pushing all of us before him as though we were his chickens, said, with that grin: "We can't stand here in the cold and argue. If we can't eat inside, we can drink. Alcohol kills all microbes."

And Guillaume brightened suddenly—he was really remarkable, as though he carried, hidden somewhere on his person, a needle filled with vitamins, which, automatically, at the blackening hour, discharged itself into his veins. "*Il y a les jeunes dedans,*" he said, and we went in.

Indeed there were young people, half a dozen at the zinc counter before glasses of red and white wine, along with others not young at all. A pockmarked boy and a very rough-looking girl were playing the pinball machine near the window. There were a few people sitting at the tables in the back, served by an astonishingly clean-looking waiter. In the gloom, the dirty walls, the sawdust-covered floor, his white jacket gleamed like snow. Behind these tables one caught a glimpse of the kitchen and the surly, obese cook. He lumbered about like one of those overloaded trucks outside, wearing one of those high, white hats, and with a dead cigar stuck between his lips.

Behind the counter sat one of those absolutely inimita-

ble and indomitable ladies, produced only in the city of
Paris, but produced there in great numbers, who would be
as outrageous and unsettling in any other city as a mer-
maid on a mountaintop. All over Paris they sit behind their
counters like a mother bird in a nest and brood over the
cash register as though it were an egg. Nothing occurring
under the circle of heaven where they sit escapes their eye,
if they have ever been surprised by anything, it was only in
a dream—a dream they long ago ceased having. They are
neither ill- nor good-natured, though they have their days
and styles, and they know, in the way, apparently, that other
people know when they have to go to the bathroom, everything about everyone who enters their domain. Though
some are white-haired and some not, some fat, some thin,
some grandmothers and some but lately virgins, they all
have exactly the same, shrewd, vacant, all-registering eye;
it is difficult to believe that they ever cried for milk or
looked at the sun; it seems they must have come into the
world hungry for banknotes, and squinting helplessly, unable to focus their eyes until they came to rest on a cash
register.

This one's hair is black and grey, and she has a face
which comes from Brittany; and she, like almost everyone
else standing at the bar, knows Giovanni and, after her
fashion, likes him. She has a big, deep bosom and she clasps
Giovanni to it; and a big, deep voice.

"Ah, mon pote!" she cries. *"Tu es revenu!* You have come
back at last! *Salaud!* Now that you are rich and have found
rich friends, you never come to see us anymore! *Canaille!"*

And she beams at us, the "rich" friends, with a friendli-
ness deliciously, deliberately vague; she would have no
trouble reconstructing every instant of our biographies
from the moment we were born until this morning. She

knows exactly who is rich—and how rich—and she knows it isn't me. For this reason, perhaps, there was a click of speculation infinitesimally double behind her eyes when she looked at me. In a moment, however, she knows that she will understand it all.

"You know how it is," says Giovanni, extricating himself and throwing back his hair, "when you work, when you become serious, you have no time to play."

"*Tiens,*" says she, with mockery. "*Sans blague?*"

"But I assure you," says Giovanni, "even when you are a young man like me, you get very tired"—she laughs—"and you go to sleep early"—she laughs again—"and *alone,*" says Giovanni, as though this proved everything, and she clicks her teeth in sympathy and laughs again.

"And now," she says, "are you coming or going? Have you come for breakfast or have you come for a nightcap? *Nom de Dieu,* you do not *look* very serious; I believe you need a drink."

"*Bien sûr,*" says someone at the bar, "after such hard work he needs a bottle of white wine—and perhaps a few dozen oysters."

Everybody laughs. Everybody, without seeming to, is looking at us and I am beginning to feel like part of a travelling circus. Everybody, also, seems very proud of Giovanni.

Giovanni turns to the voice at the bar. "An excellent idea, friend," he says, "and exactly what I had in mind." Now he turns to us. "You have not met my friends," he says, looking at me, then at the woman. "This is Monsieur Guillaume," he tells her, and with the most subtle flattening of his voice, "my *patron.* He can tell you if I am serious."

"Ah," she dares to say, "but I cannot tell if *he* is," and covers this daring with a laugh.

Guillaume, raising his eyes with difficulty from the young men at the bar, stretches out his hand and smiles. "But you are right, Madame," he says. "He is so much more serious than I am that I fear he will own my bar one day."

He will when lions fly, she is thinking, but professes herself enchanted by him and shakes his hand with energy.

"And Monsieur Jacques," says Giovanni, "one of our finest customers."

"Enchanté, Madame," says Jacques, with his most dazzling smile, of which she, in responding, produces the most artless parody.

"And this is *monsieur l'américain,"* says Giovanni, "otherwise known as: *Monsieur David. Madame Clothilde."*

And he stands back slightly. Something is burning in his eyes and it lights up all his face, it is joy and pride.

"Je suis ravie, monsieur," she tells me and looks at me and shakes my hand and smiles.

I am smiling too, I scarcely know why; everything in me is jumping up and down. Giovanni carelessly puts an arm around my shoulder. "What have you got good to eat?" he cried. "We are hungry."

"But we must have a drink first!" cried Jacques.

"But we can drink sitting down," said Giovanni, "no?"

"No," said Guillaume, to whom leaving the bar, at the moment, would have seemed like being driven from the promised land, "let us first have a drink, here at the bar, with Madame."

Guillaume's suggestion had the effect—but subtly, as though a wind had blown over everything or a light been imperceptibly intensified—of creating among the people at the bar, a *troupe*, who would now play various roles in a play they knew very well. Madame Clothilde would demur, as, indeed, she instantly did, but only for a moment; then she would accept, it would be something expensive; it turned out to be champagne. She would sip it, making the most noncommittal conversation, so that she could vanish out of it a split second before Guillaume had established contact with one of the boys at the bar. As for the boys at the bar, they were each invisibly preening, having already calculated how much money he and his *copain* would need for the next few days, having already appraised Guillaume to within a decimal of that figure, and having already estimated how long Guillaume, as a fountainhead, would last, and also how long they would be able to endure him. The only question left was whether they would be *vache* with him, or *chic*, but they knew that they would probably be *vache*. There was also Jacques, who might turn out to be a bonus, or merely a consolation prize. There was me, of course, another matter altogether, innocent of apartments, soft beds, or food, a candidate, therefore, for affection, but, as Giovanni's *môme*, out of honorable reach. Their only means, practically at least, of conveying their affection for Giovanni and me was to relieve us of these two old men. So that there was added, to the roles they were about to play, a certain jolly aura of conviction and, to self-interest, an altruistic glow.

I ordered black coffee and a cognac, a large one. Giovanni was far from me, drinking *marc* between an old man, who looked like a receptacle of all the world's dirt and disease, and a young boy, a redhead, who would look like that man one day, if one could read, in the dullness of his eye, anything so real as a future. Now, however, he had something of a horse's dreadful beauty; some suggestion, too, of the storm trooper; covertly, he was watching Guillaume; he knew that both Guillaume and Jacques were watching him. Guillaume chatted, meanwhile, with Madame Clothilde; they were agreeing that business was awful, that all standards had been debased by the *nouveau riche,* and that the country needed de Gaulle. Luckily, they had both had this conversation so many times before that it ran, so to speak, all by itself, demanding of them nothing in the way of concentration. Jacques would shortly offer one of the boys a drink but, for the moment, he wished to play uncle to me.

"How do you feel?" he asked me. "This is a very important day for you."

"I feel fine," I said. "How do you feel?"

"Like a man," he said, "who has seen a vision."

"Yes?" I said. "Tell me about this vision."

"I am not joking," he said. "I am talking about you. *You* were the vision. You should have seen yourself tonight. You should see yourself now."

I looked at him and said nothing.

"You are—how old? Twenty-six or seven? I am nearly twice that and, let me tell you, you are lucky. You are lucky that what is happening to you now is happening *now* and not when you are forty, or something like that, when there would be no hope for you and you would simply be destroyed."

"What is happening to me?" I asked. I had meant to sound sardonic, but I did not sound sardonic at all.

He did not answer this, but sighed, looking briefly in the direction of the redhead. Then he turned to me. "Are you going to write to Hella?"

"I very often do," I said. "I suppose I will again."

"That does not answer my question."

"Oh. I was under the impression that you had asked me if I was going to write to Hella."

"Well. Let's put it another way. Are you going to write to Hella about this night and this morning?"

"I really don't see what there is to write about. But what's it to you if I do or I don't?"

He gave me a look full of a certain despair which I had not, till that moment, known was in him. It frightened me. "It's not," he said, "what it is to *me*. It's what it is to *you*. And to her. And to that poor boy, yonder, who doesn't know that when he looks at you the way he does, he is simply putting his head in the lion's mouth. Are you going to treat them as you've treated me?"

"*You?* What have *you* to do with all this? How have I treated *you*?"

"You have been very unfair to me," he said. "You have been very dishonest."

This time I did sound sardonic. "I suppose you mean that I would have been fair, I would have been honest if I had—if—"

"I mean you could have been fair to me by despising me a little less."

"I'm sorry. But I think, since you bring it up, that a lot of your life *is* despicable."

"I could say the same about yours," said Jacques. "There are so many ways of being despicable it quite makes one's head spin. But the way to be really despicable is to be contemptuous of other people's pain. You ought to have some apprehension that the man you see before you was once even younger than you are now and arrived at his present wretchedness by imperceptible degrees."

There was silence for a moment, threatened, from a distance, by that laugh of Giovanni's.

"Tell me," I said at last, "is there really no other way for you but this? To kneel down forever before an army of boys for just five dirty minutes in the dark?"

"Think," said Jacques, "of the men who have kneeled before you while you thought of something else and pretended that nothing was happening down there in the dark between your legs."

I stared at the amber cognac and at the wet rings on the metal. Deep below, trapped in the metal, the outline of my own face looked upward hopelessly at me.

"You think," he persisted, "that my life is shameful because my encounters are. And they are. But you should ask yourself *why* they are."

"Why are they—shameful?" I asked him.

"Because there is no affection in them, and no joy. It's like putting an electric plug in a dead socket. Touch, but no contact. All touch, but no contact and no light."

I asked him: "Why?"

"That you must ask yourself," he told me, "and perhaps one day, this morning will not be ashes in your mouth."

I looked over at Giovanni, who now had one arm around the ruined-looking girl, who could have once been very beautiful but who never would be now.

Jacques followed my look. "He is very fond of you," he said, "already. But this doesn't make you happy or proud, as it should. It makes you frightened and ashamed. Why?"

"I don't understand him," I said at last. "I don't know what his friendship means; I don't know what he means by friendship."

Jacques laughed. "You don't know what he means by

friendship but you have the feeling it may not be safe. You are afraid it may change you. What kind of friendship have you had?"

I said nothing.

"Or for that matter," he continued, "what kind of love affairs?"

I was silent for so long that he teased me, saying, "Come out, come out, wherever you are!"

And I grinned, feeling chilled.

"Love him," said Jacques, with vehemence, "love him and let him love you. Do you think anything else under heaven really matters? And how long, at the best, can it last? since you are both men and still have everywhere to go? Only five minutes, I assure you, only five minutes, and most of that, *hélas!* in the dark. And if you think of them as dirty, then they *will* be dirty—they will be dirty because you will be giving nothing, you will be despising your flesh and his. But you can make your time together anything but dirty; you can give each other something which will make both of you better—forever—if you will *not* be ashamed, if you will only *not* play it safe." He paused, watching me, and then looked down to his cognac. "You play it safe long enough," he said, in a different tone, "and you'll end up trapped in your own dirty body, forever and forever and forever—like me." And he finished his cognac, ringing his glass slightly on the bar to attract the attention of Madame Clothilde.

She came at once, beaming; and in that moment Guillaume dared to smile at the redhead. Mme. Clothilde poured Jacques a fresh cognac and looked questioningly at me, the bottle poised over my half full glass. I hesitated.

"Et pourquoi pas?" she asked, with a smile.

So I finished my glass and she filled it. Then, for the briefest of seconds, she glanced at Guillaume; who cried, "*Et le rouquin là!* What's the redhead drinking?"

Mme. Clothilde turned with the air of an actress about to deliver the severely restrained last lines of an exhausting and mighty part. "*On t'offre, Pierre,*" she said, majestically. "What will you have?"—holding slightly aloft meanwhile the bottle containing the most expensive cognac in the house.

"*Je prendrai un petit cognac,*" Pierre mumbled after a moment and, oddly enough, he blushed, which made him, in the light of the pale, just-rising sun, resemble a freshly fallen angel.

Mme. Clothilde filled Pierre's glass and, amid a beautifully resolving tension, as of slowly dimming lights, replaced the bottle on the shelf and walked back to the cash register; offstage, in effect, into the wings, where she began to recover herself by finishing the last of the champagne. She sighed and sipped and looked outward contentedly into the slowly rising morning. Guillaume had murmured a "*Je m'excuse un instant, Madame,*" and now passed behind us on his way to the redhead.

I smiled. "Things my father never told me."

"*Somebody,*" said Jacques, "your father or mine, should have told us that not many people have ever died of love. But multitudes have perished, and are perishing every hour—and in the oddest places!—for the lack of it." And then: "Here comes your baby. *Sois sage. Sois chic.*"

He moved slightly away and began talking to the boy next to him.

And here my baby came indeed, through all that sunlight, his face flushed and his hair flying, his eyes, unbelievably, like morning stars. "It was not very nice of me to go off for so long," he said, "I hope you have not been too bored."

"*You* certainly haven't been," I told him. "You look like a kid about five years old waking up on Christmas morning."

This delighted, even flattered him, as I could see from the way he now humorously pursed his lips. "I am sure I cannot look like that," he said. "I was always disappointed on Christmas morning."

"Well, I mean very *early* on Christmas morning, before you saw what was under the tree." But his eyes have somehow made of my last statement a *double entendre*, and we are both laughing.

"Are you hungry?" he asked.

"Perhaps I would be if I were alive and sober. I don't know. Are you?"

"I think we should eat," he said with no conviction whatever, and we began to laugh again.

"Well," I said, "What shall we eat?"

"I scarcely dare suggest white wine and oysters," said Giovanni, "but that is really the best thing after such a night."

"Well, let's do that," I said, "while we can still walk to the dining room." I looked beyond him to Guillaume and the redhead. They had apparently found something to talk about; I could not imagine what it was. And Jacques was deep in conversation with the tall, very young, pock-marked boy, whose turtleneck black sweater made him seem even paler and thinner than he actually was. He had been playing the pinball machine when we came in; his name appeared to be Yves. "Are they going to eat now?" I asked Giovanni.

"Perhaps not now," said Giovanni, "but they are certainly going to eat. Everyone is very hungry." I took this to refer more to the boys than to our friends, and we passed into the dining room, which was now empty, the waiter nowhere in sight.

"Mme. Clothilde!" shouted Giovanni, *"On mange ici, non?"*

This shout produced an answering shout from Mme. Clothilde and also produced the waiter, whose jacket was less spotless, seen in closeup, than it had seemed from a distance. It also officially announced our presence in the dining room to Jacques and Guillaume and must have definitely increased, in the eyes of the boys they were talking to, a certain tigerish intensity of affection.

"We'll eat quickly and go," said Giovanni. "After all, I have to work tonight."

"Did you meet Guillaume here?" I asked him.

He grimaced, looking down. "No. That is a long story." He grinned. "No, I did not meet him here. I met him"—he laughed—"in a cinema!" We both laughed. *"C'était un film du far west, avec Gary Cooper."* This seemed terribly funny, too; we kept laughing until the waiter came with our bottle of white wine.

"Well," said Giovanni, sipping the wine, his eyes damp, "after the last gun shot had been fired and all the music came up to celebrate the triumph of goodness and I came up the aisle, I bumped into this man—Guillaume—and I excused myself and walked into the lobby. Then here he came, after me, with a long story about leaving his scarf in *my* seat because, it appeared, he had been sitting *behind* me, you understand, with his coat and his scarf on the seat *before* him and when I sat down I pulled his scarf down with me. Well, I told him I didn't work for the cinema and I told him what he could do with his scarf—but I did not really get angry because he made me want to laugh. He said that all the people who worked for the cinema were thieves and he was sure that they would keep it if they so much as laid eyes on it, and it was very expensive, and a gift from his mother and—oh, I assure you, not even Garbo ever gave such a performance. So I went back and of course there was no scarf there and when I told him this it seemed he would fall dead right there in the lobby. And by this time, you understand, everybody thought we were together and I didn't know whether to kick him or the people who were looking at us; but he was very well dressed, of course, and I was not and so I thought, well, we had better get out of this lobby. So we went to a cafe and sat on the terrace and when he had got over his grief about the scarf and what his mother would say and so on and so on, he asked me to have supper with him. Well, naturally, I said no; I had certainly had enough of him by that time, but the only way I could prevent another scene, right there on the terrace, was to promise to have supper with him a few days later—I did not intend to go," he said, with a shy grin, "but when the day came, I had not eaten for a long time and I was very hungry." He looked at me and I saw in his face again something which I have fleetingly seen there during these hours: under his beauty and his bravado, terror, and a terrible desire to please; dreadfully, dreadfully moving, and it made me want, in anguish, to reach out and comfort him.

Our oysters came and we began to eat. Giovanni sat in the sun, his black hair gathering to itself the yellow glow of the wine and the many dull colors of the oyster where the sun struck it.

"Well"—with his mouth turned down—"dinner was awful, of course, since he can make scenes in his apartment, too. But by this time I knew he owned a bar and was a French citizen. I am not and I had no job and no *carte de travail*. So I saw that he could be useful if I could only find some way to make him keep his hands off me. I did not, I must say"—this with that look at me—"altogether succeed in remaining untouched by him; he has more hands than an octopus, and no dignity whatever, *but*"—grimly throwing down another oyster and refilling our glasses of wine— "I *do* now have a *carte de travail* and I have a job. Which pays very well," he grinned. "It appears that I am good for business. For this reason, he leaves me mostly alone." He looked out into the bar. "He is really not a man at all," he said, with a sorrow and bewilderment at once childlike and ancient, "I do not know what he is, he is horrible. But I will keep my *carte de travail*. The job is another matter, but"— he knocked wood—"we have had no trouble now for nearly three weeks."

"But you think that trouble is coming," I said.

"Oh, yes," said Giovanni, with a quick, startled look at me, as if he were wondering if I had understood a word of what he had said, "we are certainly going to have a little trouble soon again. Not right away, of course; that is not his style. But he will invent something to be angry at me about."

Then we sat in silence for awhile, smoking cigarettes, surrounded by oyster shells, and finishing the wine. I was all at once very tired. I looked out into the narrow street, this strange, crooked corner where we sat, which was brazen now with the sunlight and heavy with people— people I would never understand. I ached abruptly, intolerably, with a longing to go home; not to that hotel, in one of the alleys of Paris, where the concierge barred the way with my unpaid bill; but home, home across the ocean, to things and people I knew and understood; to those things, those places, those people which I would always, helplessly, and in whatever bitterness of spirit, love above all else. I had never realized such a sentiment in myself before, and it frightened me. I saw myself, sharply, as a wanderer, an adventurer, rocking through the world, unanchored. I looked at Giovanni's face, which did not help me. He belonged to this strange city, which did not belong to me. I began to see that, while what was happening to me was not so strange as it would have comforted me to believe, yet it was strange beyond belief. It was not really so strange, so unprecedented, though voices deep within me boomed, For shame! For shame! that I should be so abruptly, so hideously entangled with a boy; what was strange was that this was but one tiny aspect of the dreadful human tangle occurring everywhere, without end, forever.

"Viens," said Giovanni.

We rose and walked back into the bar and Giovanni paid our bill. Another bottle of champagne had been opened and Jacques and Guillaume were now really beginning to be drunk. It was going to be ghastly and I wondered if those poor, patient boys were ever going to get anything to eat. Giovanni talked to Guillaume for a moment, agreeing to open up the bar; Jacques was too busy with the pale tall boy to have much time for me; we said good-morning and left them.

"I must go home," I said to Giovanni when we were in the street. "I must pay my hotel bill."

Giovanni stared. *"Mais tu es fou,"* he said mildly. "There is certainly no point in going home now, to face an ugly concierge and then go to sleep in that room all by yourself and then wake up later, with a terrible stomach and a sour mouth, wanting to commit suicide. Come with me; we will rise at a civilized hour and have a gentle aperitif somewhere and then a little dinner. It will be much more cheer-ful like that," he said with a smile, "you will see."

"But I must get my clothes," I said.

He took my arm. "*Bien sûr.* But you do not have to get them *now.*" I held back. He stopped. "Come. I am sure that I am much prettier than your wallpaper—or your con-cierge. I will smile at you when you wake up. They will not."

"Ah," I could only say, "*tu es vache.*"

"It is you who are *vache,*" he said, "to want to leave me alone in this lonely place when you know that I am far too drunk to reach my home unaided."

We laughed together, both caught up in a stinging, teas-ing sort of game. We reached the Boulevard de Sébastopol. "But we will not any longer discuss the painful subject of how you desired to desert Giovanni, at so dangerous an hour, in the middle of a hostile city." I began to realize that he, too, was nervous. Far down the boulevard a cab mean-dered toward us, and he put up his hand. "I will show you my room," he said. "It is perfectly clear that you would have to see it one of these days, anyway." The taxi stopped beside us, and Giovanni, as though he were suddenly afraid that I would really turn and run, pushed me in before him. He got in beside me and told the driver: "*Nation.*"

The street he lived on was wide, respectable rather than elegant, and massive with fairly recent apartment build-ings; the street ended in a small park. His room was in the back, on the ground floor of the last building on this street. We passed the vestibule and the elevator into a short, dark corridor which led to his room. The room was small, I only made out the outlines of clutter and disorder, there was the smell of the alcohol he burned in his stove. He locked the door behind us, and then for a moment, in the gloom, we simply stared at each other—with dismay, with relief, and breathing hard. I was trembling. I thought, if I do not open the door at once and get out of here, I am lost. But I knew I could not open the door, I knew it was too late; soon it was too late to do anything but moan. He pulled me against him, putting himself into my arms as though he were giving me himself to carry, and slowly pulled me down with him to that bed. With everything in me screaming *No!* yet the sum of me sighed *Yes*.

———

Here in the south of France it does not often snow; but snowflakes, in the beginning rather gently and now with more force, have been falling for the last half hour. It falls as though it might quite possibly decide to turn into a blizzard. It has been cold down here this winter, though he people of the region seem to take it as a mark of ill-breeding in a foreigner if he makes any reference to this fact. They themselves, even when their faces are burning in that wind which seems to blow from everywhere at once, and which penetrates everything, are as radiantly cheerful as children at the seashore. "*Il fait beau bien?*—throwing their faces toward the lowering sky in which the celebrated southern sun has not made an appearance in days.

I leave the window of the big room and walk through the house. While I am in the kitchen, staring into the mirror—I have decided to shave before all the water turns cold—I hear a knocking at the door. Some vague, wild hope leaps in me for a second and then I realize that it is only the caretaker from across the road come to make certain that I have not stolen the silver or smashed the dishes or chopped up the furniture for firewood. And, indeed, she rattles the door and I hear her voice out there, cracking,

M'sieu! M'sieu! M'sieu, l'américain!" I wonder, with annoyance, why on earth she should sound so worried.

But she smiles at once when I open the door, a smile which weds the coquette and the mother. She is quite old and not really French; she came many years ago, "when I was a very young girl, sir," from just across the border, out of Italy. She seems, like most of the women down here, to have gone into mourning directly the last child moved out of childhood. Hella thought that they were all widows, but, it turned out, most of them had husbands living yet. These husbands might have been their sons. They sometimes played *belote* in the sunshine in a flat field near our house, and their eyes, when they looked at Hella, contained the proud watchfulness of a father and the watchful speculation of a man. I sometimes played billiards with them, and drank red wine, in the *tabac*. But they made me tense— with their ribaldries, their good-nature, their fellowship, the life written on their hands and in their faces and in their eyes. They treated me as the son who has but lately been initiated into manhood; but at the same time, with great distance, for I did not really belong to any of them; and they also sensed (or I felt they did) something else about me, something which it was no longer worth their while to pursue. This seemed to be in their eyes when I walked with Hella and they passed us on the road, saying, very respectfully, *Salut, Monsieur-dame.* They might have been the sons of these women in black, come home after a lifetime of storming and conquering the world, home to rest and be scolded and wait for death, home to those breasts, now dry, which had nourished them in their beginnings.

Flakes of snow have drifted across the shawl which covers her head; and hang on her eyelashes and on the wisps of black and white hair not covered by the shawl. She is very strong yet, though, now, a little bent, a little breathless.

"Bonsoir, monsieur. Vous n'êtes pas malade?"

"No," I say, "I have not been sick. Come in."

She comes in, closing the door behind her, and allowing the shawl to fall from her head. I still have my drink in my hand and she notices this, in silence.

"Eh bien," she says. "*Tant mieux.* But we have not seen you for several days. You have been staying in the house?"

And her eyes search my face.

I am embarrassed and resentful; yet it is impossible to rebuff something at once shrewd and gentle in her eyes and voice. "Yes," I say, "the weather has been bad."

"It is not the middle of August, to be sure," says she, "but you do not have the air of an invalid. It is not good to sit in the house alone."

"I am leaving in the morning," I say, desperately. "Did you want to take the inventory?"

"Yes," she says, and produces from one of her pockets the list of household goods I signed upon arrival. "It will not be long. Let me start from the back."

We start toward the kitchen. On the way I put my drink down on the night table in my bedroom.

"It doesn't matter to me if you drink," she says, not turning around. But I leave my drink behind anyway.

We walk into the kitchen. The kitchen is suspiciously clean and neat. "Where have you been eating?" she asks, sharply. "They tell me at the *tabac* you have not been seen for days. Have you been going to town?"

"Yes," I say lamely, "sometimes."

"On foot?" she inquires. "Because the bus driver, he has not seen you, either." All this time she is not looking at me but around the kitchen, checking off the list in her hand with a short, yellow pencil.

I can make no answer to her last, sardonic thrust, having forgotten that in a small village almost every move is made under the village's collective eye and ear.

She looks briefly in the bathroom. "I'm going to clean that tonight," I say.

"I should hope so," she says. "Everything was clean when you moved in." We walk back through the kitchen. She has failed to notice that two glasses are missing, broken by me, and I have not the energy to tell her. I will leave some money in the cupboard. She turns on the light in the guest room. My dirty clothes are lying all over.

"Those go with me," I say, trying to smile.

"You could have come just across the road," she says. "I would have been glad to give you something to eat. A little soup, something nourishing. I cook every day for my husband; what difference does one more make?"

This touches me, but I do not know how to indicate it, and I cannot say, of course, that eating with her and her husband would have stretched my nerves to the breaking point.

She is examining a decorative pillow. "Are you going to join your fiancée?" she asks.

I know I ought to lie, but somehow I cannot. I am afraid of her eyes. I wish, now, that I had my drink with me. "No," I say, flatly, "she has gone to America."

"*Tiens!*" she says. "And you—do you stay in France?" She looks directly at me.

"For awhile," I say. I am beginning to sweat. It has come to me that this woman, a peasant from Italy, must resemble, in so many ways, the mother of Giovanni. I keep trying not to hear her howls of anguish, I keep trying not to see in her eyes what would surely be there if she knew that her son would be dead by morning, if she knew what I had done to her son.

But, of course, she is not Giovanni's mother.

"It is not good," she says, "it is not right for a young man like you to be sitting alone in a great big house with no woman." She looks, for a moment, very sad; starts to say something more and thinks better of it. I know she wants to say something about Hella, whom neither she nor any of the other women here had liked. But she turns out the light in the guest room and we go into the big bedroom, the master bedroom, which Hella and I had used, not the one in which I have left my drink. This, too, is very clean and orderly. She looks about the room and looks at me, and smiles.

"You have not been using this room lately," she says.

I feel myself blushing painfully. She laughs.

"But you will be happy again," she says. "You must go and find yourself another woman, a *good* woman, and get married, and have babies. *Yes,* that is what you ought to do," she says, as though I had contradicted her, and before I can say anything, "Where is your *maman?*"

"She is dead."

"Ah!" She clicks her teeth in sympathy. "That is sad. And your Papa—is he dead, too?"

"No. He is in America."

"Pauvre bambino!" She looks at my face. I am really helpless in front of her and if she does not leave soon, she will reduce me to tears or curses. "But you do not have the intention of just wandering through the world like a sailor? I am sure that would make your mother very unhappy. You will make a home someday?"

"Yes, surely. Someday."

She puts her strong hand on my arm. "Even if your *maman*, she is dead—that is very sad!—your Papa will be very happy to see bambinos from you." She pauses, her black eyes soften; she is looking at me, but she is looking beyond me, too. "We had three sons. Two of them were killed in the war. In the war, too, we lost all our money. It is sad, is it not, to have worked so hard all one's life in order to have a little peace in one's old age and then to have it all taken away? It almost killed my husband; he has never been the same since." Then I see that her eyes are not merely shrewd; they are also bitter and very sad. She shrugs her shoulders. "Ah! What can one do? It is better not to think about it." Then she smiles. "But our last son, he lives in the north; he came to see us two years ago, and he brought with him his little boy. His little boy, he was only four years old then. He was so beautiful! Mario, he is called." She gestures. "It is my husband's name. They stayed about ten days and we felt young again." She smiles again. "Especially my husband." And she stands there a moment with this smile on her face. Then she asks, abruptly, "Do you pray?"

I wonder if I can stand this another moment. "No," I stammer. "No. Not often."

"But you are a believer?"

I smile. It is not even a patronizing smile, though, perhaps, I wish it could be, "Yes."

But I wonder what my smile could have looked like. It did not reassure her. "You must pray," she says, very soberly. "I assure you. Even just a little prayer, from time to time. Light a little candle. If it were not for the prayers of the blessed saints, one could not live in this world at all. I speak to you," she says, drawing herself up slightly, "as though I were your *maman*. Do not be offended."

"But I am not offended. You are very nice. You are very nice to speak to me this way."

She smiles a satisfied smile. "Men—not just babies like you, but old men, too—they always need a woman to tell them the truth. *Les hommes, ils sont impossibles.*" And she smiles, and forces me to smile at the cunning of this universal joke, and turns out the light in the master bedroom. We go down the hall again, thank heaven, to my drink. This bedroom, of course, is quite untidy, the light burning, my bathrobe, books, dirty socks, and a couple of dirty glasses, and a coffee cup half full of stale coffee—lying around, all over the place; and the sheets on the bed a tangled mess.

"I'll fix this up before morning," I say.

"Bien sûr." She sighs. "You really must take my advice, monsieur, and get married." At this, suddenly, we both laugh. Then I finish my drink.

The inventory is almost done. We go into the last room, the big room, where the bottle is, before the window. She looks at the bottle, then at me. "But you will be drunk by morning," she says.

"Oh, no! I'm taking the bottle *with* me."

It is quite clear that she knows this is not true. But she shrugs her shoulders again. Then she becomes, by the act of wrapping the shawl around her head, very formal, even a little shy. Now that I see she is about to leave, I wish I could think of something to make her stay. When she has gone back across the road, the night will be blacker and longer than ever. I have something to say to her—to her?— but of course it will never be said. I feel that I want to be forgiven; I want *her* to forgive me. But I do not know how to state my crime. My crime, in some odd way, is in being a man and she knows all about this already. It is terrible how naked she makes me feel, like a half-grown boy, naked before his mother.

She puts out her hand. I take it, awkwardly.

"*Bon voyage, monsieur.* I hope that you were happy while you were here and that, perhaps, one day, you will visit us again." She is smiling and her eyes are kind but now the smile is purely social, it is the graceful termination of a business deal.

"Thank you," I say. "Perhaps I will be back next year." She releases my hand and we walk to the door.

"Oh!" she says, at the door, "please do not wake me up in the morning. Put the keys in my mailbox. I do not, any more, have any reason to get up so early."

"Surely." I smile and open the door. "Good-night, Madame."

"*Bonsoir, Monsieur. Adieu!*" She steps out into the darkness. But there is a light coming from my house and from her house across the road. The town lights glimmer beneath us and I hear, briefly, the sea again.

She walks a little away from me, and turns. "*Souvenez-vous,*" she tells me. "One must make a little prayer from time to time."

And I close the door.

She has made me realize that I have much to do before morning. I decide to clean the bathroom before I allow myself another drink. And I begin to do this, first scrubbing out the tub, then running water into the pail to mop the floor. The bathroom is tiny and square, with one frosted window. It reminds me of that claustrophobic room in Paris. Giovanni had had great plans for remodelling the room and there was a time, when he had actually begun to do this, when we lived with plaster all over everything and bricks piled on the floor. We took packages of bricks out of the house at night and left them in the streets.

I suppose they will come for him early in the morning, perhaps just before dawn, so that the last thing Giovanni will ever see will be that grey, lightless sky over Paris, beneath which we stumbled homeward together so many desperate and drunken mornings.

PART TWO

ONE

I remember that life in that room seemed to be occurring beneath the sea. Time flowed past indifferently above us; hours and days had no meaning. In the beginning, our life together held a joy and amazement which was newborn every day. Beneath the joy, of course, was anguish and beneath the amazement was fear; but they did not work themselves to the beginning until our high beginning was aloes on our tongues. By then anguish and fear had become the surface on which we slipped and slid, losing balance, dignity, and pride. Giovanni's face, which I had memorized so many mornings, noons, and nights, hardened before my eyes, began to give in secret places, began to crack. The light in the eyes became a glitter; the wide and beautiful brow began to suggest the skull beneath. The sensual lips turned inward, busy with the sorrow overflowing from his heart. It became a stranger's face—or it made me so guilty to look on him that I wished it were a stranger's face. Not all my memorizing had prepared me for the metamorphosis which my memorizing had helped to bring about.

Our day began before daybreak, when I drifted over to Guillaume's bar in time for a preclosing drink. Sometimes, when Guillaume had closed the bar to the public, a few friends and Giovanni and myself stayed behind for breakfast and music. Sometimes Jacques was there—from the time of our meeting with Giovanni he seemed to come out more and more. If we had breakfast with Guillaume, we usually left around seven o'clock in the morning. Sometimes, when Jacques was there, he offered to drive us home in the car which he had suddenly and inexplicably bought, but we almost always walked the long way home along the river.

Spring was approaching Paris. Walking up and down this house tonight, I see again the river, the cobblestoned *quais,* the bridges. Low boats passed beneath the bridges and on those boats one sometimes saw women hanging washing out to dry. Sometimes we saw a young man in a canoe, energetically rowing, looking rather helpless, and also rather silly. There were yachts tied up along the banks from time to time, and houseboats, and barges; we passed the firehouse so often on our way home that the firemen got to know us. When winter came again and Giovanni found himself in hiding in one of these barges, it was a fireman who, seeing him crawl back into hiding with a loaf of bread one night, tipped off the police.

The trees grew green those mornings, the river dropped, and the brown winter smoke dropped downward out of it, and fishermen appeared. Giovanni was right about the fishermen; they certainly never seemed to catch anything, but it gave them something to do. Along the *quais* the bookstalls seemed to become almost festive, awaiting the weather which would allow the passerby to leaf idly through the dog-eared books, and which would inform the tourist with a passionate desire to carry off to the United States, or Denmark, more colored prints than he could afford, or, when he got home, know what to do with. Also, the girls appeared on their bicycles, along with boys similarly equipped; and we sometimes saw them along the river, as the light began to fade, their bicycles put away until the morrow. This was after Giovanni had lost his job and we walked around in the evenings. Those evenings were bitter. Giovanni knew that I was going to leave him, but he did not dare accuse me for fear of being corroborated. I did not dare to tell him. Hella was on her way back from Spain and my father had agreed to send me money, which I was not going to use to help Giovanni, who had done so much to help me. I was going to use it to escape his room.

Every morning the sky and the sun seemed to be a little higher and the river stretched before us with a greater haze of promise. Every day the bookstall keepers seemed to have taken off another garment, so that the shape of their bodies appeared to be undergoing a most striking and continual metamorphosis. One began to wonder what the final shape would be. It was observable, through open windows on the *quais* and sidestreets, that *hôteliers* had called in painters to paint the rooms; the women in the dairies had taken off their blue sweaters and rolled up the sleeves of their dresses, so that one saw their powerful arms; the bread seemed warmer and fresher in the bakeries. The small school children had taken off their capes and their knees were no longer scarlet with the cold. There seemed to be more chatter—in that curiously measured and vehement language, which sometimes reminds me of stiffening egg white and sometimes of stringed instruments but always of the underside and aftermath of passion.

But we did not often have breakfast in Guillaume's

bar because Guillaume did not like me. Usually I simply waited around, as inconspicuously as possible, until Giovanni had finished cleaning up the bar and had changed his clothes. Then we said good-night and left. The habitués had evolved toward us a curious attitude, composed of an unpleasant maternalism, and envy, and disguised dislike. They could not, somehow, speak to us as they spoke to one another, and they resented the strain we imposed on them of speaking in any other way. And it made them furious that the dead center of their lives was, in this instance, none of their business. It made them feel their poverty again, through the narcotics of chatter, and dreams of conquest, and mutual contempt.

Wherever we ate breakfast and wherever we walked, when we got home we were always too tired to sleep right away. We made coffee and sometimes drank cognac with it; we sat on the bed and talked and smoked. We seemed to have a great deal to tell—or Giovanni did. Even at my most candid, even when I tried hardest to give myself to him as he gave himself to me, I was holding something back. I did not, for example, really tell him about Hella until I had been living in the room a month. I told him about her then because her letters had begun to sound as though she would be coming back to Paris very soon.

"What is she doing, wandering around through Spain alone?" asked Giovanni.

"She likes to travel," I said.

"Oh," said Giovanni, "nobody likes to travel, especially not women. There must be some other reason." He raised his eyebrows suggestively. "Perhaps she has a Spanish lover and is afraid to tell you—? Perhaps she is with a *torero*."

Perhaps she is, I thought. "But she wouldn't be afraid to tell me."

Giovanni laughed. "I do not understand Americans at all," he said.

"I don't see that there's anything very hard to understand. We aren't married, you know."

"But she is your mistress, no?" asked Giovanni.

"Yes."

"And she is still your mistress?"

I stared at him. "Of course," I said.

"Well then," said Giovanni, "I do not understand what she is doing in Spain while you are in Paris." Another thought struck him. "How old is she?"

"She's two years younger than I am." I watched him. "What's that got to do with it?"

"Is she married? I mean to somebody else, naturally."

I laughed. He laughed too. "Of course not."

"Well, I thought she might be an older woman," said Giovanni, "with a husband somewhere and perhaps she had to go away with him from time to time in order to be able to continue her affair with you. That would be a nice arrangement. Those women are sometimes *very* interesting and they usually have a little money. If *that* woman was in Spain, she would bring back a wonderful gift for you. But a young girl, bouncing around in a foreign country by herself—I do not like that at all. You should find another mistress."

It all seemed very funny. I could not stop laughing. "Do *you* have a mistress?" I asked him.

"Not now," he said, "but perhaps I will again one day." He half frowned, half smiled. "I don't seem to be very interested in women right now—I don't know why. I used to be. Perhaps I will be again." He shrugged. "Perhaps it is because women are just a little more trouble than I can afford right now. *Et puis*—" He stopped.

I wanted to say that it seemed to me that he had taken a most peculiar road out of his trouble; but I only said, after a moment, cautiously: "You don't seem to have a very high opinion of women."

"Oh, women! There is no need, thank heaven, to have an opinion about *women*. Women are like water. They are tempting like that, and they can be that treacherous, and they can seem to be that bottomless, you know?—and they can be that shallow. And that dirty." He stopped. "I perhaps don't like women very much, that's true. That hasn't stopped me from making love to many and loving one or two. But most of the time—most of the time I made love only with the body."

"That can make one very lonely," I said. I had not expected to say it.

He had not expected to hear it. He looked at me and reached out and touched me on the cheek. "Yes," he said. Then: "I am not trying to be *méchant* when I talk about women. I respect women—very much—for their inside life, which is not like the life of a man."

"Women don't seem to like that idea," I said.

"Oh, well," said Giovanni, "these absurd women running around today, full of ideas and nonsense, and thinking themselves equal to men—*quelle rigolade!*—they need to be beaten half to death so that they can find out who rules the world."

I laughed. "Did the women you knew like to get beaten?"

He smiled. "I don't know if they liked it. But a beating never made them go away." We both laughed. "They were not, anyway, like that silly little girl of yours, wandering all over Spain and sending postcards back to Paris. What does she think she is doing? Does she want you or does she not want you?"

"She went to Spain," I said, "to find out."

Giovanni opened his eyes wide. He was indignant. "To Spain? Why not to China? What is she doing, testing all the Spaniards and comparing them with you?"

I was a little annoyed. "You don't understand," I said. "She is a very intelligent, very complex girl; she wanted to go away and think."

"What is there to think about? She sounds rather silly, I must say. She just can't make up her mind what bed to sleep in. She wants to eat her cake and she wants to have it all."

"If she were in Paris now," I said, abruptly, "then I would not be in this room with you."

"You would possibly not be living here," he conceded, "but we would certainly be seeing each other, why not?"

"Why *not*? Suppose she found out?"

"Found *out*? Found out what?"

"Oh, stop it," I said. "You know what there is to find out."

He looked at me very soberly. "She sounds more and more impossible, this little girl of yours. What does she do, follow you everywhere? Or will she hire detectives to sleep under our bed? And what business is it of hers, anyway?"

"You can't possibly be serious," I said.

"I certainly can be," he retorted, "and I am. You are the incomprehensible one." He groaned and poured more coffee and picked up our cognac from the floor. "*Chez toi* everything sounds extremely feverish and complicated, like one of those English murder mysteries. To find out, to find out, you keep saying, as though we were accomplices in a crime. We have not committed any crime." He poured the cognac.

"It's just that she'll be terribly hurt if she does find out, that's all. People have very dirty words for—for this situation." I stopped. His face suggested that my reasoning was flimsy. I added, defensively, "Besides, it *is* a crime—in my country and, after all, I didn't grow up here, I grew up *there*."

"If dirty words frighten you," said Giovanni, "I really do not know how you have managed to live so long. People are full of dirty words. The only time they do not use them, most people I mean, is when they are describing something dirty." He paused and we watched each other. In spite of what he was saying, he looked rather frightened himself. "If your countrymen think that privacy is a crime, so much the worse for your country. And as for this girl of yours—are you always at her side when she is here? I mean, all day, every day? You go out sometimes to have a drink alone, no? Maybe you sometimes take a walk without her—to think, as you say. The Americans seem to do a great deal of thinking. And perhaps while you are thinking and having that drink, you look at another girl who passes, no? Maybe you even look up at that sky and feel your own blood in you? Or does everything stop when Hella comes? No drinks alone, no looks at other girls, no sky? Eh? Answer me."

"I've told you already that we're not married. But I don't seem to be able to make you understand anything at all this morning."

"But anyway—when Hella is here you do sometimes see other people—without Hella?"

"Of course."

"And does she make you tell her everything you have done while you were not with her?"

I sighed. I had lost control of the conversation somewhere along the line and I simply wanted it to end. I drank my cognac too fast and it burned my throat. "Of course not."

"Well. You are a very charming and good-looking and civilized boy and, unless you are impotent, I do not see what she has to complain about, or what you have to worry about. To arrange, *mon cher, la vie pratique,* is very simple— it only has to be done." He reflected. "Sometimes things go wrong, I agree; then you have to arrange it another way. But it is certainly not the English melodrama you make it. Why, that way, life would simply be unbearable." He poured more cognac and grinned at me, as though he had solved all my problems. And there was something so artless in this smile that I had to smile back. Giovanni liked to believe that he was hard-headed and that I was not and that he was teaching me the stony facts of life. It was very important for him to feel this: it was because he knew, unwillingly, at the very bottom of his heart, that I, helplessly, at the very bottom of mine, resisted him with all my strength.

Eventually we grew still, we fell silent, and we slept. We awoke around three or four in the afternoon, when the dull sun was prying at odd corners of the cluttered room. We arose and washed and shaved, bumping into each other and making jokes and furious with the unstated desire to escape the room. Then we danced out into the streets, into Paris, and ate quickly somewhere, and I left Giovanni at the door to Guillaume's bar.

Then I, alone, and relieved to be alone, perhaps went to a movie, or walked, or returned home and read, or sat in a park and read, or sat on a cafe terrace, or talked to people, or wrote letters. I wrote to Hella, telling her nothing, or I wrote to my father asking for money. And no matter what I was doing, another me sat in my belly, absolutely cold with terror over the question of my life.

Giovanni had awakened an itch, had released a gnaw in me. I realized it one afternoon, when I was taking him to work via the Boulevard Montparnasse. We had bought a kilo of cherries and we were eating them as we walked along. We were both insufferably childish and high-spirited that afternoon and the spectacle we presented, two grown men jostling each other on the wide sidewalk and aiming the cherry pits, as though they were spitballs, into each other's faces, must have been outrageous. And I realized that such childishness was fantastic at my age and the happiness out of which it sprang yet more so; for that moment I really loved Giovanni, who had never seemed more beautiful than he was that afternoon. And, watching his face, I realized that it meant much to me that I could make his face so bright. I saw that I might be willing to give a great deal not to lose that power. And I felt myself flow toward him, as a river rushes when the ice breaks up. Yet, at that very moment, there passed between us on the pavement another boy, a stranger, and I invested him at once with Giovanni's beauty and what I felt for Giovanni I also felt for him. Giovanni saw this and saw my face and it made him laugh the more. I blushed and he kept laughing and then the boulevard, the light, the sound of his laughter turned into a scene from a nightmare. I kept looking at the trees, the light falling through the leaves. I felt sorrow and shame and panic and great bitterness. At the same time—it was part of my turmoil and also outside it—I felt the muscles in my neck tighten with the effort I was making not to turn my head and watch that boy diminish down the bright avenue. The beast which Giovanni had awakened in me would never go to sleep again; but one day I would not be with Giovanni anymore. And would I then, like all the others, find myself turning and following all kinds of boys down God knows what dark avenues, into what dark places?

With this fearful intimation there opened in me a hatred for Giovanni which was as powerful as my love and which was nourished by the same roots.

Two

I scarcely know how to describe that room. It became, in a way, every room I had ever been in and every room I find myself in hereafter will remind me of Giovanni's room. I did not really stay there very long—we met before the spring began and I left there during the summer—but it still seems to me that I spent a lifetime there. Life in that room seemed to be occurring underwater, as I say, and it is certain that I underwent a sea change there.

To begin with, the room was not large enough for two. It looked out on a small courtyard. "Looked out" means only that the room had two windows, against which the court-yard malevolently pressed, encroaching day by day, as though it had confused itself with a jungle. We, or rather Giovanni, kept the windows closed most of the time. He had never bought any curtains; neither did we buy any while I was in the room. To insure privacy, Giovanni had obscured the window panes with a heavy, white cleaning polish. We sometimes heard children playing outside our window, sometimes strange shapes loomed against it. At such moments, Giovanni, working in the room, or lying in bed, would stiffen like a hunting dog and remain perfectly silent until whatever seemed to threaten our safety had moved away.

He had always had great plans for remodelling this room, and before I arrived he had already begun. One of the walls was a dirty, streaked white where he had torn off the wallpaper. The wall facing it was destined never to be uncovered, and on this wall a lady in a hoop skirt and a man in knee breeches perpetually walked together, hemmed in by roses. The wallpaper lay on the floor, in great sheets and scrolls, in dust. On the floor also lay our dirty laundry, along with Giovanni's tools and the paint brushes and the bottles of oil and turpentine. Our suitcases teetered on top of something, so that we dreaded ever having to open them and sometimes went without some minor necessity, such as clean socks, for days.

No one ever came to see us, except Jacques, and he did not come often. We were far from the center of the city and we had no phone.

I remembered the first afternoon I woke up there, with Giovanni fast asleep beside me, heavy as a fallen rock. The sun filtered through the room so faintly that I was worried about the time. I stealthily lit a cigarette, for I did not want to wake Giovanni. I did not yet know how I would face his eyes. I looked about me. Giovanni had said something in the taxi about his room being very dirty. "I'm sure it is," I had said lightly, and turned away from him, looking out of the window. Then we had both been silent. When I woke up in his room, I remembered that there had been something strained and painful in the quality of that silence, which had been broken when Giovanni said, with a shy, bitter smile: "I must find some poetic figure."

And he spread his heavy fingers in the air, as though a metaphor were tangible. I watched him.

"Look at the garbage of this city," he said, finally, and his fingers indicated the flying street, "all of the garbage of this city? Where do they take it? I don't know where they take it—but it might very well be my room."

"It's much more likely," I said, "that they dump it into the Seine."

But I sensed, when I woke up and looked around the room, the bravado and the cowardice of his figure of speech. This was not the garbage of Paris, which would have been anonymous: this was Giovanni's regurgitated life.

Before and beside me and all over the room, towering like a wall, were boxes of cardboard and leather, some tied with string, some locked, some bursting, and out of the topmost box before me spilled down sheets of violin music. There was a violin in the room, lying on the table in its warped, cracked case—it was impossible to guess from looking at it whether it had been laid to rest there yesterday or a hundred years before. The table was loaded with yellowing newspapers and empty bottles and it held a single brown and wrinkled potato in which even the sprouting eyes were rotten. Red wine had been spilled on the floor; it had been allowed to dry and it made the air in the room sweet and heavy. But it was not the room's disorder which was frightening; it was the fact that when one began searching for the key to this disorder, one realized that it was not to be found in any of the usual places. For this was not a matter of habit or circumstance or temperament; it was a matter of punishment and grief. I do not know how I knew this, but I knew it at once; perhaps I knew it because

I wanted to live. And I stared at the room with the same, nervous, calculating extension of the intelligence and of all one's forces which occurs when gauging a mortal and unavoidable danger: at the silent walls of the room with its distant, archaic lovers trapped in an interminable rose garden, and the staring windows, staring like two great eyes of ice and fire, and the ceiling which lowered like those clouds out of which fiends have sometimes spoken and which obscured but failed to soften its malevolence behind the yellow light which hung like a diseased and undefinable sex in its center. Under this blunted arrow, this smashed flower of light lay the terrors which encompassed Giovanni's soul. I understood why Giovanni had wanted me and had brought me to his last retreat. I was to destroy this room and give to Giovanni a new and better life. This life could only be my own, which, in order to transform Giovanni's, must first become a part of Giovanni's room.

In the beginning, because the motives which led me to Giovanni's room were so mixed, had so little to do with his hopes and desires, and were so deeply a part of my own desperation, I invented in myself a kind of pleasure in playing the housewife after Giovanni had gone to work. I threw out the paper, the bottles, the fantastic accumulation of trash; I examined the contents of the innumerable boxes and suitcases and disposed of them. But I am not a housewife—men never can be housewives. And the pleasure was never real or deep, though Giovanni smiled his humble, grateful smile and told me in as many ways as he could find how wonderful it was to have me there, how I stood, with my love and my ingenuity, between him and the dark. Each day he invited me to witness how he had changed, how love had changed him, how he worked and sang and cherished me. I was in a terrible confusion. Sometimes I thought, but this *is* your life. Stop fighting it. Stop fighting. Or I thought, but I am happy. And he loves me. I am safe. Sometimes, when he was not near me, I thought, I will never let him touch me again. Then, when he touched me, I thought, it doesn't matter, it is only the body, it will soon be over. When it was over, I lay in the dark and listened to his breathing and dreamed of the touch of hands, of Giovanni's hands, or anybody's hands, hands which would have the power to crush me and make me whole again.

Sometimes I left Giovanni over our afternoon breakfast, blue smoke from a cigarette circling around his head, and went off to the American Express office at Opéra, where my mail would be, if I had any. Sometimes, but rarely, Giovanni came with me; he said that he could not endure being surrounded by so many Americans. He said they all looked alike—as I am sure they did, to him. But they didn't look alike to me. I was aware that they all had in common something that made them Americans, but I could never put my finger on what it was. I knew that whatever this common quality was, I shared it. And I knew that Giovanni had been attracted to me partly because of it. When Giovanni wanted me to know that he was displeased with me, he said I was a *"vrai américain"*; conversely, when delighted, he said that I was not an American at all; and on both occasions he was striking, deep in me, a nerve which did not throb in him. And I resented this: resented being called an American (and resented resenting it) because it seemed to make me nothing more than that, whatever that was; and I resented being called *not* an American because it seemed to make me nothing.

Yet, walking into the American Express Office one harshly bright, midsummer afternoon, I was forced to admit that this active, so disquietingly cheerful horde struck the eye, at once, as a unit. At home, I could have distinguished patterns, habits, accents of speech—with no effort whatever: now everybody sounded, unless I listened hard, as though they had just arrived from Nebraska. At home I could have seen the clothes they were wearing, but here I only saw bags, cameras, belts, and hats, all clearly from the same department store. At home I would have had some sense of the individual womanhood of the woman I faced: here the most ferociously accomplished seemed to be involved in some ice-cold or sun-dried travesty of sex, and even grandmothers seemed to have had no traffic with the flesh. And what distinguished the men was that they seemed incapable of age; they smelled of soap, which seemed indeed to be their preservative against the dangers and exigencies of any more intimate odor; the boy he had been shone, somehow, unsoiled, untouched, unchanged, through the eyes of the man of sixty, booking passage, with his smiling wife, to Rome. His wife might have been his mother, forcing more oatmeal down his throat, and Rome might have been the movie she had promised to allow him to see. Yet I also suspected that what I was seeing was but a part of the truth and perhaps not even the most important part; beneath these faces, these clothes, accents, rudenesses, was power and sorrow, both unadmitted, unrealized, the power of inventors, the sorrow of the disconnected.

I took my place in the mail line behind two girls who had decided that they wanted to stay on in Europe and who were hoping to find jobs with the American government in

Germany. One of them had fallen in love with a Swiss boy; so I gathered, from the low, intense, and troubled conversation she was having with her friend. The friend was urging her to "put her foot down"—on what principle I could not discover; and the girl in love kept nodding her head, but more in perplexity than agreement. She had the choked and halting air of someone who has something more to say but finds no way of saying it. "You mustn't be a fool about this," the friend was saying. "I know, I know," said the girl. One had the impression that, though she certainly did not wish to be a fool, she had lost one definition of the word and might never be able to find another.

There were two letters for me, one from my father and one from Hella. Hella had been sending me only postcards for quite awhile. I was afraid her letter might be important and I did not want to read it. I opened the letter from my father first. I read it, standing just beyond reach of the sunlight, beside the endlessly swinging double doors.

Dear Butch, my father said, *aren't you ever coming home? Don't think I'm only being selfish but it's true I'd like to see you. I think you have been away long enough, God knows I don't know what you're doing over there, and you don't write enough for me even to guess. But my guess is you're going to be sorry one of these fine days that you stayed over there, looking at your navel, and let the world pass you by. There's nothing over there for you. You're as American as pork and beans, though maybe you don't want to think so anymore. And maybe you won't mind my saying that you're getting a little old for studying, after all, if that's what you're doing. You're pushing thirty. I'm getting along, too, and you're all I've got. I'd like to see you.*

You keep asking me to send you your money and I guess you think I'm being a bastard about it. I'm not trying to starve you out

*and you know if you really need anything, I'll be the first to help you
but I really don't think I'd be doing you a favor by letting you spend
what little money you've got over there and then coming home to
nothing. What the hell are you doing? Let your old man in on the secret, can't you? You may not believe this, but once I was a young
man, too.*

And then he went on about my stepmother and how she
wanted to see me, and about some of our friends and what
they were doing. It was clear that my absence was beginning to frighten him. He did not know what it meant. But
he was living, obviously, in a pit of suspicions which daily
became blacker and vaguer—he would not have known
how to put them into words, even if he had dared. The
question he longed to ask was not in the letter and neither
was the offer: *Is it a woman, David? Bring her on home. I don't
care who she is. Bring her on home and I'll help you get set up.* He
could not risk this question because he could not have endured an answer in the negative. An answer in the negative
would have revealed what strangers we had become. I
folded the letter and put it in my back pocket and looked
out for a moment at the wide, sunlit foreign avenue.

There was a sailor, dressed all in white, coming across
the boulevard, walking with that funny roll sailors have
and with that aura, hopeful and hard, of having to make a
great deal happen in a hurry. I was staring at him, though I
did not know it, and wishing I were he. He seemed—
somehow—younger than I had ever been, and blonder and
more beautiful, and he wore his masculinity as unequivo-
cally as he wore his skin. He made me think of home—
perhaps home is not a place but simply an irrevocable
condition. I knew how he drank and how he was with his
friends and how pain and women baffled him. I wondered

if my father had ever been like that, if I had ever been like that—though it was hard to imagine, for this boy, striding across the avenue like light itself, any antecedents, any connections at all. We came abreast and, as though he had seen some all-revealing panic in my eyes, he gave me a look contemptuously lewd and knowing; just such a look as he might have given, but a few hours ago, to the desperately well-dressed nymphomaniac or trollop who was trying to make him believe she was a lady. And in another second, had our contact lasted, I was certain that there would erupt into speech, out of all that light and beauty, some brutal variation of *Look, baby, I know you.* I felt my face flame, I felt my heart harden and shake as I hurried past him, trying to look stonily beyond him. He had caught me by surprise, for I had, somehow, not really been thinking of him but of the letter in my pocket, of Hella and Giovanni. I got to the other side of the boulevard, not daring to look back, and I wondered what he had seen in me to elicit such instantaneous contempt. I was too old to suppose that it had anything to do with my walk, or the way I held my hands, or my voice—which, anyway, he had not heard. It was something else and I would never see it. I would never dare to see it. It would be like looking at the naked sun. But, hurrying, and not daring now to look at anyone, male or female, who passed me on the wide sidewalks, I knew that what the sailor had seen in my unguarded eyes was envy and desire: I had seen it often in Jacques' eyes and my reaction and the sailor's had been the same. But if I were still able to feel affection and if he had seen it in my eyes, it would not have helped, for affection, for the boys I was doomed to look at, was vastly more frightening than lust.

I walked farther than I had intended, for I did not dare to stop while the sailor might still be watching. Near the river, on rue des Pyramides, I sat down at a cafe table and opened Hella's letter.

Mon cher, she began, *Spain is my favorite country mais ca n'empêche que Paris est toujours ma ville préférée. I long to be again among all those foolish people, running for métros and jumping off of buses and dodging motorcycles and having traffic jams and admiring all that crazy statuary in all those absurd parks. I weep for the fishy ladies in the Place de la Concorde. Spain is not like that at all. Whatever else Spain is, it is not frivolous. I think, really, that I would stay in Spain forever—if I had never been to Paris. Spain is very beautiful, stony and sunny and lonely. But by and by you get tired of olive oil and fish and castanets and tambourines—or, anyway, I do. I want to come home, to come home to Paris. It's funny, I've never felt anyplace was home before.*

Nothing has happened to me here—I suppose that pleases you, I confess it rather pleases me. The Spaniards are nice, but, of course, most of them are terribly poor, the ones who aren't are impossible, I don't like the tourists, mainly English and American dipsomaniacs, paid, my dear, by their families to stay away. (I wish I had a family.) I'm on Mallorca now and it would be a pretty place if you could dump all the pensioned widows into the sea and make dry-martini drinking illegal. I've never seen anything like it! The way these old hags guzzle and make eyes at anything in pants, especially anything about eighteen—well, I said to myself, Hella, my girl, take a good look. You may be looking at your future. The trouble is that I love myself too much. And so I've decided to let two try it, this business of loving me, I mean, and see how that works out. (I feel fine, now that I've made the decision, I hope you'll feel fine, too, dear knight in Gimble's armor.)

I've been trapped into some dreary expedition to Seville with an English family I met in Barcelona. They adore Spain and they want to take me to see a bullfight—I never have, you know, all the time I've been wandering around here. They're really quite nice, he's some kind of poet with the B.B.C. and she's his efficient and adoring spouse. Quite nice, really. They do have an impossibly lunatick son who imagines himself mad about me, but he's much too English and much, much too young. I leave tomorrow and shall be gone ten days. Then, they to England and I—to you!

I folded this letter, which I now realized I had been awaiting for many days and nights, and the waiter came and asked me what I wanted to drink. I had meant to order an aperitif but now, in some grotesque spirit of celebration, ordered a Scotch and soda. And over this drink, which had never seemed more American than it did at that moment, I stared at absurd Paris, which was as cluttered now, under the scalding sun, as the landscape of my heart. I wondered what I was going to do.

I cannot say that I was frightened. Or, it would be better to say that I did not feel any fear—the way men who are shot do not, I am told, feel any pain for awhile. I felt a certain relief. It seemed that the necessity for decision had been taken from my hands. I told myself that we both had always known, Giovanni and myself, that our idyll could not last forever. And it was not as though I had not been honest with him—he knew all about Hella. He knew that she would be returning to Paris one day. Now she would be coming back and my life with Giovanni would be finished. It would be something that had happened to me once—it would be something that had happened to many men once. I paid for my drink and got up and walked across the river to Montparnasse.

I felt elated—yet, as I walked down Raspail toward the cafes of Montparnasse, I could not fail to remember that Hella and I had walked here, Giovanni and I had walked here. And with each step, the face that glowed insistently before me was not her face but his. I was beginning to wonder how he would take my news. I did not think he would fight me, but I was afraid of what I would see in his face. I was afraid of the pain I would see there. But even this was not my real fear. My real fear was buried and was driving me to Montparnasse. I wanted to find a girl, any girl at all.

But the terraces seemed oddly deserted. I walked along slowly, on both sides of the street, looking at the tables. I saw no one I knew. I walked down as far as the *Closerie des Lilas* and I had a solitary drink there. I read my letters again. I thought of finding Giovanni at once and telling him I was leaving him but I knew he would not yet have opened the bar and he might be almost anywhere in Paris at this hour. I walked slowly back up the boulevard. Then I saw a couple of girls, French whores, but they were not very attractive. I told myself that I could do better than *that*. I got to the *Sélect* and sat down. I watched the people pass, and I drank. No one I knew appeared on the boulevard for the longest while.

The person who appeared, and whom I did not know very well, was a girl named Sue, blonde and rather puffy, with the quality, in spite of the fact that she was not pretty, of the girls who are selected each year to be Miss Rheingold. She wore her curly blond hair cut very short, she had small breasts and a big behind, and in order, no doubt, to indicate to the world how little she cared for appearance or sensuality, she almost always wore tight blue jeans. I think she came from Philadelphia and her family was very rich. Sometimes, when she was drunk, she reviled them, and, sometimes, drunk in another way, she extolled their virutes of thrift and fidelity. I was both dismayed and relieved to see her. The moment she appeared I began, mentally, to take off all her clothes.

"Sit down," I said. "Have a drink."

"I'm glad to *see* you," she cried, sitting down, and looking about for the waiter. "You'd rather dropped out of sight. How've you been?"—abandoning her search for the waiter and leaning forward to me with a friendly grin.

"I've been fine," I told her. "And you?"

"Oh, *me*! Nothing ever happens to me." And she turned down the corners of her rather predatory and also vulnerable mouth to indicate that she was both joking and not joking. "I'm built like a brick stone wall." We both laughed. She peered at me. "They tell me you're living way out at the end of Paris, near the zoo."

"I found a maid's room out there. Very cheap."

"Are you living alone?"

I did not know whether she knew about Giovanni or not. I felt a hint of sweat on my forehead. "Sort of," I said.

"Sort of? What the hell does *that* mean? Do you have a monkey with you, or something?"

I grinned. "No. But this French kid I know, he lives with his mistress, but they fight a lot and it's really *his* room so sometimes, when his mistress throws him out, he bunks with me for a couple of days."

"Ah!" she sighed. *"Chagrin d'amour!"*

"He's having a good time," I said. "He loves it." I looked at her. "Aren't you?"

"Stone walls," she said, "are impenetrable."

The waiter arrived. "Doesn't it," I dared, "depend on the weapon?"

"What are you buying me to drink?" she asked.

"What do you want?" We were both grinning. The waiter stood above us, manifesting a kind of surly *joie de vivre*.

"I believe I'll have"—she batted the eyelashes of her tight blue eyes—"*un ricard*. With a hell of a lot of ice."

"*Deux ricards*," I said to the waiter "*avec beaucoup de la glace.*"

"*Oui, monsieur.*" I was sure he despised us both. I thought of Giovanni and of how many times in an evening the phrase, *Oui, monsieur* fell from his lips. With this fleeting thought there came another, equally fleeting: a new sense of Giovanni, his private life and pain, and all that moved like a flood in him when we lay together at night.

"To continue," I said.

"To continue?" She made her eyes very wide and blank. "Where were we?" She was trying to be coquettish and she was trying to be hard-headed. I felt that I was doing something very cruel.

But I could not stop. "We were talking about stone walls and how they could be entered."

"I never knew," she simpered, "that you had any interest in stone walls."

"There's a lot about me you don't know." The waiter returned with our drinks. "Don't you think discoveries are fun?"

She stared discontentedly at her drink. "Frankly," she said, turning toward me again, with those eyes, "no."

"Oh, you're much too young for that," I said. "*Everything* should be a discovery."

She was silent for a moment. She sipped her drink. "I've made," she said, finally, "all the discoveries that I can stand." But I watched the way her thighs moved against the cloth of her jeans.

"But you can't just go on being a brick stone wall forever."

"I don't see why not," she said. "Nor do I see *how* not."

"Baby," I said, "I'm making you a proposition."

She picked up her glass again and sipped it, staring straight outward at the boulevard. "And what's the proposition?"

"Invite me for a drink. *Chez toi.*"

"I don't believe," she said, turning to me, "that I've got anything in the house."

"We can pick up something on the way," I said.

She stared at me for a long time. I forced myself not to drop my eyes. "I'm sure that I shouldn't," she said at last.

"Why not?"

She made a small, helpless movement in the wicker chair. "I don't know. I don't know what you want."

I laughed. "If you invite me home for a drink," I said, "I'll show you."

"I think you're being impossible," she said, and for the first time there was something genuine in her eyes and voice.

"Well," I said, "I think *you* are." I looked at her with a smile which was, I hoped, both boyish and insistent. "I don't know what I've said that's so impossible. I've put all my cards on the table. But you're still holding yours. I don't know why you should think a man's being impossible when he declares himself attracted to you."

"Oh, please," she said, and finished her drink, "I'm sure it's just the summer sun."

"The summer sun," I said, "has nothing to do with it." And when she still made no answer, "All you've got to do," I said desperately, "is decide whether we'll have another drink here or at your place."

She snapped her fingers abruptly but did not succeed in appearing jaunty. "Come along," she said. "I'm certain to regret it. But you really will have to buy something to drink. There *isn't* anything in the house. And that way," she added, after a moment, "I'll be sure to get something out of the deal."

It was I, then, who felt a dreadful holding back. To avoid looking at her, I made a great show of getting the waiter. And he came, as surly as ever, and I paid him, and we rose and started walking towards the rue de Sévres, where Sue had a small apartment.

Her apartment was dark and full of furniture. "None of it is mine," she said. "It all belongs to the French lady of a certain age from whom I rented it, who is now in Monte Carlo for her nerves." She was very nervous, too, and I saw that this nervousness could be, for a little while, a great help to me. I had bought a small bottle of cognac and I put it down on her marble-topped table and took her in my arms. For some reason I was terribly aware that it was after seven in the evening, that soon the sun would have disappeared from the river, that all the Paris night was about to begin, and that Giovanni was now at work.

She was very big and she was disquietingly fluid—fluid without, however, being able to flow. I felt a hardness and a constriction in her, a grave distrust, created already by too many men like me ever to be conquered now. What we were about to do would not be pretty.

And, as though she felt this, she moved away from me. "Let's have a drink," she said. "Unless, of course, you're in a hurry. I'll try not to keep you any longer than absolutely necessary."

She smiled and I smiled, too. We were as close in that instant as we would ever get—like two thieves. "Let's have several drinks," I said.

"But not *too* many," she said, and simpered again suggestively, like a broken-down movie queen facing the cruel cameras again after a long eclipse.

She took the cognac and disappeared into her corner of a kitchen. "Make yourself comfortable," she shouted out to me. "Take off your shoes. Take off your socks. Look at my books—I often wonder what I'd do if there weren't any books in the world."

I took off my shoes and lay back on her sofa. I tried not to think. But I was thinking that what I did with Giovanni could not possibly be more immoral than what I was about to do with Sue.

She came back with two great brandy snifters. She came close to me on the sofa and we touched glasses. We drank a little, she watching me all the while, and then I touched her breasts. Her lips parted and she put her glass down with extraordinary clumsiness and lay against me. It was a gesture of great despair and I knew that she was giving herself, not to me, but to that lover who would never come.

And I—I thought of many things, lying coupled with Sue in that dark place. I wondered if she had done anything to prevent herself from becoming pregnant; and the thought of a child belonging to Sue and me, of my being trapped that way—in the very act, so to speak, of trying to escape—almost precipitated a laughing jag. I wondered if her blue jeans had been thrown on top of the cigarette she had been smoking. I wondered if anyone else had a key to her apartment, if we could be heard through the inadequate walls, how much, in a few moments, we would hate each other. I also approached Sue as though she were a job of work, a job which it was necessary to do in an unforgettable manner. Somewhere, at the very bottom of myself, I realized that I was doing something awful to her and it became a matter of my honor not to let this fact become too obvious. I tried to convey, through this grisly act of love, the intelligence, at least, that it was not her, not *her* flesh, that I despised—it would not be her I could not face when we became vertical again. Again, somewhere at the bottom of me, I realized that my fears had been excessive and groundless and, in effect, a lie: it became clearer every instant that what I had been afraid of had nothing to do with my body. Sue was not Hella and she did not lessen my terror of what would happen when Hella came: she increased it, she made it more real than it had been before. At the same time, I realized that my performance with Sue was succeeding even too well, and I tried not to despise her for feeling so little what her laborer felt. I travelled through a network of Sue's cries, of Sue's tom-tom fists on my back, and judged by means of her thighs, by means of her legs, how soon I could be free. Then I thought, *The end is coming soon,* her sobs became even higher and harsher, I was terribly aware of the small of my back and the cold sweat there, I thought, *Well, let her have it for Christ sake, get it over with;* then it was ending and I hated her and me, then it was over, and the dark, tiny room rushed back. And I wanted only to get out of there.

She lay still for a long time. I felt the night outside and it was calling me. I leaned up at last and found a cigarette.

"Perhaps," she said, "we should finish our drinks."

She sat up and switched on the lamp which stood beside her bed. I had been dreading this moment. But she saw nothing in my eyes—she stared at me as though I had made a long journey on a white charger all the way to her prison house. She lifted her glass.

"*À la votre,*" I said.

"*À la* votre?" She giggled. "*À la* tienne, *chéri!*" She leaned over and kissed me on the mouth. Then, for a moment, she felt something; she leaned back and stared at me, her eyes not quite tightening yet; and she said, lightly, "Do you suppose we could do this again sometime?"

"I don't see why not," I told her, trying to laugh. "We carry our own equipment."

She was silent. Then: "Could we have supper together— tonight?"

"I'm sorry," I said. "I'm really sorry, Sue, but I've got a date."

"Oh. Tomorrow, maybe?"

"Look, Sue. I hate to make dates. I'll just surprise you."

She finished her drink. "I doubt that," she said.

She got up and walked away from me. "I'll just put on some clothes and come down with you."

She disappeared and I heard the water running. I sat there, still naked, but with my socks on, and poured myself another brandy. Now I was afraid to go out into that night which had seemed to be calling me only a few moments before.

When she came back she was wearing a dress and some real shoes, and she had sort of fluffed up her hair. I had to admit she looked better that way, really more like a girl, like a schoolgirl. I rose and started putting on my clothes. "You look nice," I said.

There were a great many things she wanted to say, but she forced herself to say nothing. I could scarcely bear to watch the struggle occurring in her face, it made me so ashamed. "Maybe you'll be lonely again," she said, finally. "I guess I won't mind if you come looking for me." She wore the strangest smile I had ever seen. It was pained and vindictive and humiliated, but she inexpertly smeared across this grimace a bright, girlish gaiety—as rigid as the skeleton beneath her flabby body. If fate ever allowed Sue to reach me, she would kill me with just that smile.

"Keep a candle," I said, "in the window"—and she opened her door and we passed out into the streets.

THREE

I left her at the nearest corner, mumbling some schoolboy excuse, and watched her stolid figure cross the boulevard towards the cafes.

I did not know what to do or where to go. I found myself at last along the river, slowly going home.

And this was perhaps the first time in my life that death occurred to me as a reality. I thought of the people before me who had looked down at the river and gone to sleep beneath it. I wondered about them. I wondered how they had done it—it, the physical act. I had thought of suicide when I was much younger, as, possibly, we all have, but then it would have been for revenge, it would have been my way of informing the world how awfully it had made me suffer. But the silence of the evening, as I wandered home, had nothing to do with that storm, that far-off boy. I simply wondered about the dead because their days had ended and I did not know how I would get through mine.

The city, Paris, which I loved so much, was absolutely silent. There seemed to be almost no one on the streets, although it was still very early in the evening. Nevertheless, beneath me—along the river bank, beneath the bridges, in the shadow of the walls, I could almost hear the collective, shivering sigh—were lovers and ruins, sleeping, embracing, coupling, drinking, staring out at the descending night. Behind the walls of the houses I passed, the French nation was clearing away the dishes, putting little Jean Pierre and Marie to bed, scowling over the eternal problems of the sou, the shop, the church, the unsteady State. Those walls, those shuttered windows held them in and protected them against the darkness and the long moan of this long night. Ten years hence, little Jean Pierre or Marie might find themselves out here beside the river and wonder, like me, how they had fallen out of the web of safety. What a long way, I thought, I've come—to be destroyed!

Yet it was true, I recalled, turning away from the river down the long street home, I wanted children. I wanted to be inside again, with the light and safety, with my manhood unquestioned, watching my woman put my children to bed. I wanted the same bed at night and the same arms and I wanted to rise in the morning, knowing where I was. I wanted a woman to be for me a steady ground, like the earth itself, where I could always be renewed. It had been so once; it had almost been so once. I could make it so again, I could make it real. It only demanded a short, hard strength for me to become myself again.

I saw a light burning beneath our door as I walked down the corridor. Before I put my key in the lock the door was opened from within. Giovanni stood there, his hair in his eyes, laughing. He held a glass of cognac in his hand. I was struck at first by what seemed to be the merriment on his face. Then I saw that it was not merriment but hysteria and despair.

I started to ask him what he was doing home, but he pulled me into the room, holding me around the neck tightly, with one hand. He was shaking. "Where have you been?" I looked into his face, pulling slightly away from him. "I have looked for you everywhere."

"Didn't you go to work?" I asked him.

"No," he said. "Have a drink. I have bought a bottle of cognac to celebrate my freedom." He poured me a cognac. I did not seem to be able to move. He came toward me again, thrusting the glass into my hand.

"Giovanni—what happened?"

He did not answer. He suddenly sat down on the edge of the bed, bent over. I saw then that he was also in a state of rage. *"Ils sont sale, les gens, tu sais?"* He looked up at me. His eyes were full of tears. "They are just dirty, all of them, low and cheap and dirty." He stretched out his hand and pulled me down to the floor beside him. "All except you. *Tous, sauf toi.*" He held my face between his hands and I suppose such tenderness has scarcely ever produced such terror as I then felt. *"Ne me laisse pas tomber, je t'en prie,"* he said, and kissed me, with a strange insistent gentleness, on the mouth.

His touch could never fail to make me feel desire; yet his hot, sweet breath also made me want to vomit. I pulled away as gently as I could and drank my cognac. "Giovanni," I said, "please tell me what happened. What's the matter?"

"He fired me," he said. "Guillaume. *Il m'a mis à la porte.*" He laughed and rose and began walking up and down the tiny room. "He told me never to come to his bar anymore. He said I was a gangster and a thief and a dirty little street boy and the only reason I ran after him—I ran after *him*—

was because I intended to rob him one night. *Après l'amour. Merde!*" He laughed again.

I could not say anything. I felt that the walls of the room were closing in on me.

Giovanni stood in front of our whitewashed windows, his back to me. "He said all these things in front of many people, right downstairs in the bar. He waited until people came. I wanted to kill him, I wanted to kill them all." He turned back into the center of the room and poured himself another cognac. He drank it at a breath, then suddenly took his glass and hurled it with all his strength against the wall. It rang briefly and fell in a thousand pieces all over our bed, all over the floor. I could not move at once; then, feeling that my feet were being held back by water but also watching myself move very fast, I grabbed him by the shoulders. He began to cry. I held him. And, while I felt his anguish entering into me, like acid in his sweat, and felt that my heart would burst for him, I also wondered, with an unwilling, unbelieving contempt, why I had ever thought him strong.

He pulled away from me and sat against the wall which had been uncovered. I sat facing him.

"I arrived at the usual time," he said. "I felt very good today. He was not there when I arrived and I cleaned the bar as usual and had a little drink and a little something to eat. Then he came and I could see at once that he was in a dangerous mood—perhaps he had just been humiliated by some young boy. It is funny"—and he smiled—"you can tell when Guillaume is in a dangerous mood because he then becomes so respectable. When something has happened to humiliate him and make him see, even for a moment, how disgusting he is, and how alone, then he remembers that he is a member of one of the best and oldest families in France. But maybe, then, he remembers that his name is going to die with him. Then he has to do something, quick, to make the feeling go away. He has to make much noise or have some *very* pretty boy or get drunk or have a fight or look at his dirty pictures." He paused and stood up and began walking up and down again. "I do not know what happened to him today, but when he came in he tried at first to be very business-like—he was trying to find fault with my work. But there was nothing wrong and he went upstairs. Then, by and by, he called me. I hate going up to that little *pied-à-terre* he has up there over the bar, it always means a scene. But I had to go and I found him in his dressing gown, covered with perfume. I do not know why, but the moment I saw him like that, I began to be angry. He looked at me as though he were some fabulous coquette—and he is ugly, ugly, he has a body just like sour milk!—and then he asked me how you were. I was a little astonished, for he never mentions you. I said you were fine. He asked me if we still lived together. I think perhaps I should have lied to him but I did not see any reason to lie to such a disgusting old fairy, so I said, *Bien sûr*. I was trying to be calm. Then he asked me terrible questions and I began to get sick watching him and listening to him. I thought it was best to be very quick with him and I said that such questions were not asked, even by a priest or a doctor, and I said he should be ashamed. Maybe he had been waiting for me to say something like that, for then he became angry and he reminded me that he had taken me out of the streets, *et il a fait ceci et il a fait cela*, everything for me because he thought I was adorable, *parce qu'il m'adorait*—and on and on and that I had no gratitude and no decency. I maybe handled it all very badly, I know how

I would have done it even a few months ago, I would have made him scream, I would have made him kiss my feet, *je te jure!*—but I did not want to do that, I really did not want to be dirty with him. I tried to be serious. I told him that I had never told him any lies and I had always said that I did not want to be lovers with him—and—he had given me the job all the same. I said I worked very hard and was very honest with him and that it was not my fault if—if—if I did not feel for him as he felt for me. Then he reminded me that once—one time—and I did not want to say yes, but I was weak from hunger and had had trouble not to vomit. I was still trying to be calm and trying to handle it right. So I said, *Mais à ce moment là je n'avais pas un copain.* I am not alone anymore, *je suis avec un gars maintenant.* I thought he would understand that, he is very fond of romance and the dream of fidelity. But not this time. He laughed and said a few more awful things about you, and he said that you were just an American boy, after all, doing things in France which you would not dare to do at home, and that you would leave me very soon. Then, at last, I got angry and I said that he did not pay me a salary for listening to slander and then I heard someone come into the bar downstairs so I turned around without saying anything more and walked out."

He stopped in front of me. "Can I have some more cognac?" he asked, with a smile. "I won't break the glass this time."

I gave him my glass. He emptied it and handed it back. He watched my face. "Don't be afraid," he said. "We will be alright. I am not afraid." Then his eyes darkened, he looked again toward the windows.

"Well," he said, "I hoped that that would be the end of it. I worked in the bar and tried not to think of Guillaume or of what he was thinking or doing upstairs. It was aperitif time, you know? and I was very busy. Then, suddenly, I heard the door slam upstairs and the moment I heard that I knew that it had happened, the awful thing had happened. He came into the bar, all dressed now, like a French businessman, and came straight to me. He did not speak to anyone as he came in, and he looked white and angry and, naturally, this attracted attention. Everyone was waiting to see what he would do. And, I must say, I thought he was going to strike me, or he had maybe gone mad and had a pistol in his pocket. So I am sure I looked frightened and this did not help matters, either. He came behind the bar and began saying that I was a *tapette* and a thief and told me to leave at once or he would call the police and have me put behind bars. I was so astonished I could not say anything and all the time his voice was rising and people were beginning to listen and, suddenly, *mon cher*, I felt that I was falling, falling from a great, high place. For a long while I could not get angry and I could feel the tears, like fire, coming up. I could not get my breath, I could not *believe* that he was really doing this to me. I kept saying, what have I done? What have I *done*? And he would not answer and then he shouted, very loud, it was like a gun going off, "*Mais tu le sais, salop!* You know very well!" And nobody knew what he meant, but it was just as though we were back in that theatre lobby again, where we met, you remember? Everybody knew that Guillaume was right and I was wrong, that I had done something awful. And he went to the cash register and took out some money—but I knew that he knew that there was not much money *in* the cash register at such an hour—and pushed it at me and said. "Take it! Take it! Better to give it to you than have you steal it from me at night! Now go!" And, oh, the faces in that bar, you should have seen them. They were so wise and tragic and they knew that *now* they knew everything, that they had always known it, and they were so glad that they had never had anything to do with me. "Ah! *Les encules!* The dirty sons of bitches! *Les gonzesses!*" He was weeping again, with rage this time. "Then, at last, I struck him and then many hands grabbed me and now I hardly know what happened, but by and by I was in the street, with all these torn bills in my hand and everybody staring at me. I did not know what to do, I hated to walk away but I knew if anything more happened, the police would come and Guillaume would have me put in jail. But I will see him again, I swear it, and on that day—!"

He stopped and sat down, staring at the wall. Then he turned to me. He watched me for a long time, in silence. Then, "If you were not here," he said, very slowly, "this would be the end of Giovanni."

I stood up. "Don't be silly," I said. "It's not so tragic as all that." I paused. "Guillaume's disgusting. They all are. But it's not the worst thing that ever happened to you. Is it?"

"Maybe everything bad that happens to you makes you weaker," said Giovanni, as though he had not heard me, "and so you can stand less and less." Then, looking up at me, "No. The worst thing happened to me long ago and my life has been awful since that day. You are not going to leave me, are you?"

I laughed, "Of course not." I started shaking the broken glass off our blanket onto the floor.

"I do not know what I would do if you left me." For the first time I felt the suggestion of a threat in his voice—or I put it there. "I have been alone so long—I do not think I would be able to live if I had to be alone again."

"You aren't alone now," I said. And then, quickly, for I

could not, at that moment, have endured his touch: "Shall we go for a walk? Come—out of this room for a minute." I grinned and cuffed him roughly, football fashion, on the neck. Then we clung together for an instant. I pushed him away. "I'll buy you a drink," I said.

"And will you bring me home again?" he asked.

"Yes. I'll bring you home again."

"*Je t'aime, tu sais?*"

"*Je le sais, mon vieux.*"

He went to the sink and started washing his face. He combed his hair. I watched him. He grinned at me in the mirror, looking, suddenly, beautiful and happy. And young—I had never in my life before felt so helpless or so old.

"But we will be alright!" he cried. "*N'est-ce pas?*"

"Certainly," I said.

He turned from the mirror. He was serious again. "But you know—I do not know how long it will be before I find another job. And we have almost no money. Do you have any money? Did any money come from New York for you today?"

"No money came from New York today," I said, calmly, "but I have a little money in my pocket." I took it all out and put it on the table. "About four thousand francs."

"And I"—he went through his pockets, scattering bills and change. He shrugged and smiled at me, that fantastically sweet and helpless and moving smile. "*Je m'excuse.* I went a little mad." He went down on his hands and knees and gathered it up and put it on the table beside the money I had placed there. About three thousand francs worth of bills had to be pasted together and we put those aside until later. The rest of the money on the table totalled about nine thousand francs.

"We are not rich," said Giovanni grimly, "but we will eat tomorrow."

I somehow did not want him to be worried. I could not endure that look on his face. "I'll write my father again tomorrow," I said. "I'll tell him some kind of lie, some kind of lie that he'll believe and I'll *make* him send me some money." And I moved toward him as though I were driven, putting my hands on his shoulders and forcing myself to look into his eyes. I smiled and I really felt at that moment that Judas and the Savior had met in me. "Don't be frightened. Don't worry."

And I also felt, standing so close to him, feeling such a passion to keep him from terror, that a decision—once again!—had been taken from my hands. For neither my father nor Hella was real at that moment. And yet even this was not as real as my despairing sense that nothing was real for me, nothing would ever be real for me again—unless, indeed, this sensation of falling was reality.

—

The hours of this night begin to dwindle and now, with every second that passes on the clock, the blood at the bottom of my heart begins to boil, to bubble, and I know that no matter what I do, anguish is about to overtake me in this house, as naked and silver as that great knife which Giovanni will be facing very soon. My executioners are here with me, walking up and down with me, washing things and packing and drinking from my bottle. They are everywhere I turn. Walls, windows, mirrors, water, the night outside—they are everywhere. I might call—as Giovanni, at this moment lying in his cell, might call. But no one will hear. I might try to explain. Giovanni tried to explain. I might ask to be forgiven—if I could name and face my crime, if there were anything or anybody anywhere with the power to forgive.

No. It would help if I were able to feel guilty. But the end of innocence is also the end of guilt.

No matter how it seems now, I must confess: I loved him. I do not think that I will ever love anyone like that again. And this might be a great relief if I did not also know that, when the knife has fallen, Giovanni, if he feels anything will feel relief.

I walk up and down this house—up and down this house. I think of prison. Long ago, before I had ever met Giovanni, I met a man at a party at Jacques' house who was celebrated because he had spent half his life in prison. He had then written a book about it which displeased the prison authorities and won a literary prize. But this man's life was over. He was fond of saying that, since to be in prison was simply not to live, the death penalty was the only merciful verdict any jury could deliver. I remember thinking that, in effect, he had never left prison. Prison was all that was real to him; he could speak of nothing else. All his movements, even to the lighting of a cigarette, were stealthy, wherever his eyes focused one saw a wall rise up. His face, the color of his face, brought to mind darkness and dampness, I felt that if one cut him, his flesh would be the flesh of mushrooms. And he described to us in avid, nostalgic detail the barred windows, the barred doors, the judas, the guards standing at far ends of corridors, under the light. It is three tiers high inside the prison and everything is the color of gunmetal. Everything is dark and cold, except for those patches of light, where authority stands. There is on the air perpetually the memory of fists against the metal, a dull, booming tom-tom possibility, like the possibility of madness. The guards move and mutter and pace the corridors and boom dully up and down the stairs. They are in black, they carry guns, they are always afraid, they scarcely dare be kind. Three tiers down, in the prison's center, in the prison's great, cold heart, there is always activity: trusted prisoners wheeling things about, going in and out of the offices, ingratiating themselves with the guards for privileges of cigarettes, alcohol, and sex. The night deepens in the prison, there is muttering everywhere, and everybody knows—somehow—that death will be entering the prison courtyard early in the morning. Very early in the morning, before the trusties begin wheeling great garbage cans of food along the corridors, three men in black will come noiselessly down the corridor, one of them will turn the key in the lock. They will lay hands on someone and rush him down the corridor, first to the priest and then to a door which will open only for him, which will allow him, perhaps, one glimpse of the morning before he is thrown forward on his belly on a board and the knife falls on his neck.

I wonder about the size of Giovanni's cell. I wonder if it is bigger than his room. I know that it is colder. I wonder if he is alone or with two or three others; if he is perhaps playing cards, or smoking, or talking, or writing a letter— to whom would he be writing a letter?—or walking up and down. I wonder if he knows that the approaching morning is the last morning of his life. (For the prisoner usually does not know; the lawyer knows and tells the family or friends but does not tell the prisoner.) I wonder if he cares. Whether he knows or not, cares or not, he is certainly afraid. Whether he is with others or not, he is certainly alone. I try to see him, his back to me, standing at the window of his cell. From where he is perhaps he can only see the opposite wing of the prison; perhaps, by straining a little, just over the high wall, a patch of the street outside. I do not know if his hair has been cut, or is long—I should think it would have been cut. I wonder if he is shaven. And now a million details, proof and fruit of intimacy, flood my mind. I wonder, for example, if he feels the need to go to the bathroom, if he has been able to eat today, if he is sweating, or dry. I wonder if anyone has made love to him in prison. And then something shakes me, I feel shaken hard and dry, like some dead thing in the desert, and I know that I am hoping that Giovanni is being sheltered in someone's arms tonight. I wish that someone were here with me. I would make love to whoever was here all night long, I would labor with Giovanni all night long.

—

Those days after Giovanni had lost his job, we dawdled; dawdled as doomed mountain climbers may be said to dawdle above the chasm, held only by a snapping rope. I did not write my father—I put it off from day to day. It would have been too definitive an act. I knew which lie I would tell him and I knew the lie would work—only—I was not sure that it would be a lie. Day after day we lingered in that room and Giovanni began to work on it again. He had some weird idea that it would be nice to have a bookcase sunk in the wall and he chipped through the wall until he came to the brick and began pounding away at the brick. It was hard work, it was insane work, but I did not have the energy or the heart to stop him. In a way he was doing it for me, to prove his love for me. He wanted me to stay in the room with him. Perhaps he was trying, with his own strength, to push back the encroaching walls, without, however, having the walls fall down.

Now—now, of course, I see something very beautiful in those days, which were such torture then. I felt, then, that

Giovanni was dragging me with him to the bottom of the sea. He could not find a job. I knew that he was not really looking for one, that he could not. He had been bruised, so to speak, so badly that the eyes of strangers lacerated him like salt. He could not endure being very far from me for very long. I was the only person on God's cold, green earth who cared about him, who knew his speech and silence, knew his arms, and did not carry a knife. The burden of his salvation seemed to be on me and I could not endure it.

And the money dwindled—it went, it did not dwindle, very fast. Giovanni tried to keep panic out of his voice when he asked me each morning, "Are you going to American Express today?"

"Certainly," I would answer.

"Do you think your money will be there today?"

"I don't know."

"What are they *doing* with your money in New York?"

Still, still I could not act. I went to Jacques and borrowed ten thousand francs from him again. I told him that Giovanni and I were going through a difficult time but that it would be over soon.

"He was very nice about it," said Giovanni.

"He *can*, sometimes, be a very nice man." We were sitting on a terrace near Odéon. I looked at Giovanni and thought for a moment how nice it would be if Jacques would take him off my hands.

"What are you thinking?" asked Giovanni.

For a moment I was frightened and I was also ashamed. "I was thinking," I said, "that I'd like to get out of Paris."

"Where would you like to go?" he asked.

"Oh, I don't know. Anywhere. I'm sick of this city," I said suddenly, with a violence that surprised us both. "I'm tired of this ancient pile of stone and all these goddam smug people. Everything you put your hands on here comes to pieces in your hands."

"That," said Giovanni gravely, "is true." He was watching me with a terrible intensity. I forced myself to look at him and smile.

"Wouldn't you like to get out of here for awhile?" I asked.

"Ah!" he said, and raised both hands briefly, palms outward, in a kind of mock resignation. "I would like to go wherever you go. I do not feel so strongly about Paris as you do, suddenly. I have never liked Paris very much."

"Perhaps," I said—I scarcely knew what I was saying—"we could go to the country. Or to Spain."

"Ah," he said, lightly, "you are lonely for your mistress."

I was guilty and irritated and full of love and pain. I wanted to kick him and I wanted to take him in my arms. "That's no reason to go to Spain," I said sullenly. "I'd just like to see it, that's all. This city is expensive."

"Well," he said brightly, "let us go to Spain. Perhaps it will remind me of Italy."

"Would you rather go to Italy? Would you rather visit your home?"

He smiled. "I do not think I have a home there anymore." And then: "No. I would not like to go to Italy—perhaps, after all, for the same reason you do not want to go to the United States."

"But I *am* going to the United States," I said, quickly. And he looked at me. "I mean, I'm certainly going to go back there one of these days."

"One of these days," he said. "Everything bad will happen—one of these days."

"Why is it bad?"

He smiled. "Why, you will go home and then you will

find that home is not home anymore. Then you will really be in trouble. As long as you stay here, you can always think: One day I will go home." He played with my thumb and grinned. *"N'est-ce pas?"*

"Beautiful logic," I said. "You mean I have a home to go to as long as I don't go there?"

He laughed. "Well, isn't it true? You don't have a home until you leave it and then, when you have left it, you never can go back."

"I seem," I said, "to have heard this song before."

"Ah, *yes,*" said Giovanni, "and you will certainly hear it again. It is one of those songs that somebody somewhere will always be singing."

We rose and started walking. "And what would happen," I asked, idly, "if I shut my ears?"

He was silent for a long while. Then: "You do, sometimes, remind me of the kind of man who is tempted to put himself in prison in order to avoid being hit by a car."

"That," I said, sharply, "would seem to apply much more to you than to me."

"What do you mean?" he asked.

"I'm talking about that room, that hideous room. Why have you buried yourself there so long?"

"Buried myself? Forgive me, *mon cher Américain,* but Paris is not like New York; it is not full of palaces for boys like me. Do you think I should be living in Versailles instead?"

"There must—there must," I said, "be other rooms."

"Ça ne manque pas, les chambres. The world is full of rooms— big rooms, little rooms, round rooms, square ones, rooms high up, rooms low down—all kinds of rooms! What kind of room do you think Giovanni should be living in? How long do you think it took me to find the room I have? And

since when, since when"—he stopped and beat with his forefinger on my chest—"have you so hated the room? Since when? Since yesterday, since always? *Dismoi.*"

Facing him, I faltered. "I don't hate it. I—I didn't mean to hurt your feelings."

His hands dropped to his sides. His eyes grew big. He laughed. "Hurt my *feelings*! Am I now a stranger that you speak to me like that, with such an American politeness?"

"All I mean, baby, is that I wish we could move."

"We can move. Tomorrow! Let us go to a hotel. Is that what you want? *Le Crillon peut-être?*"

I sighed, speechless, and we started walking again.

"I know," he burst out, after a moment, "I know! You want to leave Paris, you want to leave the room—ah! you are wicked. *Comme tu es méchant!*"

"You misunderstand me," I said. "You misunderstand me."

He smiled grimly, to himself. *"J'espère bien."*

Later, when we were back in the room putting the loose bricks Giovanni had taken out of the wall into a sack, he asked me, "This girl of yours—have you heard from her lately?"

"Not lately," I said. I did not look up. "But I expect her to turn up in Paris almost any day now."

He stood up, standing in the center of the room under the light, looking at me. I stood up, too, half smiling, but also, in some strange, dim way, a little frightened.

"Viens m'embrasser," he said.

I was vividly aware that he held a brick in his hand, I held a brick in mine. It really seemed for an instant that if I did not go to him, we would use these bricks to beat each other to death.

Yet, I could not move at once. We stared at each other

across a narrow space that was full of danger, that almost seemed to roar, like flame.

"Come," he said.

I dropped my brick and went to him. In a moment I heard his fall. And at moments like this I felt that we were merely enduring and committing the longer and lesser and more perpetual murder.

FOUR

At last there came the note which I had been waiting for, from Hella, telling me what day and hour she would arrive in Paris. I did not tell this to Giovanni but walked out alone that day and went to the station to meet her.

I had hoped that when I saw her something instantaneous, definitive, would have happened in me, something to make me know where I should be and where I was. But nothing happened. I recognized her at once, before she saw me. She was wearing green, her hair was a little shorter, and her face was tan, and she wore the same brilliant smile. I loved her as much as ever and I still did not know how much that was.

When she saw me she stood stock-still on the platform, her hands clasped in front of her, with her wide-legged, boyish stance, smiling. For a moment we simply stared at each other.

"Eh bien," she said, *"t'embrasse pas ta femme?"*

Then I took her in my arms and something happened then. I was terribly glad to see her. It really seemed, with

Hella in the circle of my arms, that my arms were home and I was welcoming her back there. She fitted in my arms, she always had, and the shock of holding her caused me to feel that my arms had been empty since she had been away.

I held her very close in that high, dark shed, with a great confusion of people all about us, just beside the breathing train. She smelled of the wind and the sea and of space and I felt in her marvellously living body the possibility of legitimate surrender.

Then she pulled away. Her eyes were damp. "Let me look at you," she said. She held me at arm's length, searching my face. "Ah. You look wonderful. I'm so happy to see you again."

I kissed her lightly on the nose and felt that I had passed the first inspection. I picked up her bags and we started towards the exit. "Did you have a good trip? And how was Seville? And how do you like bullfights? Did you meet any bullfighters? Tell me everything."

She laughed. "Everything is a very tall order. I had a terrible trip, I hate trains, I wish I'd flown but I've been in one Spanish airplane and I swore never, never again. It rattled, my dear, in the middle of the air just like a model T Ford—it had probably *been* a model T Ford at one time—and I just sat there, praying and drinking brandy. I was sure I'd never see land again." We passed through the barrier, into the streets. Hella looked about delightedly at all of it, the cafes, the self-contained people, the violent snarl of the traffic, the blue-caped traffic policeman and his white, gleaming club. "Coming back to Paris," she said, after a moment, "is always so lovely, no matter where you've been." We got into a cab and our driver made a wide, reckless circle into the stream of traffic. "I should think that even if you returned here in some awful sorrow, you might—well, you might find it possible here to begin to be reconciled."

"Let's hope," I said, "that we never have to put Paris to that test."

Her smile was at once bright and melancholy. "Let's hope." Then she suddenly took my face between her hands and kissed me. There was a great question in her eyes and I knew that she burned to have this question answered at once. But I could not do it yet. I held her close and kissed her, closing my eyes. Everything was as it had been between us, and at the same time everything was different.

I told myself I would not think about Giovanni yet, I would not worry about him yet; for tonight, anyway, Hella and I should be together with nothing to divide us. Still, I knew very well that this was not really possible: he had already divided us. I tried not to think of him sitting alone in that room, wondering why I stayed away so long.

Then we were sitting together in Hella's room on the rue de Tournon, sampling Fundador. "It's much too sweet," I said. "Is this what they drink in Spain?"

"I never saw any Spaniards drinking it," she said, and laughed. "*They* drink wine. *I* drank gin-fizz—in Spain I somehow had the feeling that it was healthy," and she laughed again.

I kept kissing her and holding her, trying to find my way in her again, as though she were a familiar, darkened room in which I fumbled to find the light. And, with my kisses, I was trying also to delay the moment which would commit me to her, or fail to commit me to her. But I think she felt that the indefinitive constraint between us was of her doing and all on her side. She was remembering that I had written her less and less often while she had been away. In Spain, until near the end, this had probably not worried her; not until she herself had come to a decision did she begin to be afraid that I might also have arrived at a decision, opposite to hers. Perhaps she had kept me dangling too long.

She was by nature forthright and impatient; she suffered when things were not clear; yet she forced herself to wait for some word or sign from me and held the reins of her strong desire tightly in her hands.

I wanted to force her to relinquish reins. Somehow, I would be tongue-tied until I took her again. I hoped to burn out, through Hella, my image of Giovanni and the reality of his touch—I hoped to drive out fire with fire. Yet, my sense of what I was doing made me double-minded. And at last she asked me, with a smile, "Have I been away too long?"

"I don't know," I said. "It's been a long time."

"It was a very lonely time," she said, unexpectedly. She turned slightly away from me, lying on her side, looking toward the window. "I felt so aimless—like a tennis ball, bouncing, bouncing—I began to wonder where I'd land. I began to feel that I'd, somewhere, missed the boat." She looked at me. "You know the boat I'm talking about. They make movies about it where I come from. It's the boat that, when you miss it, it's a boat, but when it comes in, it's a ship." I watched her face. It was stiller than I had ever known it to be before.

"Didn't you like Spain," I asked, nervously, "at all?"

She ran one hand, impatiently, through her hair. "Oh. Of course, I liked Spain, why not? It's very beautiful. I just didn't know what I was doing there. And I'm beginning to be tired of being in places for no particular reason."

I lit a cigarette and smiled. "But you went to Spain to get away from me—remember?"

She smiled and stroked my cheek. "I haven't been very nice to you, have I?"

"You've been very honest." I stood up and walked a little away from her. "Did you get much thinking done, Hella?"

"I told you in my letter—don't *you* remember?"

For a moment everything seemed perfectly still. Even the faint street noises died. I had my back to her but I felt her eyes. I felt her waiting—everything seemed to be waiting.

"I wasn't sure about that letter." I was thinking. *Perhaps I can get out of it without having to tell her anything.* "You were so sort of—offhand—I couldn't be sure whether you were glad or sorry to be throwing in with me."

"Oh," she said, "but we've always been offhand. It's the only way I could have said it. I was afraid of embarrassing you—don't you understand that?"

What I wanted to suggest was that she was taking me out of desperation, less because she wanted me than because I was there. But I could not say it. I sensed that, though it might be true, she no longer knew it.

"But, perhaps," she said, carefully, "you feel differently now. Please say so if you do." She waited for my answer for a moment. Then: "You know, I'm not really the emancipated girl I try to be at all. I guess I just want a man to come home to me every night. I want to be able to sleep with a man without being afraid he's going to knock me up. Hell, I want to be knocked up. I want to start having babies. In a way, it's really all I'm good for." There was silence again. "Is that what you want?"

"Yes," I said, "I've always wanted that."

I turned to face her, very quickly, or as though strong hands on my shoulders had turned me around. The room was darkening. She lay on the bed watching me, her mouth slightly open and her eyes like lights. I was terribly aware of her body, and of mine. I walked over to her and put my head on her breast. I wanted to lie there, hidden and still. But then, deep within, I felt her moving, rushing to open the gates of her strong, walled city and let the king of glory come in.

Dear Dad, I wrote, *I won't keep any secrets from you anymore, I found a girl and I want to marry her and it wasn't that I was keeping secrets from you, I just wasn't sure she wanted to marry me. But she's finally agreed to risk it, poor soft-headed thing that she is, and we're planning to tie the knot while we're still over here and make our way home by easy stages. She's not French, in case you're worried (I know you don't dislike the French, it's just that you don't think they have our virtues—I might add, they don't.) Anyway, Hella—her name is Hella Lincoln, she comes from Minneapolis, her father and mother still live there, he's a corporation lawyer, she's just the little woman—Hella would like us to honeymoon here and it goes without saying that I like anything she likes. So. Now will you send your loving son some of his hard-earned money.* Tout de suite. *That's French for pronto.*

Hella—the photo doesn't really do her justice—came over here a couple of years ago to study painting. Then she discovered she wasn't a painter and just about the time she was ready to throw herself into the Seine, we met, and the rest, as they say, is history. I know you'll love her, Dad, and she'll love you. She's already made me a very happy man.

Hella and Giovanni met by accident, after Hella had been in Paris for three days. During those three days I had not seen him and I had not mentioned his name.

We had been wandering about the city all day and all day Hella had been full of a subject which I had never heard her discuss at such length before: women. She claimed it was hard to be one.

"I don't see what's so hard about being a woman. At least, not as long as she's got a man."

"That's just it," said she. "Hasn't it ever struck you that that's a sort of humiliating necessity?"

"Oh, please," I said. "It never seemed to humiliate any of the women I knew."

"Well," she said, "I'm sure you never thought about any of them—in that way."

"I certainly didn't. I hope they didn't, either. And why are *you*? What's *your* beef?"

"I've got no *beef*," she said. She hummed, low in her throat, a kind of playful Mozart tune. "I've got no beef at all. But it does seem—well, difficult—to be at the mercy of some gross, unshaven stranger before you can begin to be yourself."

"I don't know if I like *that*," I said. "Since when have I been gross? or a stranger? It may be true that I need a shave but that's *your* fault, I haven't been able to tear myself away from you." And I grinned and kissed her.

"Well," she said, "you may not be a stranger *now*. But you were once and I'm sure you will be again—many times."

"If it comes to that," I said, "so will you be, for me."

She looked at me with a quick, bright smile. "Will I?" Then: "But what I mean about being a woman is, we might get married now and stay married for fifty years and I might be a stranger to you every instant of that time and you might never know it."

"But if *I* were a stranger—*you* would know it?"

"For a woman," she said, "I think a man is always a stranger. And there's something awful about being at the mercy of a stranger."

"But men are at the mercy of women, too. Have you never thought of that?"

"Ah!" she said, "men may be at the mercy of women—I think men like that idea, it strokes the misogynist in them. But if a particular *man* is ever at the mercy of a particular *woman*—why, he's somehow stopped being a man. And the lady, then, is more neatly trapped than ever."

"You mean, I can't be at your mercy? But you can be at mine?" I laughed. "I'd like to see you at *anybody's* mercy, Hella."

"You may laugh," she said, humorously, "but there is something in what I say. I began to realize it in Spain—that I wasn't free, that I couldn't be free until I was attached— no, *committed*—to someone."

"To someone? Not some*thing*?"

She was silent. "I don't know," she said at last, "but I'm beginning to think that women get attached to some*thing* really by default. They'd give it up, if they could, anytime, for a man. Of course they can't admit this, and neither can most of them let go of what they have. But I think it kills them—perhaps I only mean," she added, after a moment, "that it would have killed *me*."

"What do you want, Hella? What have you got now that makes such a difference?"

She laughed. "It isn't what I've *got*. It isn't even what I *want*. It's that *you've* got me. So now I can be—your obedient and most loving servant."

I felt cold. I shook my head in mock confusion. "I don't know what you're talking about."

"Why," she said, "I'm talking about my life. I've got you

to take care of and feed and torment and trick and love—
I've got you to put up with. From now on, I can have a wonderful time complaining about being a woman. But I won't
be terrified that I'm *not* one." She looked at my face, and
laughed. "Oh, I'll be doing other *things*," she cried. "I won't
stop being intelligent. I'll read and argue and *think* and all
that—and I'll make a great point of not thinking *your*
thoughts—and you'll be pleased because I'm sure the resulting confusion will cause you to see that I've only got a
finite woman's mind, after all. And, if God is good, you'll
love me more and more and we'll be quite happy." She
laughed again. "Don't bother your head about it, sweet-
heart. Leave it to me."

Her amusement was contagious and I shook my head
again, laughing with her. "You're adorable," I said. "I don't
understand you at all."

She laughed again. "There," she said, "that's fine. We're
both taking to it like ducks to water."

We were passing a bookstore and she stopped. "Can we
go in for just a minute?" she asked. "There's a book I'd like
to get. Quite," she added, as we entered the shop, "a trivial
book."

I watched her with amusement as she went over to speak
to the woman who ran the shop. I wandered idly over to the
farthest book shelf, where a man stood, his back to me,
leafing through a magazine. As I stood beside him, he
closed the magazine and put it down, and turned. We recognized each other at once. It was Jacques.

"*Tiens!*" he cried. "Here you are! We were beginning to
think that you had gone back to America."

"Me?" I laughed. "No, I'm still in Paris. I've just been
busy." Then, with a terrible suspicion, I asked, "Who's *we*?"

"Why," said Jacques, with a hard, insistent smile, "your baby. It seems you left him alone in that room without any food, without any money, without, even, any cigarettes. He finally persuaded his concierge to allow him to put a phone call on his bill and called me. The poor boy sounded as though he would have put his head in the gas oven. If," he laughed, "he had *had* a gas oven."

We stared at each other. He, deliberately, said nothing. I did not know what to say.

"I threw a few provisions in my car," said Jacques, "and hurried out to get him. He thought we should drag the river for you. But I assured him that he did not know Americans as well as I and that you had not drowned your-self. You had only disappeared in order—to think. And I see that I was right. You have thought so much that now you must find what others have thought before you. One book," he said, finally, "that you can surely spare yourself the trouble of reading is the Marquis de Sade."

"Where is Giovanni now?" I asked.

"I finally remembered the name of Hella's hotel," said Jacques. "Giovanni said that you were more or less expect-ing her and so I gave him the bright idea of calling you there. He has stepped out for an instant to do just that. He'll be along presently."

Hella had returned, with her book.

"You two have met before," I said, awkwardly. "Hella, you remember Jacques."

She remembered him and also remembered that she disliked him. She smiled politely and held out her hand. "How are you?"

"*Je suis ravi, mademoiselle,*" said Jacques. He knew that Hella disliked him and this amused him. And, to corroborate her dislike, and also because at that moment he really hated me, he bowed low over her outstretched hand and became, in an instant, outrageously and offensively effeminate. I watched him as though I were watching an imminent disaster from many miles away. He turned playfully to me. "David has been hiding from us," he murmured, "now that you are back."

"Oh?" said Hella, and moved closer to me, taking my hand, "that was very naughty of him. I'd never have allowed it—if I'd known we were hiding." She grinned. "But, then, he never tells me anything."

Jacques looked at her. "No doubt," he said, "he finds more fascinating topics when you are together than why he hides from old friends."

I felt a great need to get out of there before Giovanni arrived. "We haven't eaten supper yet," I said, trying to smile. "Perhaps we can meet you later?" I knew that my smile was begging him to be kind to me.

But at that moment the tiny bell which announced every entry into the shop rang, and Jacques said, "Ah. Here is Giovanni." And, indeed, I felt him behind me, standing stock-still, staring, and felt in Hella's clasp, in her entire body, a kind of wild shrinking and not all of her composure kept this from showing in her face. When Giovanni spoke, his voice was thick with fury and relief and unshed tears.

"Where have you been?" he cried. "I thought you were dead! I thought you had been knocked down by a car or thrown into the river—what have you been doing all these days?"

I was able, oddly enough, to smile. And I was astonished at my calm. "Giovanni," I said, "I want you to meet my fiancée. Mlle Hella. Monsieur Giovanni."

He had seen her before his outburst ended and now he touched her hand with a still, astounded politeness and stared at her with black, steady eyes as though he had never seen a woman before.

"Enchanté, mademoiselle," he said. And his voice was dead and cold. He looked briefly at me, then back at Hella. For a moment we, all four, stood there as though we were posing for a tableau.

"Really," said Jacques, "now that we are all together, I think we should have one drink together. A very short one," he said to Hella, cutting off her attempt at polite refusal and taking her arm. "It's not every day," he said, "that old friends get together." He forced us to move, Hella and he together, Giovanni and I ahead. The bell rang viciously as Giovanni opened the door. The evening air hit us like a blaze. We started walking away from the river, toward the boulevard.

"When I decide to leave a place," said Giovanni, "I tell the concierge, so that at least she will know where to forward my mail."

I flared briefly, unhappily. I had noticed that he was shaven and wore a clean, white shirt and tie—a tie which surely belonged to Jacques. "I don't see what you've got to complain about," I said. "You sure knew where to go."

But with the look he gave me then my anger left me and I wanted to cry. "You are not nice," he said. *"Tu n'est pas chic du tout."* Then he said no more and we walked to the boulevard in silence. Behind us I could hear the murmur of Jacques' voice. On the corner we stood and waited for them to catch up with us.

"Darling," said Hella, as she reached me, "you stay and have a drink if you want to, I can't, I really can't, I don't feel well at all." She turned to Giovanni. "Please forgive me," she said, "but I've just come back from Spain and I've hardly sat down a moment since I got off the train. Another time, truly—but I *must* get some sleep tonight." She smiled and held out her hand but he did not seem to see it.

"I'll walk Hella home," I said, "and then I'll come back. If you'll tell me where you're going to be."

Giovanni laughed, abruptly. "Why, we will be in the quarter," he said. "We will not be difficult to find."

"I am sorry," said Jacques, to Hella, "that you do not feel well. Perhaps another time." And Hella's hand, which was still uncertainly outstretched, he bowed over and kissed a second time. He straightened and looked at me. "You must bring Hella to dinner at my house one night." He made a face. "There is no need to hide your fiancée from us."

"No need whatever," said Giovanni. "She is very charming. And we"—with a grin, to Hella—"will try to be charming, too."

"Well," I said, and took Hella by the arm, "I'll see you later."

"If I am not here" said Giovanni, both vindictive and near tears, "by the time you come back again, I will be at home. You remember where that is—? It is near a zoo."

"I remember," I said. I started backing away, as though I were backing out of a cage. "I'll see you later. *A tout à l'heure.*"

"*À la prochaine,*" said Giovanni.

I felt their eyes on our backs as we walked away from them. For a long while Hella was silent—possibly because, like me, she was afraid to say anything. Then: "I really can't stand that man. He gives me the creeps." After a moment: "I didn't know you'd seen so much of him while I was away."

"I didn't," I said. To do something with my hands, to give myself a moment of privacy, I stopped and lit a cigarette. I felt her eyes. But she was not suspicious; she was only troubled.

"And who is Giovanni?" she asked, when we started walking again. She gave a little laugh. "I just realized that I haven't even asked you where you were living. Are you living with him?"

"We've been sharing a maid's room out at the end of Paris," I said.

"Then it wasn't very nice of you," said Hella, "to go off for so long without any warning."

"Well, my God," I said, "he's only my roommate. How was I to know he'd start dragging the river just because I stayed out a couple of nights?"

"Jacques said you left him there without any money, without any cigarettes, or anything, and you didn't even tell him you were going to be with me."

"There are lots of things I didn't tell Giovanni. But he's never made any kind of scene before—I guess he must be drunk. I'll talk to him later."

"Are you going to go back there later?"

"Well," I said, "if I don't go back there later, I'll go on over to the room. I've been meaning to do that anyway." I grinned. "I have to get shaved."

Hella sighed. "I didn't mean to get your friends mad at you," she said. "You ought to go back and have a drink with them. You said you were going to."

"Well, I may, I may not. I'm not married to them, you know."

"Well, the fact that you're going to be married to *me* doesn't mean you have to break your word to your friends.

It doesn't even mean," she added, shortly, "that I have to *like* your friends."

"Hella," I said, "I am perfectly aware of that."

We turned off the boulevard, toward her hotel.

"He's very intense, isn't he?" she said. I was staring at the dark mound of the Senate, which ended our dark, slightly uphill street.

"Who is?"

"Giovanni. He's certainly very fond of you."

"He's Italian," I said. "Italians are theatrical."

"Well, this one," she laughed, "must be special, even in Italy! How long have you been living with him?"

"A couple of months." I threw away my cigarette. "I ran out of money while you were away—you know, I'm still waiting for money—and I moved in with him because it was cheaper. At that time he had a job and was living with his mistress most of the time."

"Oh?" she said. "He has a mistress?"

"He had a mistress," I said. "He also had a job. He's lost both."

"Poor boy," she said. "No wonder he looks so lost."

"He'll be alright," I said, briefly. We were before her door. She pressed the night bell.

"Is he a very good friend of Jacques?" she asked.

"Perhaps," I said, "not quite good enough to please Jacques."

She laughed. "I always feel a cold wind go over me," she said, "when I find myself in the presence of a man who dislikes women as much as Jacques does."

"Well, then," I said, "we'll just keep him away from you. We don't want no cold winds blowing over this girl." I kissed her on the tip of her nose. At the same moment there was a rumble from deep within the hotel and the door unlocked itself with a small, violent shudder. Hella looked humorously into the blackness. "I always wonder," she said, "if I *dare* go in." Then she looked up at me. "Well? Do you want to have a drink upstairs before you go back to join your friends?"

"Sure," I said. We tiptoed into the hotel, closing the door gently behind us. My fingers finally found the *minuterie,* and the weak, yellow light spilled over us. A voice, completely unintelligible, shouted out at us and Hella shouted back her name, which she tried to pronounce with a French accent. As we started up the stairs, the light went out and Hella and I began to giggle like two children. We were unable to find the minute-switch on any of the landings—I don't know why we both found this so hilarious, but we did, and we held on to each other, giggling, all the way to Hella's top-floor room.

"Tell me about Giovanni," she asked, much later, while we lay in bed and watched the black night tease her stiff, white curtains. "He interests me."

"That's a pretty tactless thing to say at this moment," I told her. "What the hell do you mean, he interests you?"

"I mean who he is, what he thinks about. How he got that face."

"What's the matter with his face?"

"Nothing. He's very beautiful, as a matter of fact. But there's something in that face—so old-fashioned."

"Go to sleep," I said. "You're babbling."

"How did you meet him?"

"Oh. In a bar one drunken night, with lots of other people."

"Was Jacques there?"

"I don't remember. Yes, I guess so. I guess he met Giovanni at the same time I did."

"What made you go to live with him?"

"I told you. I was broke and he had this room—"

"But that can't have been the *only* reason."

"Oh, well," I said, "I liked him."

"And don't you like him any more?"

"I'm very fond of Giovanni. You didn't see him at his best tonight, but he's a very nice man." I laughed; covered by the night, emboldened by Hella's body and my own, and protected by the tone of my voice, I found great relief in adding: "I love him, in a way. I really do."

"He seems to feel that you have a funny way of showing it."

"Oh, well," I said, "these people have another style from us. They're much more demonstrative. I can't help it. I just can't—do all that."

"Yes," she said, thoughtfully, "I've noticed that."

"You've noticed what?"

"Kids here—they think nothing of showing a lot of affection for each other. It's sort of a shock at first. Then you begin to think it's sort of nice."

"It *is* sort of nice," I said.

"Well," said Hella, "I think we ought to take Giovanni out to dinner or something one of these days. After all, he did sort of rescue you."

"That's a good idea," I said. "I don't know what he's doing these days but I imagine he'll have a free evening."

"Does he hang around with Jacques much?"

"No, I don't think so. I think he just ran into Jacques tonight." I paused. "I'm beginning to see," I said, carefully, "that kids like Giovanni are in a difficult position. This isn't, you know, the land of opportunity—there's no provision made for them. Giovanni's poor, I mean he comes from poor folks, and there isn't really much that he can do. And for what he *can* do, there's terrific competition. And, at that, very little money, not enough for them to be able to think of building any kind of future. That's why so many of them wander the streets and turn into gigolos and gangsters and God knows what."

"It's cold," she said, "out here in the Old World."

"Well, it's pretty cold out there in the New One, too," I said. "It's cold out here, period."

She laughed. "But we—we have our love to keep us warm."

"We're not the first people who thought that as they lay in bed." Nevertheless, we lay silent and still in each other's arms for awhile. "Hella," I said at last.

"Yes?"

"Hella, when the money gets here, let's take it and get out of Paris."

"Get out of Paris? Where do you want to go?"

"I don't care. Just out. I'm sick of Paris. I want to leave it for awhile. Let's go south. Maybe there'll be some sun."

"Shall we get married in the south?"

"Hella," I said, "you have to believe me, I can't do anything or decide anything. I can't even see straight until we get out of this town. I don't want to get married here; I don't even want to think about getting married here. Let's just get out."

"I didn't know you felt this way," she said.

"I've been living in Giovanni's room for months," I said, "and I just can't stand it anymore. I have to get out of there. Please."

She laughed nervously and moved slightly away from me. "Well, I really don't see why getting out of Giovanni's room means getting out of Paris."

I sighed. "Please, Hella. I don't feel like going into long explanations now. Maybe it's just that if I stay in Paris I'll keep running into Giovanni and—" I stopped.

"Why should that disturb you?"

"Well—I can't do anything to help him and I can't stand having him watch me—as though—I'm an American, Hella, he thinks I'm *rich*." I paused and sat up, looking outward. She watched me. "He's a very nice man, as I say, but he's very persistent—and he's got this *thing* about me, he thinks I'm God. And that room is so stinking and dirty. And soon winter'll be here and it's going to be cold—" I turned to her again and took her in my arms. "Look. Let's just go. I'll explain a lot of things to you later—later—when we get out."

There was a long silence.

"And you want to leave right away?" she said.

"Yes. As soon as that money comes, let's rent a house."

"You're sure," she said, "that you don't just want to go back to the States?"

I groaned. "No. Not yet. That isn't what I mean."

She kissed me. "I don't care where we go," she said, "as long as we're together." Then she pushed me away. "It's almost morning," she said. "We'd better get some sleep."

———

I got to Giovanni's room very late the next evening. I had been walking by the river with Hella and, later, I drank too much in several bistros. The light crashed on as I came into the room and Giovanni sat up in bed, crying out in a voice of terror, *"Qui est là? Qui est là?"*

I stopped in the doorway, weaving a little in the light, and I said, "It's me, Giovanni. Shut up."

Giovanni stared at me and turned on his side, facing the wall, and began to cry.

I thought, *Sweet Jesus!* and I carefully closed the door. I took my cigarettes out of my jacket pocket and hung my jacket over the chair. With my cigarettes in my hand I went to the bed and leaned over Giovanni. I said, "Baby, stop crying. Please stop crying."

Giovanni turned and looked at me. His eyes were red and wet, but he wore a strange smile, it was composed of cruelty and shame and delight. He held out his arms and I leaned down, brushing his hair from his eyes.

"You smell of wine," said Giovanni, then.

"I haven't been drinking wine. Is that what frightened you? Is that why you are crying?"

"No."

"What is the matter?"

"Why have you gone away from me?"

I did not know what to say. Giovanni turned to the wall again. I had hoped, I had supposed that I would feel nothing: but I felt a tightening in a far corner of my heart, as though a finger had touched me there.

"I have never reached you," said Giovanni. "You have never really been here. I do not think you have ever lied to me, but I know that you have never told me the truth—why? Sometimes you were here all day long and you read or you opened the window or you cooked something—and I watched you—and you never said anything—and you looked at me with such eyes, as though you did not see me. All day, while I worked, to make this room for you."

I said nothing. I looked beyond Giovanni's head at the square windows which held back the feeble moonlight.

"What are you doing all the time? And why do you say nothing? You are evil, you know, and sometimes when you smiled at me, I hated you. I wanted to strike you. I wanted to make you bleed. You smiled at me the way you smiled at everyone, you told me what you told everyone—and you tell nothing but lies. What are you always hiding? And do you think I did not know when you made love to me, you were making love to no one? *No one!* Or everyone—but not *me*, certainly. I am nothing to you, nothing, and you bring me fever but no delight."

I moved, looking for a cigarette. They were in my hand. I lit one. In a moment, I thought, I will say something. I will say something and then I will walk out of this room forever.

"You know I cannot be alone. I have told you. What is the matter? Can we never have a life together?"

He began to cry again. I watched the hot tears roll from the corners of his eyes onto the dirty pillow.

"If you cannot love me, I will die. Before you came I wanted to die, I have told you many times. It is cruel to have made me want to live only to make my death more bloody."

I wanted to say so many things. Yet, when I opened my mouth, I made no sound. And yet—I do not know what I felt for Giovanni. I felt nothing for Giovanni. I felt terror and pity and a rising lust.

He took my cigarette from my lips and puffed on it, sitting up in bed, his hair in his eyes again.

"I have never known anyone like you before. I was never like this before you came. Listen. In Italy I had a woman and she was very good to me. She loved me, she loved *me*, and she took care of me and she was always there when

I came in from work, in from the vineyards, and there was never any trouble between us, never. I was young then and did not know the things I learned later or the terrible things you have taught me. I thought all women were like that. I thought all men were like me—I thought I was like all other men. I was not unhappy then and I was not lonely—for she was there—and I did not want to die. I wanted to stay forever in our village and work in the vineyards and drink the wine we made and make love to my girl. I have told you about my village—? It is very old and in the south, it is on a hill. At night, when we walked by the wall, the world seemed to fall down before us, the whole, far-off, dirty world. I did not ever want to see it. Once we made love under the wall.

"Yes, I wanted to stay there forever and eat much spaghetti and drink much wine and make many babies and grow fat. You would not have liked me if I had stayed. I can see you, many years from now, coming through our village in the ugly, fat, American motor car you will surely have by then and looking at me and looking at all of us and tasting our wine and shitting on us with those empty smiles Americans wear everywhere and which you wear all the time and driving off with a great roar of the motors and a great sound of tires and telling all the other Americans you meet that they must come and see our village because it is so picturesque. And you will have no idea of the life there, dripping and bursting and beautiful and terrible, as you have no idea of my life now. But I think I would have been happier there and I would not have minded your smiles. I would have had my life. I have lain here many nights, waiting for you to come home, and thought how far away is my village and how terrible it is to be in this cold city, among people whom I hate, where it is cold and wet and never dry and hot as it was there, and where Giovanni has no one to talk to, and no one to be with, and where he has found a lover who is neither man nor woman, nothing that I can know or touch. You do not know, do you, what it is like to lie awake at night and wait for someone to come home? But I am sure you do not know. You do not know anything. You do not know any of the terrible things—that is why you smile and dance the way you do and you think that the comedy you are playing with the short-haired, moon-faced little girl is love."

He dropped the cigarette to the floor, where it lay burning faintly. He began to cry again. I looked at the room, thinking: I cannot bear it.

"I left my village one wild, sweet day. I will never forget that day. It was the day of my death—I wish it had been the day of my death. I remember the sun was hot and scratchy on the back of my neck as I walked the road away from my village and the road went upward and I walked bent over. I remember everything, the brown dust at my feet, and the little pebbles which rushed before me, and the short trees along the road and all the flat houses and all their colors under the sun. I remember I was weeping, but not as I am weeping now, much worse, more terrible—since I am with you, I cannot even cry as I cried then. That was the first time in my life that I wanted to die. I had just buried my baby in the churchyard where my father and my father's fathers were and I had left my girl screaming in my mother's house. Yes, I had made a baby but it was born dead. It was all grey and twisted when I saw it and it made no sound—and we spanked it on the buttocks and we sprinkled it with holy water and we prayed but it never made a sound, it was dead. It was a little boy, it would have been a wonderful, strong man, perhaps even the kind of man *you* and Jacques and Guillaume and all your disgusting band of fairies spend all your days and nights looking for, and dreaming of—but it was dead, it was my baby and we had made it, my girl and I, and it was dead. When I knew that it was dead, I took our crucifix off the wall and I spat on it and I threw it on the floor and my mother and my girl screamed and I went out. We buried it right away, the next day, and then I left my village and I came to this city where surely God has punished me for all my sins and for spitting on His holy Son, and where I will surely die. I do not think that I will ever see my village again."

I stood up. My head was turning. Salt was in my mouth. The room seemed to rock, as it had the first time I had come here, so many lifetimes ago. I heard Giovanni's moan behind me. "*Chéri. Mon très cher.* Don't leave me. Please don't leave me." I turned and held him in my arms, staring above his head at the wall, at the man and woman on the wall who walked together among roses. He was sobbing, it would have been said, as though his heart would break. But I felt that it was my heart which was broken. Something had broken in me to make me so cold and so perfectly still and far away.

Still, I had to speak.

"Giovanni," I said. "Giovanni."

He began to be still, he was listening; I felt, unwillingly, not for the first time, the cunning of the desperate.

"Giovanni," I said, "you always knew that I would leave one day. You knew my fiancée was coming back to Paris."

"You are not leaving me for her," he said. "You are leaving me for some other reason. You lie so much, you have come to believe all your own lies. But I, *I* have senses. You are not leaving me for a *woman*. If you were really in love with this little girl, you would not have had to be so cruel to me."

"She's not a little girl," I said. "She's a woman and no matter what you think, I *do* love her—"

"You do not," cried Giovanni, sitting up, "love anyone! You never have loved anyone, I am sure you never will! You love your purity, you love your mirror—you are just like a little virgin, you walk around with your hands in front of you as though you had some precious metal, gold, silver, rubies, maybe *diamonds* down there between your legs! You will never give it to anybody, you will never let anybody *touch it*—man *or* woman. You want to be *clean*. You think you came here covered with soap and you think you will go out covered with soap—and you do not want to *stink*, not even for five minutes, in the meantime." He grasped me by the collar, wrestling and caressing at once, fluid and iron at once, saliva spraying from his lips and his eyes full of tears, but with the bones of his face showing and the muscles leaping in his arms and neck. "You want to leave Giovanni because he makes you stink. You want to despise Giovanni because he is not afraid of the stink of love. You want to *kill* him in the name of all your lying little moralities. And you—you are *immoral*. You are, by far, the most immoral man I have met in all my life. Look, *look* what you have done to me. Do you think you could have done this if I did not love you? Is *this* what you should do to love?"

"Giovanni, stop it! For God's sake, *stop* it! What in the world do you want me to do? I can't *help* the way I feel."

"Do you *know* how you feel? *Do* you feel? *What* do you feel?"

"I feel nothing now," I said, "nothing. I want to get out of this room, I want to get away from you, I want to end this terrible scene."

"You want to get away from me." He laughed; he watched me; the look in his eyes was so bottomlessly bitter it was almost benevolent. "At last you are beginning to be honest. And do you know *why* you want to get away from me?"

Inside me something locked. "I—I cannot have a life with you," I said.

"But you can have a life with Hella. With that moon-faced little girl who thinks babies come out of cabbages—or Frigidaires, I am not acquainted with the mythology of your country. You can have a life with her."

"Yes," I said, wearily, "I can have a life with her." I stood up. I was shaking. "What kind of life can we have in this room?—this filthy little room. What kind of life can two men have together, anyway? All this love you talk about—isn't it just that you want to be made to feel strong? You want to go out and be the big laborer and bring home the money, and you want me to stay here and wash the dishes and cook the food and clean this miserable closet of a room and kiss you when you come in through that door and lie with you at night and be your little *girl*. That's what you want. That's what you mean and that's *all* you mean when you say you love me. You say I want to kill *you*. What do you think you've been doing to me?"

"I am not trying to make you a little girl. If I wanted a little girl, I would be *with* a little girl."

"Why aren't you? Isn't it just that you're afraid? And you take *me* because you haven't got the guts to go after a woman, which is what you *really* want?"

He was pale. "You are the one who keeps talking about *what* I want. But I have only been talking about *who* I want."

"But I'm a man," I cried, "a man! What do you think can *happen* between us?"

"You know very well," said Giovanni slowly, "what can happen between us. It is for that reason you are leaving me." He got up and walked to the window and opened it. *"Bon,"* he said. He struck his fist once against the window sill. *"If* I could make you stay, I would," he shouted. "If I had to beat you, chain you, starve you—*if* I could make you stay, I would." He turned back into the room; the wind blew his hair. He shook his finger at me, grotesquely playful. "One day, perhaps, you will wish I had."

"It's cold," I said. "Close the window."

He smiled. "Now that you are leaving—you want the windows closed. *Bien sûr.*" He closed the window and we stood staring at each other in the center of the room. "We will not fight any more," he said. "Fighting will not make you stay. In French we have what is called *une séparation de corps*—not a divorce, you understand, just a separation. Well. We will separate. But I know you belong with me. I believe, I must believe—that you will come back."

"Giovanni," I said, "I'll not be coming back. You know I won't be back."

He waved his hand. "I said we would not fight any more. The Americans have no sense of doom, none whatever. They do not recognize doom when they see it." He produced a bottle from beneath the sink. "Jacques left a bottle of cognac here. Let us have a little drink—for the road, as I believe you people say sometimes."

I watched him. He carefully poured two drinks. I saw that he was shaking—with rage, or pain, or both.

He handed me my glass.

"*À la tienne,*" he said.

"*À la tienne.*"

We drank. I could not keep myself from asking: "Giovanni. What are you going to do now?"

"Oh," he said, "I have friends. I will think of things to do. Tonight, for example, I shall have supper with Jacques. No doubt, tomorrow night I shall also have supper with Jacques. He has become very fond of me. He thinks you are a monster."

"Giovanni," I said, helplessly, "be careful. Please be careful."

He gave me an ironical smile. "Thank you," he said. "You should have given me that advice the night we met."

That was the last time we really spoke to one another. I stayed with him until morning and then I threw my things into a bag and took them away with me, to Hella's place.

I will not forget the last time he looked at me. The morning light filled the room, reminding me of so many mornings and of the morning I had first come there. Giovanni sat on the bed, completely naked, holding a glass of cognac between his hands. His body was dead white, his face was wet and grey. I was at the door with my suitcase. With my hand on the knob, I looked at him. Then I wanted to beg him to forgive me. But this would have been too great a confession; any yielding at that moment would have locked me forever in that room with him. And in a way this was exactly what I wanted. I felt a tremor go through me, like the beginning of an earthquake, and felt, for an instant, that I was drowning in his eyes. His body, which I had come to know so well, glowed in the light and charged and thickened the air between us. Then something opened in my brain, a secret, noiseless door swung open, frightening me: it had not occurred to me until that instant that, in fleeing from his body, I confirmed and perpetuated his body's power over me. Now, as though I had been branded, his body was burned into my mind, into my dreams. And all this time he did not take his eyes from me. He seemed to find my face more transparent than a shop window. He did not smile, he was neither grave, nor vindictive, nor sad; he was still. He was waiting, I think, for me to cross that space and take him in my arms again— waiting, as one waits at a deathbed for the miracle one dare not disbelieve, which will not happen. I had to get out of there for my face showed too much, the war in my body was dragging me down. My feet refused to carry me over to him again. The wind of my life was blowing me away.

"*Au revoir, Giovanni.*"

"*Au revoir, mon cher.*"

I turned from him, unlocked the door. The weary exhale of his breath seemed to ruffle my hair and brush my brow like the very wind of madness. I walked down the short corridor, expecting every instant to hear his voice behind me, passed through the vestibule, passed the *loge* of the still sleeping concierge, into the morning streets. And with every step I took it became more impossible for me to turn back. And my mind was empty—or it was as though my mind had become one enormous, anaesthetized wound. I thought only, *One day I'll weep for this. One of these days I'll start to cry.*

At the corner, in a faint patch of the morning sun, I looked in my wallet to count my bus tickets. In the wallet I found three hundred francs, taken from Hella, my *carte d'identité,* my address in the United States, and paper, paper, scraps of paper, cards, photographs. On each piece of paper I found addresses, telephone numbers, memos of various rendezvous made and kept—or perhaps not kept—people met and remembered, or perhaps not remembered, hopes probably not fulfilled: certainly not fulfilled, or I would not have been standing on that street corner.

I found four bus tickets in my wallet and I walked to the *arrêt*. There was a policeman standing there, his blue hood, weighted, hanging down behind, his white club gleaming. He looked at me and smiled and cried, "*Ça va?*"

"*Oui, merci.* And you?"

"*Toujours.* It's a nice day, no?"

"Yes." But my voice trembled. "The autumn is beginning."

"*C'est ça.*" And he turned away, back to his contemplation of the boulevard. I smoothed my hair with my hand, feeling foolish for feeling shaken. I watched a woman pass, coming from the market, her string bag full; at the top, precariously, a liter of red wine. She was not young but she was clear-faced and bold, she had a strong, thick body and strong, thick hands. The policeman shouted something to her and she shouted back—something bawdy and good-natured. The policeman laughed; but refused to look at me again. I watched the woman continue down the street—home, I thought, to her husband, dressed in blue working clothes, dirty, and to her children. She passed the corner where the patch of sunlight fell and crossed the street. The bus came and the policeman and I, the only people waiting, got on—he stood on the platform, far from me. The policeman was not young, either, but he had a gusto which I admired. I looked out of the window and the streets rolled by. Ages ago, in another city, on another bus, I sat so at the windows, looking outward, inventing for each flying face which trapped my brief attention some life, some destiny, in which I played a part. I was looking for some whisper, or promise, of my possible salvation. But it seemed to me that morning that my ancient self had been dreaming the most dangerous dream of all.

The days that followed seemed to fly. It seemed to turn cold overnight. The tourists in their thousands disappeared, conjured away by timetables. When one walked through the gardens, leaves fell about one's head and sighed and crashed beneath one's feet. The stone of the city, which had been luminous and changing, faded slowly, but with no hesitation, into simple grey stone again. It was apparent that the stone was hard. Daily, fishermen disappeared from the river until, one day, the river banks were clear. The bodies of young boys and girls began to be compromised by heavy underwear, by sweaters and mufflers, hoods and capes. Old men seemed older, old women slower. The colors on the river faded, the rain began, and the river began to rise. It was apparent that the sun would soon give up the tremendous struggle it cost her to get to Paris for a few hours every day.

"But it will be warm in the south," I said.

The money had come. Hella and I were busy every day, on the track of a house in Eze, in Cagnes-sur-Mer, in Vence, in Monte Carlo, in Antibes, in Grasse. We were scarcely ever seen in the quarter. We stayed in her room, we made love a lot, we went to the movies and had long, frequently rather melancholy dinners in strange restaurants on the right bank. It is hard to say what produced this melancholy, which sometimes settled over us like the shadow of some vast, some predatory, waiting bird. I do not think that Hella was unhappy, for I had never before clung to her as I clung to her during that time. But perhaps she sensed, from time to time, that my clutch was too insistent to be trusted, certainly too insistent to last.

And from time to time, around the quarter, I ran into Giovanni. I dreaded seeing him, not only because he was almost always with Jacques, but also because, though he was often rather better dressed, he did not look well. I could not endure something at once abject and vicious which I began to see in his eyes, nor the way he giggled at Jacques' jokes, nor the mannerisms, a fairy's mannerisms, which he was beginning, sometimes, to affect. I did not want to know what his status was with Jacques; yet the day came when it was revealed to me in Jacques' spiteful and triumphant eyes. And Giovanni, during this short encounter, in the middle of the boulevard as dusk fell, with people hurrying all about us, was really amazingly giddy and girlish, and very drunk—it was as though he were forcing me to taste the cup of his humiliation. And I hated him for this.

The next time I saw him it was in the morning. He was buying a newspaper. He looked up at me insolently, into my eyes, and looked away. I watched him diminish down the boulevard. When I got home, I told Hella about it, trying to laugh.

Then I began to see him around the quarter without Jacques, with the street boys of the quarter, whom he had once described to me as *"lamentable."* He was no longer so well dressed, he was beginning to look like one of them. His special friend among them seemed to be the same, tall, pockmarked boy, named Yves, whom I remembered having seen briefly, playing the pinball machine, and, later, talking to Jacques on that first morning in Les Halles. One night, quite drunk myself, and wandering about the quarter alone, I ran into this boy and bought him a drink. I did not mention Giovanni but Yves volunteered the information that he was not with Jacques anymore. But it seemed that he might be able to get back his old job in Guillaume's bar. It was certainly not more than a week after this that Guillaume was found dead in the private quarters above his bar, strangled with the sash of his dressing gown.

FIVE

It was a terrific scandal. If you were in Paris at the time you certainly heard of it, and saw the picture printed in all the newspapers, of Giovanni just after he was captured. Editorials were written and speeches were made, and many bars of the genre of Guillaume's bar were closed. (But they did not stay closed long.) Plainclothes policemen descended on the quarter, asking to see everyone's papers, and the bars were emptied of *tapettes*. Giovanni was nowhere to be found. All of the evidence, above all, of course, his disappearance, pointed to him as the murderer. Such a scandal always threatens, before its reverberations cease, to rock the very foundations of the state. It is necessary to find an explanation, a solution, and a victim with the utmost possible speed. Most of the men picked up in connection with this crime were not picked up on suspicion of murder. They were picked up on suspicion of having what the French, with a delicacy I take to be sardonic, call *les goûts particuliers*. These "tastes," which do not constitute a crime in France, are nevertheless regarded with extreme disapprobation by the bulk of the populace, which also looks on its rulers and "betters" with a stony lack of affection. When Guillaume's corpse was discovered, it was not only the boys of the street who were frightened; they, in fact, were a good deal less frightened than the men who roamed the streets to buy them, whose careers, positions, aspirations, could never have survived such notoriety. Fathers of families, sons of great houses, and itching adventurers from Belleville were all desperately anxious that the case be closed, so that things might, in effect, go back to normal and the dreadful whiplash of public morality not fall on their backs. Until the case was closed they could not be certain which way to jump, whether they should cry out that they were martyrs, or remain what, at heart, of course, they were: simple citizens, bitter against outrage and anxious to see justice done and the health of the state preserved.

It was fortunate, therefore, that Giovanni was a foreigner. As though by some magnificently tacit agreement, with every day that he was at large, the press became more vituperative against him and more gentle towards Guillaume. It was remembered that there perished with Guillaume one of the oldest names in France. Sunday supplements were run on the history of his family; and his old, aristocratic mother, who did not survive the trial of his murderer, testified to the sterling qualities of her son and regretted that corruption had become so vast in France that such a crime could go so long unpunished. With this sentiment the populace was, of course, more than ready to agree. It is perhaps not as incredible as it certainly seemed to me, but Guillaume's name became fantastically entangled with French history, French honor, and French glory, and very nearly became, indeed, a symbol of French manhood.

"But listen," I said to Hella, "he was just a disgusting old fairy. That's *all* he was!"

"Well, how in the world do you expect the people who read newspapers to know that? *If* that's what he was, I'm sure he didn't advertise it—and he must have moved in a pretty limited circle."

"Well—*somebody* knows it. Some of the people who write this drivel know it."

"There doesn't seem to be much point," she said, quietly, "in defaming the dead."

"But isn't there some point in telling the truth?"

"They're telling the truth. He's a member of a very important family and he's been murdered. I know what *you* mean. There's another truth they're *not* telling. But newspapers never do, that's not what they're for."

I sighed. "Poor, poor, poor Giovanni."

"Do you believe he did it?"

"I don't know. It certainly *looks* as though he did it. He was there that night. People saw him go upstairs before the bar closed and they don't remember seeing him come down."

"Was he working there that night?"

"Apparently not. He was just drinking. He and Guillaume seemed to have become friendly again."

"You certainly made some peculiar friends while I was away."

"They wouldn't seem so damn peculiar if one of them hadn't got murdered. Anyway, none of them were my friends—except Giovanni."

"You lived with him. Can't you tell whether he'd commit murder or not?"

"How? You live with me. Can I commit a murder?"

"You? Of course not."

"How do you *know* that? You don't know that. How do you know I'm what you see?"

"Because—" she leaned over and kissed me—"I love you."

"Ah! I loved Giovanni—"

"Not as I love you," said Hella.

"I might have committed murder already, for all you know. How do you know?"

"Why are you so upset?"

"Wouldn't *you* be upset if a friend of yours was accused of murder and was hiding somewhere? What do you mean, why am I so upset? What do you want me to do, sing Christmas carols?"

"Don't shout. It's just that I never realized he meant so much to you."

"He was a nice man," I said finally. "I just hate to see him in trouble."

She came to me and put her hand lightly on my arm. "We'll leave this city soon, David. You won't have to think about it anymore. People get into trouble, David. But don't act as though it were, somehow, your fault. It's not your fault."

"*I* know it's not my fault!" But my voice, and Hella's eyes, astounded me into silence. I felt, with terror, that I was about to cry.

Giovanni stayed at large nearly a week. As I watched, from Hella's window, each night creeping over Paris, I thought of Giovanni somewhere outside, perhaps under one of those bridges, frightened and cold and not knowing where to go. I wondered if he had, perhaps, found friends to hide him—it was astonishing that in so small and po-

liced a city he should prove so hard to find. I feared, sometimes, that he might come to find me—to beg me to help
him or to kill me. Then I thought that he probably considered it beneath him to ask me for help; he no doubt felt by
now that I was not worth killing. I looked to Hella for help.
I tried to bury each night, in her, all my guilt and terror.
The need to act was like a fever in me, the only act possible was the act of love.

He was finally caught, very early one morning, in a
barge tied up along the river. Newspaper speculation had
already placed him in Argentina, so it was a great shock to
discover that he had got no farther than the Seine. This
lack, on his part, of "dash" did nothing to endear him to the
public. He was a criminal, Giovanni, of the dullest kind, a
bungler; robbery, for example, had been insisted on as the
motive for Guillaume's murder; but, though Giovanni had
taken all the money Guillaume had in his pockets, he had
not touched the cash register and had not even suspected,
apparently, that Guillaume had over one hundred thousand francs hidden in another wallet at the bottom of his
closet. The money he had taken from Guillaume was still
in his pockets when he was caught; he had not been able to
spend it. He had not eaten for two or three days and was
weak and pale and unattractive. His face was on news-
stands all over Paris. He looked young, bewildered, terrified, depraved; as though he could not believe that he,
Giovanni, had come to this, had come to this and would go
no further, his short road ending in a common knife. He
seemed already to be rearing back, every inch of his flesh
revolting before that icy vision. And it seemed, as it had
seemed so many times, that he looked to me for help. The
newsprint told the unforgiving world how Giovanni re-
pented, cried for mercy, called on God, wept that he had

not meant to do it. And told us, too, in delicious detail, *how* he had done it: but not why. Why was too black for the newsprint to carry and too deep for Giovanni to tell.

I may have been the only man in Paris who knew that he had not meant to do it, who could read *why* he had done it beneath the details printed in the newspapers. I remembered again the evening I had found him at home and he told me how Guillaume had fired him. I heard his voice again and saw the vehemence of his body and saw his tears. I knew his bravado, how he liked to feel himself *débrouillard,* more than equal to any challenge, and saw him swagger into Guillaume's bar. He must have felt that, having surrendered to Jacques, his apprenticeship was over, love was over, and he could do with Guillaume anything he liked. He could, indeed, have done with Guillaume anything at all—but he could not do anything about being Giovanni. Guillaume certainly knew, Jacques would have lost no time in telling him, that Giovanni was no longer with *le jeune Américain;* perhaps Guillaume had even attended one or two of Jacques' parties, armed with his own entourage; and he certainly knew, all his circle knew, that Giovanni's new freedom, his loverless state, would turn into license, into riot—it had happened to every one of them. It must have been a great evening for the bar when Giovanni swaggered in alone.

I could hear the conversation:

"Alors, tu es revenu?" This from Guillaume, with a seductive, sardonic, speaking look.

Giovanni sees that he does not wish to be reminded of his last, disastrous tantrum, that he wishes to be friendly. At the same moment Guillaume's face, voice, manner, smell, hit him; he is actually facing Guillaume, not conjuring him up in his mind; the smile with which he responds to Guil-

laume almost causes him to vomit. But Guillaume does not
see this, of course, and offers Giovanni a drink.

"I thought you might need a barman," Giovanni says.

"But are you looking for work? I thought your American
would have bought you an oil well in Texas by now."

"No. My American"—he makes a gesture—"has flown!"
They both laugh.

"The Americans always fly. They are not serious," says
Guillaume.

"C'est vrai," says Giovanni. He finishes his drink, looking
away from Guillaume, looking dreadfully self-conscious,
perhaps almost unconsciously, whistling. Guillaume, now,
can hardly keep his eyes off him, or control his hands.

"Come back, later, at closing, and we will talk about this
job," he says at last.

And Giovanni nods and leaves. I can imagine him, then,
finding some of his street cronies, drinking with them, and
laughing, stiffening up his courage as the hours tick by. He
is dying for someone to tell him not to go back to Guillaume, not to let Guillaume touch him. But his friends tell
him how rich Guillaume is, how he is a silly old queen,
how much he can get out of Guillaume if he will only be
smart.

No one appears on the boulevards to speak to him, to
save him. He feels that he is dying.

Then the hour comes when he must go back to Guillaume's bar. He walks there alone. He stands outside awhile.
He wants to turn away, to run away. But there is no place
to run. He looks up the long, dark, curving street as though
he were looking for someone. But there is no one there.
He goes into the bar. Guillaume sees him at once and
discreetly motions him upstairs. He climbs the stairs. His
legs are weak. He finds himself in Guillaume's rooms,

surrounded by Guillaume's silks, colors, perfumes, staring at Guillaume's bed.

Then Guillaume enters and Giovanni tries to smile. They have a drink. Guillaume is precipitate, flabby, and moist, and, with each touch of his hand, Giovanni shrinks further and more furiously away. Guillaume disappears to change his clothes and comes back in his theatrical dressing gown. He wants Giovanni to undress—

Perhaps at this moment Giovanni realizes that he cannot go through with it, that his will cannot carry him through. He remembers the job. He tries to talk, to be practical, to be reasonable, but, of course, it is too late. Guillaume seems to surround him like the sea itself. And I think that Giovanni, tortured into a state like madness, feels himself going under, is overcome, and Guillaume has his will. I think if this had not happened, Giovanni would not have killed him.

For, with his pleasure taken, and while Giovanni still lies suffocating, Guillaume becomes a business man once more and, walking up and down, gives excellent reasons why Giovanni cannot work for him anymore. Beneath whatever reasons Guillaume invents, the real one lies hidden, and they both, dimly, in their different fashions, see it: Giovanni, like a falling movie star, has lost his drawing power. Everything is known about him, his secrecy has been discovered. Giovanni certainly feels this and the rage which has been building in him for many months begins to be swollen now with the memory of Guillaume's hands and mouth. He stares at Guillaume in silence for a moment and then begins to shout. And Guillaume answers him. With every word exchanged Giovanni's head begins to roar and a blackness comes and goes before his eyes. And Guillaume is in seventh heaven and begins to prance about the room—he has scarcely ever gotten so much for so little before. He plays this scene for all it's worth, deeply rejoicing in the fact that Giovanni's face grows scarlet, and his voice thick, watching with pure delight the bone-hard muscles in his neck. And he says something, for he thinks the tables have been turned; he says something, one phrase, one insult, one mockery too many; and in a split second, in his own shocked silence, in Giovanni's eyes, he realizes that he has unleashed something he cannot turn back.

Giovanni certainly did not mean to do it. But he grabbed him, he struck him. And with that touch, and with each blow, the intolerable weight at the bottom of his heart began to lift: now it was Giovanni's turn to be delighted. The room was overturned, the fabrics were shredded, the odor of perfume was thick. Guillaume struggled to get out of the room, but Giovanni followed him everywhere: now it was Guillaume's turn to be surrounded. And perhaps at the very moment Guillaume thought he had broken free, when he had reached the door perhaps, Giovanni lunged after him and caught him by the sash of the dressing gown and wrapped the sash around his neck. Then he simply held on, sobbing, becoming lighter every moment as Guillaume grew heavier, tightening the sash and cursing. Then Guillaume fell. And Giovanni fell—back into the room, the streets, the world, into the presence and the shadow of death.

———

By the time we found this great house it was clear that I had no right to come here. By the time we found it, I did not even want to see it. But by this time, also, there was nothing else to do. There was nothing else I wanted to do. I thought, it is true, of remaining in Paris in order to be close to the trial, perhaps to visit him in prison. But I knew there was no reason to do this. Jacques, who was in constant touch with Giovanni's lawyer and in constant touch with me, had seen Giovanni once. He told me what I knew already, that there was nothing I, or anyone, could do for Giovanni anymore.

Perhaps he wanted to die. He pleaded guilty, with robbery as the motive. The circumstances under which Guillaume had fired him received great play in the press. And from the press one received the impression that Guillaume had been a good-hearted, a perhaps somewhat erratic philanthropist who had had the bad judgment to befriend the hardened and ungrateful adventurer, Giovanni. Then the case drifted downward from the headlines. Giovanni was taken to prison to await trial.

And Hella and I came here. I may have thought—I am sure I thought in the beginning—that, though I could do nothing for Giovanni, I might, perhaps, be able to do something for Hella. I must have hoped that there would be something Hella could do for me. And this might have been possible if the days had not dragged by, for me, like days in prison. I could not get Giovanni out of my mind, I was at the mercy of the bulletins which sporadically arrived from Jacques. All that I remember of the autumn is waiting for Giovanni to come to trial. Then, at last, he came to trial, was found guilty, and placed under sentence of death. All winter long I counted the days. And the nightmare of this house began.

Much has been written of love turning to hatred, of the heart growing cold with the death of love. It is a remarkable process. It is far more terrible than anything I have ever read about it, more terrible than anything I will ever be able to say.

I don't know, now, when I first looked at Hella and found

her stale, found her body uninteresting, her presence grating. It seemed to happen all at once—I suppose that only means that it had been happening for a long time. I trace it to something as fleeting as the tip of her breast lightly touching my forcarm as she leaned over me to serve my supper. I felt my flesh recoil. Her underclothes, drying in the bathroom, which I had often thought of as smelling even rather improbably sweet and as being washed much too often, now began to seem unaesthetic and unclean. A body which had to be covered with such crazy, catty-cornered bits of stuff began to seem grotesque. I sometimes watched her naked body move and wished that it were harder and firmer, I was fantastically intimidated by her breasts, and when I entered her I began to feel that I would never get out alive. All that had once delighted me seemed to have turned sour on my stomach.

I think—I think that I have never been more frightened in my life. When my fingers began, involuntarily, to loose their hold on Hella, I realized that I was dangling from a high place and that I had been clinging to her for my very life. With each moment, as my fingers slipped, I felt the roaring air beneath me and felt everything in me bitterly contracting, crawling furiously upward against that long fall.

I thought that it was only, perhaps, that we were alone too much and so, for a while, we were always going out. We made expeditions to Nice and Monte Carlo and Cannes and Antibes. But we were not rich and the south of France, in the wintertime, is a playground for the rich. Hella and I went to a lot of movies and found ourselves, very often, sitting in empty, fifth-rate bars. We walked a lot, in silence. We no longer seemed to see things to point out to each other. We drank too much, especially me. Hella, who had been so brown and confident and glowing on her return from Spain, began to lose all this; she began to be pale and watchful and uncertain. She ceased to ask me what the matter was, for it was borne in on her that I either did not know or would not say. She watched me. I felt her watching and it made me wary and it made me hate her. My guilt, when I looked into her closing face, was more than I could bear.

We were at the mercy of bus schedules and often found ourselves in the wintry dawn huddled sleepily together in a waiting room or freezing on the street corner of some totally deserted town. We arrived home in the grey morning, crippled with weariness, and went straight to bed.

I was able, for some reason, to make love in the mornings. It may have been due to nervous exhaustion; or wandering about at night engendered in me a curious, irrepressible excitement. But it was not the same, something was gone: the astonishment, the power, and the joy were gone, the peace was gone.

I had nightmares and sometimes my own cries woke me up and sometimes my moaning made Hella shake me awake.

"I wish," she said, one day, "you'd tell me what it is. Tell me what it is; let me help you."

I shook my head in bewilderment and sorrow and sighed. We were sitting in the big room, where I am standing now. She was sitting in the easy chair, under the lamp, with a book open on her lap.

"You're sweet," I said. Then: "It's nothing. It'll go away. It's probably just nerves."

"It's Giovanni," she said.

I watched her.

"Isn't it," she asked, carefully, "that you think you've done something awful to him by leaving him in that room? I think you blame yourself for what happened to him. But, darling, nothing you could have done would have helped him. Stop torturing yourself."

"He was so beautiful," I said. I had not meant to say it. I felt myself beginning to shake. She watched me while I walked to the table—there was a bottle there then as now—and poured myself a drink.

I could not stop talking, though I feared at every instant that I would say too much. Perhaps I wanted to say too much.

"I can't help feeling that I placed him in the shadow of the knife. He wanted me to stay in that room with him; he begged me to stay. I didn't tell you—we had an awful fight the night I went there to get my things." I paused. I sipped my drink. "He cried."

"He was in love with you," said Hella. "Why didn't you tell me that? Or didn't you know it?"

I turned away, feeling my face flame.

"It's not your fault," she said. "Don't you understand that? You couldn't keep him from falling in love with you. You couldn't have kept him from—from killing that awful man."

"You don't know anything about it," I muttered. "You don't know anything about it."

"I know how you feel—"

"You *don't* know how I feel."

"David. Don't shut me out. Please don't shut me out. Let me help you."

"Hella. Baby. I know you want to help me. But just let me be for awhile. I'll be all right."

"You've been saying that now," she said, wearily, "for a long time." She looked at me steadily for awhile and then she said, "David. Don't you think we ought to go home?"

"Go home? What for?"

"What are we staying here for? How long do you want to sit in this house, eating your heart out? And what do you think it's doing to me?" She rose and came to me. "Please. I want to go home. I want to get married. I want to start having kids. I want us to live someplace, I want *you*. Please David. What are we marking time over here for?"

I moved away from her, quickly. At my back she stood perfectly still.

"What's the *matter*, David? What do you *want*?"

"I don't know. I don't *know*."

"What is it you're not telling me? Why don't you tell me the truth? Tell me the *truth*."

I turned and faced her. "Hella—bear with me, *bear* with me—a little while."

"I want to," she cried, "but where *are* you? You've gone away somewhere and I can't find you. If you'd only let me reach you—!"

She began to cry. I held her in my arms. I felt nothing at all.

I kissed her salty tears and murmured, murmured I don't know what. I felt her body straining, straining to meet mine and I felt my own contracting and drawing away and I knew that I had begun the long fall down. I stepped away from her. She swayed where I had left her, like a puppet dangling from a string.

"David, please let me be a woman. I don't care what you do to me. I don't care what it costs. I'll wear my hair long, I'll give up cigarettes, I'll throw away the books." She tried to smile; my heart turned over. "Just let me be a woman, take me. It's what I want. It's *all* I want. I don't care about anything else." She moved toward me. I stood perfectly still. She touched me, raising her face, with a desperate and terribly moving trust, to mine. "Don't throw me back into the sea, David. Let me stay here with you." Then she kissed me, watching my face. My lips were cold. I felt nothing on my lips. She kissed me again and I closed my eyes, feeling that strong chains were dragging me to fire. It seemed that my body, next to her warmth, her insistence, under her hands, would never awaken. But when it awakened, I had moved out of it. From a great height, where the air all around me was colder than ice, I watched my body in a stranger's arms.

It was that evening, or an evening very soon thereafter, that I left her sleeping in the bedroom and went, alone, to Nice.

I roamed all the bars of that glittering town, and at the end of the first night, blind with alcohol and grim with lust, I climbed the stairs of a dark hotel in company with a sailor. It turned out, late the next day, that the sailor's leave was not yet ended and that the sailor had friends. We went to visit them. We stayed the night. We spent the next day together, and the next. On the final night of the sailor's leave, we stood drinking together in a crowded bar. We faced the mirror. I was very drunk. I was almost penniless. In the mirror, suddenly, I saw Hella's face. I thought for a moment that I had gone mad, and I turned. She looked very tired and drab and small.

For a long time we said nothing to each other. I felt the sailor staring at both of us.

"Hasn't she got the wrong bar?" he asked me, finally.

Hella looked at him. She smiled.

"It's not the only thing I got wrong," she said.

Now the sailor stared at me.

"Well," I said to Hella, "now you know."

"I think I've known it for a long time," she said. She turned and started away from me. I moved to follow her. The sailor grabbed me.

"Are you—is she—?"

I nodded. His face, open-mouthed, was comical. He let me go and I passed him and, as I reached the doors, I heard his laughter.

We walked for a long time in the stone-cold streets, in silence. There seemed to be no one on the streets at all. It seemed inconceivable that the day would ever break.

"Well," said Hella, "I'm going home. I wish I'd never left it."

———

"If I stay here much longer," she said, later that same morning, as she packed her bag, "I'll forget what it's like to be a woman."

She was extremely cold, she was very bitterly handsome.

"I'm not sure any woman *can* forget that," I said.

"There are women who have forgotten that to be a woman doesn't simply mean humiliation, doesn't simply mean bitterness. I haven't forgotten it yet," she added, "in spite of you. I'm not going to forget it. I'm getting out of this house, away from you, just as fast as taxis, trains, and boats will carry me."

And in the room which had been our bedroom in the beginning of our life in this house, she moved with the desperate haste of someone about to flee—from the open suitcase on the bed, to the chest of drawers, to the closet. I stood in the doorway, watching her. I stood there the way a small boy who has wet his pants stands before his teacher.

All the words I wanted to say closed my throat, like weeds, and stopped my mouth.

"I wish, anyway," I said at last, "that you'd believe me when I say that, if I was lying, I wasn't lying to *you*."

She turned toward me with a terrible face. "I was the one you were talking to. *I* was the one you wanted to come with you to this terrible house in the middle of nowhere. I was the one you said you wanted to marry!"

"I mean," I said, "I was lying to myself."

"Oh," said Hella, "I see. That makes everything different, of course."

"I only mean to say," I shouted, "that whatever I've done to hurt you, I didn't mean to do!"

"Don't shout," said Hella. "I'll soon be gone. Then you can shout it to those hills out there, shout it to the peasants, how guilty you are, how you love to be guilty!"

She started moving back and forth again, more slowly, from the suitcase to the chest of drawers. Her hair was damp and fell over her forehead, and her face was damp. I longed to reach out and take her in my arms and comfort her. But that would not be comfort anymore, only torture, for both of us.

She did not look at me as she moved, but kept looking at the clothes she was packing, as though she were not sure they were hers.

"But I *knew*," she said, "I knew. This is what makes me so ashamed. I knew it every time you looked at me. I knew it every time we went to bed. If only you had told me the truth *then*. Don't you see how unjust it was to wait for *me* to find it out? To put all the burden on *me*? I had the *right* to expect to hear from you—women are always waiting for the *man* to speak. Or hadn't you heard?"

I said nothing.

"I wouldn't have had to spend all this time in this *house*; I wouldn't be wondering how in the name of God I'm going to stand that long trip back. I'd *be* home by now, dancing with some man who wanted to make me. And I'd *let* him make me, too, why not?" And she smiled bewilderedly at a crowd of nylon stockings in her hand and carefully crushed them in the suitcase.

"Perhaps *I* didn't know it then. I only knew I had to get out of Giovanni's room."

"Well," she said, "you're out. And now I'm getting out. It's only poor Giovanni who's—lost his head."

It was an ugly joke and made with the intention of wounding me; yet she couldn't quite manage the sardonic smile she tried to wear.

"I'll never understand it," she said at last, and she raised her eyes to mine as though I could help her to understand. "That sordid little gangster has wrecked your life. I think he's wrecked mine, too. Americans should never come to Europe," she said, and tried to laugh and began to cry, "it means they never can be happy again. What's the good of an American who isn't happy? Happiness was all we had." And she fell forward into my arms, into my arms for the last time, sobbing.

"Don't believe it," I muttered, "don't believe it. We've got much more than that, we've always had much more than that. Only—only—it's sometimes hard to bear."

"Oh, God, I wanted you," she said. "Every man I come across will make me think of you." She tried to laugh again. "Poor man! Poor men! Poor *me*!"

"Hella. Hella. One day, when you're happy, try to forgive me."

She moved away. "Ah. I don't know anything about happiness anymore. I don't know anything about forgiveness.

But if women are supposed to be led by men and there aren't any men to lead them, what happens then? What happens then?" She went to the closet and got her coat; dug in her handbag and found her compact and, looking into the tiny mirror, carefully dried her eyes and began to apply her lipstick. "There's a difference between little boys and little girls, just like they say in those little blue books. Little girls want little boys. But little boys—!" She snapped her compact shut. "I'll never again, as long as I live, know *what* they want. And now I know they'll never tell me. I don't think they know how." She ran her fingers through her hair, brushing it back from her forehead, and, now, with the lipstick, and in the heavy, black coat, she looked again cold, brilliant, and bitterly helpless, a terrifying woman. "Mix me a drink," she said, "we can drink to old times' sake before the taxi comes. No, I don't want you to come to the station with me. I wish I could drink all the way to Paris and all the way across that criminal ocean."

We drank in silence, waiting to hear the sound of tires on gravel. Then we heard it, saw the lights, and the driver began honking his horn. Hella put down her drink and wrapped her coat around her and started for the door. I picked up her bags and followed. The driver and I arranged the baggage in the car; all the time I was trying to think of some last thing to say to Hella, something to help wipe away the bitterness. But I could not think of anything. She said nothing to me. She stood very erect beneath the dark winter sky, looking far out. And when all was ready, I turned to her.

"Are you sure you wouldn't like me to come with you as far as the station, Hella?"

She looked at me and held out her hand.

"Good-bye, David."

I took her hand. It was cold and dry, like her lips.

"Good-bye, Hella."

She got into the taxi. I watched it back down the drive, onto the road. I waved one last time, but Hella did not wave back.

———

Outside my window the horizon begins to lighten, turning the grey sky a purplish blue.

I have packed my bags and I have cleaned the house. The keys to the house are on the table before me. I have only to change my clothes. When the horizon has become a little lighter the bus which will take me to town, to the station, to the train which will take me to Paris, will appear at the bend of the highway. Still, I cannot move.

On the table, also, is a small, blue envelope, the note from Jacques informing me of the date of Giovanni's execution.

I pour myself a very little drink, watching, in the window pane, my reflection, which steadily becomes more faint. I seem to be fading away before my eyes—this fancy amuses me, and I laugh to myself.

It should be now that gates are opening before Giovanni and clanging shut behind him, never, for him, to be opened or shut anymore. Or perhaps it is already over. Perhaps it is only beginning. Perhaps he still sits in his cell, watching, with me, the arrival of the morning. Perhaps now there are whispers at the end of the corridor, three heavy men in black taking off their shoes, one of them holding the ring of keys, all of the prison silent, waiting, charged with dread. Three tiers down, the activity on the stone floor has become silent, is suspended, someone lights a cigarette. Will he die alone? I do not know if death, in this country, is a solitary or a mass-produced affair. And what will he say to the priest?

Take off your clothes, something tells me, *it's getting late.*

I walk into the bedroom where the clothes I will wear are lying on the bed and my bag lies open and ready. I begin to undress. There is a mirror in this room, a large mirror. I am terribly aware of the mirror.

Giovanni's face swings before me like an unexpected lantern on a dark, dark night. His eyes—his eyes, they glow like a tiger's eyes, they stare straight out, watching the approach of his last enemy, the hair of his flesh stands up. I cannot read what is in his eyes: if it is terror, then I have never seen terror, if it is anguish, then anguish has never laid hands on me. Now they approach, now the key turns in the lock, now they have him. He cries out once. They look at him from far away. They pull him to the door of his cell, the corridor stretches before him like the graveyard of his past, the prison spins around him. Perhaps he begins to moan, perhaps he makes no sound. The journey begins. Or, perhaps, when he cries out, he does not stop crying; perhaps his voice is crying now, in all that stone and iron. I see his legs buckle, his thighs jelly, the buttocks quiver, the secret hammer there begins to knock. He is sweating, or he is dry. They drag him, or he walks. Their grip is terrible, his arms are not his own anymore.

Down that long corridor, down those metal stairs, into the heart of the prison and out of it, into the office of the priest. He kneels. A candle burns, the Virgin watches him.

Mary, blessed mother of God.

My own hands are clammy, my body is dull and white and dry. I see it in the mirror, out of the corner of my eye.

Mary, blessed mother of God.

He kisses the cross and clings to it. The priest gently lifts the cross away. Then they lift Giovanni. The journey begins. They move off, toward another door. He moans. He wants to spit, but his mouth is dry. He cannot ask that they let him pause for a moment to urinate—all that, in a moment, will take care of itself. He knows that beyond the door which comes so deliberately closer, the knife is waiting. That door is the gateway he has sought so long out of this dirty world, this dirty body.

It's getting late.

The body in the mirror forces me to turn and face it. And I look at my body, which is under sentence of death. It is lean, hard, and cold, the incarnation of a mystery. And I do not know what moves in this body, what this body is searching. It is trapped in my mirror as it is trapped in time and it hurries toward revelation.

When I was a child, I spake as a child, I understood as a child, I thought as a child: but when I became a man, I put away childish things.

I long to make this prophecy come true. I long to crack that mirror and be free. I look at my sex, my troubling sex, and wonder how it can be redeemed, how I can save it from the knife. The journey to the grave is already begun, the journey to corruption is, always, already, half over. Yet, the key to my salvation, which cannot save my body, is hidden in my flesh.

Then the door is before him. There is darkness all around him, there is silence in him. Then the door opens and he stands alone, the whole world falling away from him. And the brief corner of the sky seems to be shrieking, though he does not hear a sound. Then the earth tilts, he is thrown forward on his face in darkness, and his journey begins.

I move at last from the mirror and begin to cover that nakedness which I must hold sacred, though it be never so vile, which must be scoured perpetually with the salt of my life. I must believe, I must believe, that the heavy grace of God, which has brought me to this place, is all that can carry me out of it.

And at last I step out into the morning and I lock the door behind me. I cross the road and drop the keys into the old lady's mailbox. And I look up the road, where a few people stand, men and women, waiting for the morning bus. They are very vivid beneath the awakening sky, and the horizon beyond them is beginning to flame. The morning weighs on my shoulders with the dreadful weight of hope and I take the blue envelope which Jacques has sent me and tear it slowly into many pieces, watching them dance in the wind, watching the wind carry them away. Yet, as I turn and begin walking toward the waiting people, the wind blows some of them back on me.

A NOTE ON THE TYPE

The principal text of this Modern Library edition
was set in a digitized version of Janson,
a typeface that dates from about 1690 and was cut by Nicholas Kis,
a Hungarian working in Amsterdam. The original matrices have
survived and are held by the Stempel foundry in Germany.
Hermann Zapf redesigned some of the weights and sizes for Stempel,
basing his revisions on the original design.